Theos Friends' Progr

CW00404861

Theos is a religion and society think tank which se
opinion about the role of faith and belief in society

We were launched in November 2006 with the sup
Dr Rowan Williams and the Cardinal Archbishop of
Cardinal Cormac Murphy-O'Connor.

We provide

- high-quality research, reports and publications;
- an events programme;
- news, information and analysis to media companies,
  parliamentarians and other opinion formers.

We can only do this with your help!

Theos Friends receive complimentary copies of all Theos publications, invitations
to selected events and monthly email bulletins.

Theos Associates receive all the benefits of Friends and in addition are invited
to attend an exclusive annual dinner with the Theos Director and team.

If you would like to become a Friend or an Associate, please visit
www.theosthinktank.co.uk or detach or photocopy the form below, and send
it with a cheque to Theos for the relevant amount. Thank you.

Yes, I would like to help change public opinion!
I enclose a cheque payable to Theos for: ☐ **£60** (Friend) ☐ **£300** (Associate)

☐ Please send me information on how to give by standing order/direct debit

Name _____

Address _____

_____ Postcode _____

Email _____

Tel _____

Data Protection Theos will use your personal data to inform you of its activities.
If you prefer not to receive this information please tick here. ☐

*By completing you are consenting to receiving communications by telephone and email.
Theos will not pass on your details to any third party.*

Please return this form to:
Theos | 77 Great Peter Street | London | SW1P 2EZ
S: 97711 D: 36701

Theos – clear thinking on religion and society

Theos is a Christian think tank working in the area of religion, politics and society. We aim to inform debate around questions of faith and secularism and the related subjects of values and identity. We were launched in November 2006, and our first report *'Doing God'; a Future for Faith in the Public Square,* written by Nick Spencer, examined the reasons why faith will play an increasingly significant role in public life.

what Theos stands for

In our post-secular age, interest in spirituality is increasing across western culture. We believe that it is impossible to understand the modern world without an understanding of religion. We also believe that much of the debate about the role and place of religion has been unnecessarily emotive and ill-informed. We reject the notion of any possible 'neutral' perspective on these issues.

what Theos works on

Theos conducts research, publishes reports and runs debates, seminars and lectures on the intersection of religion, politics and society in the contemporary world. We also provide regular comment for print and broadcast media. Research areas include religion in relation to public services, the constitution, law, the economy, pluralism and education.

what Theos provides

In addition to our independently driven work, Theos provides research, analysis and advice to individuals and organisations across the private, public and not-for-profit sectors. Our unique position within the think tank sector means that we have the capacity to develop proposals that carry values – with an eye to demonstrating what really works.

what Theos believes

Theos was launched with the support of the Archbishop of Canterbury and the Cardinal Archbishop of Westminster, but it is independent of any particular denomination. We are an ecumenical Christian organisation, committed to the belief that religion in general and Christianity in particular has much to offer for the common good of society as a whole. We are committed to the traditional creeds of the Christian faith and draw on social and political thought from a wide range of theological traditions. We also work with many non-Christian and non-religious individuals and organisations.

More than an Educated Guess:

Assessing the evidence on faith schools

Elizabeth Oldfield, Liane Hartnett and Emma Bailey

Published by Theos in 2013
© Theos

ISBN 978-0-9574743-2-1

Some rights reserved – see copyright licence for details
For further information and subscription details please contact:

Theos
Licence Department
77 Great Peter Street
London
SW1P 2EZ

T 020 7828 7777
E hello@theosthinktank.co.uk
www.theosthinktank.co.uk

contents

acknowledgements

The authors would like to acknowledge the support of the Jerusalem Trust. Thanks also go to Beth Greene, Mike Simmons, Trevor Cooling, Howard Worsley, Paul Bickley, Nick Spencer, Alanna Harris and Polly Parrott. We are grateful to Simon Barrow, the Right Rev John Prichard, Bishop of Oxford and the Right Rev Malcolm McMahon OP, Bishop of Nottingham for being willing to respond to the report and engage in what we hope will be an ongoing conversation.

executive summary

Around one in three maintained (i.e. state funded) schools in England have a religious character. This reflects the substantial historic contribution of the churches in providing public education. *More than an Educated Guess: Assessing the evidence on faith schools* summarises research around maintained schools with a religious character, with a view to informing debate around their place in a plural society and their effect on students.

The report argues that this heated debate is often a proxy for wider disputes around the role of faith in contemporary society in general and education in particular – what is the purpose of education in a plural society, is it possible to create 'neutral' public spaces, and what place can and should strongly held religious beliefs have in schools? Different answers to these questions generate fiercely defended positions on what are popularly known as faith schools.

More than an Educated Guess offers a cool-headed reassessment of the evidence base in relation to voluntary aided and voluntary controlled faith schools, but does not touch on free schools, academies or foundation schools because there is not yet enough evidence on which to draw. The report considers research grouped around four key and closely related questions. First, are faith schools socially divisive – do they compound the effect of existing community divides, such as those of race or ethnicity? Second, are faith schools exclusive and elitist – does the ability of some faith schools to act as their own admissions authority result in a degree of social or economic sorting? Third, is there a 'faith school effect' – is there anything about the ethos or practice of faith schools which offers an educational advantage over non-faith or community schools? Fourth, do faith schools offer a distinctive education experience – what is the impact of the kind of education that faith schools offer?

The evidence reviewed suggests that there is little reason to think that faith schools are socially divisive. Rather, they are as successful as community schools at reflecting the multicultural make-up of English communities and promoting cohesion.

The balance of the available evidence suggests that when schools act as their own admission authorities – as many do – a degree of socio-economic 'sorting' can result (e.g., with faith schools admitting a lower than proportionate number of pupils eligible for free school meals compared with their locality). However, faith-based selection criteria are likely to be only one cause amongst others of this phenomenon.

There is a clear 'faith school effect' across a range of measures, including academic performance, but the cause of this is disputed. Evidence suggests that the profile of the school intake is an important cause, and that once this is accounted for the 'faith school effect' is much weaker.

There is comparatively little research on the nature and use of a distinctively Christian or other faith-based approach to education (or ethos), and therefore no conclusions can be drawn about the possible impact of this.

The report concludes by noting that there is a significant diversity of schools grouped under the term faith schools, which contributes to the patchy nature of the evidence base. Further research would be welcome, though research is unlikely ever to offer comprehensive or final answers to questions around their overall legitimacy.

The report recommends that those engaged in the debate acknowledge the partiality and contested nature of many of the conclusions and seek to make conversations more constructive. Supporters of faith schools should move away from a justification based on academic outcomes and instead develop a stronger understanding and articulation of the value of an education in a school with a religious character, possibly in relation to ethos, a more holistic approach and development of character. For Christian schools in particular, there are strong reasons to reassess policies around pupil selection, to avoid what looks like a degree of indirect socio-economic sorting, especially given their historic ethic of concern for the poorest in society.

introduction

More than an Educated Guess: Assessing the evidence on faith schools is a summary and analysis of the evidence on state-maintained faith schools in England. Drawing on, as far as possible, all available and relevant research, it asks two interrelated questions: What do state-maintained faith schools offer students? and, How do state-maintained faith schools impact society?

Theos acknowledges at the outset that 'in law, there is no such thing as a faith school'.[1] There are, however, schools with a religious character. The term 'faith schools' is both problematic and contested and is rejected, for example, by the major churches. Our decision to use 'faith schools' as shorthand for a range of schools 'with a religious character' merely seeks to reflect the language of the public debate. For the purposes of this report, 'faith school' simply refers to a state-maintained school within England which teaches the wider, general curriculum, but which is affiliated to a particular religious denomination or organisation.

Faith schools constitute about a third of all state-maintained or non-fee paying schools in England.[2] Over 99% of these schools are Christian, but some are Jewish, Muslim, Sikh, or Hindu.[3] State-maintained schools may be community schools, voluntary aided schools, voluntary controlled schools, foundation schools, academies or free schools. The next chapter offers a more detailed discussion of the types of state-maintained schools and the differences between them. In summary, these differences relate to governance, property ownership, curricula, admissions and employment.

This report is primarily focussed on voluntary schools. Voluntary schools may be voluntary aided or controlled.[4] Although the next chapter will provide greater detail, it will suffice to note that each of these schools receives, or can receive, a different amount of state funding and that the extent of the formal influence of the associated religious group varies. In fact, the vast majority (about 95%) of faith schools are either voluntary aided or controlled.[5] In 2012, about 4 per cent were academies or free schools, although this is growing rapidly, and less than one per cent are foundation schools.[6] Although academies and free schools have a growing impact on the landscape of state-maintained faith schooling in England, the research on these schools is so far limited, so we do not address them here. Similarly, independent or fee-paying schools are not within the scope of this report. As the faith school debate has largely centred on equality of access to education, it is the existence of non-fee-paying faith schools that is most contentious, and therefore they are the focus of this report.

an arena for proxy debates

The existence of faith schools is controversial, in part, because the debate around faith schools serves as a proxy for other contentious issues. Often the faith school debate is in fact about the role of religion in the public square. This manifests itself in the seemingly intractable tensions between the religious advocates of faith schools, for example, the Church of England and the Roman Catholic Church, and their secular opponents, such as, the British Humanist Association and the National Secular Society. However, people's positions on the various components of the debate cannot be neatly categorised – for instance, they do not necessarily align with religious affiliation. For example, the Accord Coalition and the newly launched Fair Admissions Campaign advance a particular model of "inclusive education",[7] "without regard to religion or belief".[8] Yet their membership base includes the British Muslims for Secular Democracy, the Christian think-tank Ekklesia, the General Assembly of Free Christian and Unitarian Churches, and the Hindu Academy. Similarly, David Conway at the religiously unaffiliated think-tank Civitas advances the merits of faith schools.[9]

> *Often the faith school debate is in fact about the role of religion in the public square.*

Discussions about faith schools occur in a particular historical context. In England, the histories of faith and education are deeply intertwined. Indeed, the provision of schooling by the Church predates the modern state education system.[10] As the next chapter will outline, these schools often had a mission of serving the poor and disenfranchised. The introduction of non-religious state-maintained schools and the evolving relationship between Church and state has problematized the role of religious institutions. Today, however, the debate is never purely about the relationship between religion and state. It is about how we choose to live in an increasingly diverse society, how much scope we allow for parental choice, how we acknowledge diversity and pluralism while promoting cohesion and respecting liberty. We must also determine how we envision common spaces like schools. Are they 'neutral' spaces that require us to disregard our religious, philosophical and cultural identities? Or can they be spaces where we come together in difference and equality?

These conversations are grounded in a more fundamental philosophical problem about the objective of education. Is worldview-neutral knowledge dissemination possible? Is it possible to teach or learn without the content being profoundly shaped by who we are or what we value? For advocates of faith schools, faith plays a pivotal role in shaping the conception of 'the good'.[11] The guiding documents of the Roman Catholic Church and the Church of England, for instance, highlight that the contribution of faith schools lies in their commitment to value-based education and the need to replace the atomistic understanding of the individual with a sense of belonging and service to the community.

Drawing on a declaration from the Second Vatican Council, the Catholic Education Service elaborates:

(T)he Church provides Catholic schools to be more than just places where pupils are equipped with learning and skills for the workplace and responsible citizenship. Rather, they are to be the communities where the spiritual, cultural and personal worlds within which we live are harmonised to form the roots from which grow our values, motivation, aspirations and the moral imperatives that inform our choices and actions as persons.[12]

Similarly for the Church of England, education has as its core the dual purpose of 'witness' and 'service'. It finds expression in:

a sense of obligation to share an enduring narrative, a set of values and ways of behaving that stem from and express the Christian foundation of the school, thereby sharing the faith with all members of the school community [and an] engagement with and service to society: the provision of education as a common good, open to all and of benefit to all.[13]

For secular and humanist critics of faith schools, however, the good is conceptualized in terms of rationality, autonomy and objectivity.[14] The National Secular Society's vision is premised on a complete separation of religion and state and the creation of spaces where religious freedoms may be exercised but never privileged.[15] In practice, they call for the elimination of the expression of religious beliefs or preferences by any state institution, including state-funded schools.[16] For the British Humanist Association, education rests on the celebration of humanism: a trust in "the scientific method, evidence, and reason to discover truths about the universe" and the placing of "human welfare and happiness at the centre of...ethical decision making".[17] To this end, they campaign to end the expansion of faith schools and promote reform within existing faith schools.

Given the competing visions of the role of faith in the public square, of diversity, liberty, cohesion and even the purpose of education, it is unsurprising that these debates remain heated. Coming to terms with our identity as a diverse and plural society fundamentally requires us to navigate our way through the seemingly competing human rights of individuals, children and families, of our rights and freedoms to religion, belief and expression.

However, making faith schools the site for all these wider debates loads a narrow issue with ideological weight that it cannot bear. While it is impossible to evade these wider themes or approach this issue from a position of neutrality, our objective is to clear the ground and provide a resource for those seeking to better understand the issues.

our approach

Drawing together evidence from a wide range of sources, including books, academic papers, newspaper reports and polls, we seek to represent the spread of evidence on these issues. This is not a meta-analysis in the classic academic sense, as it casts its net beyond academic research where appropriate, but it should function as a similarly useful resource for those interested in the field. We did not conduct any primary research. Instead, using an evidence-based approach, we aim to highlight points of consensus, divergence and gaps in existing research. Our report is aimed at a non-technical audience and we have attempted to combine rigour with clarity and accessibility.

Engaging with the available evidence and the core arguments of advocates and opponents of faith schools, our central focus is the impact of state-maintained faith schools on society and students. Our focus is narrow and our aim is to look at the main areas of the debate dispassionately, without seeking to privilege or problematize either faith or community schools. The report is structured around a series of questions that seek to reflect the tenor of the debate and grapple with the core critique and defence of faith schools:

- Are faith schools socially divisive?

- Are faith schools exclusive and elitist?

- Is there a faith school effect?

- Do faith schools offer a distinctive education experience?

These chapters are preceded by another section entitled 'facts and figures' laying out the meaning of the key terms and the most useful statistics.

It is worth noting at this juncture that there are some limitations to this report. First, the faith school landscape varies significantly across the United Kingdom and consequently this report has chosen to focus primarily on faith schools in England and not Wales, Scotland or Northern Ireland. Second, the report may appear to prioritise research on Church of England and Roman Catholic schools to the detriment of schools of other denominations and religions. However, this is merely reflective of the fact that around 98% of faith schools are either Catholic or Anglican and the vast majority of available research centres on them.[18] Third, there are some components of the debate which fall outside the scope of this report. For example, we do not discuss allegations of homophobia in faith schools, for two reasons. First, the most recent Stonewall School Report found pupils in faith schools are now no more likely than pupils in non-faith schools to report homophobic bullying.[19] Second, a discussion about homophobic bullying necessarily entails engaging with the debate about the content of religious education and school curricula, which are beyond the purview of this report. These issues in turn are bound to the deeply contentious issue of proselytism, which merits greater consideration than this report allows, and will be focus of a forthcoming Theos report. Finally, this report does not explore the relationship between faith schools and human rights and equality legislation. Although there is significant research on the law and possible areas for legal reform, a rigorous discussion of this issue would require further primary research and access to data on admissions and employment, which is outside the ambit of the project.

> **98% of faith schools are either Catholic or Anglican.**

In 2003, a researcher at the University of London Institute of Education wrote:

> Much of the political and public debate about faith-based schooling is conducted at the level of generalised assertion and counter- assertion, with little reference to educational scholarship or research. There is a tendency in these debates to draw upon historical images of faith schooling (idealised and critical); to use ideological advocacy (both for and against) and to deploy strong claims about the effects of faith- based schooling upon personal and intellectual autonomy and the wider consequences of such schooling for social harmony, race relations and the common good of society.[20]

Ten years later, the problem is as deeply entrenched. We hope that our report begins a process that turns a debate grounded primarily in ideology into one that pays due attention to the facts.

introduction – references

1   Rachel Barker and John Anderson, 'Segregation or cohesion: Church of England Schools in Bradford', in Roy Gardner et al. *Faith Schools: Consensus or Conflict*, (Routledge, 2005), p. 122.

2   http://www.education.gov.uk/schools/leadership/typesofschools/maintained/b00198369/voluntary-and-faith-schools.

3   See table: Data on Faith Schools https://humanism.org.uk/wp-content/uploads/data-on-faith-schools.xlsx (Correct at January 2012, and obtained by FOI from the Department of Education) http://humanism.org.uk/campaigns/schools-and-education/faith-schools/.

4   For a more detailed discussion of voluntary aided and voluntary controlled schools see page 20 and 21.

5   Data on Faith Schools table.

6   Ibid.

7   http://accordcoalition.org.uk/about-us/.

8   http://fairadmissions.org.uk/about/.

9   David Conway, 'Faith Schools: Enrichment or Division?', Paper delivered to the London Society for the Study of Religion on 7 June 2011, http://www.civitas.org.uk/pdf/Conway_FaithSchools.pdf.

10   http://www.education.gov.uk/schools/leadership/typesofschools/b0066996/faith-schools.

11   Trevor Cooling, *Doing God in Education* (Theos, 2010).

12   *Gravissium Educationatis*, as cited in *Christ at the Centre* (Catholic Truth Society, 2013), p. 7.

13   Church School of the Future Review (Church of England Archbishops Council Education Division, 2012), p. 8.

14   Cooling, *Doing God in Education* (Theos, 2010), Chapter 1.

15   http://www.secularism.org.uk/what-is-secularism.html.

16   http://www.secularism.org.uk/secularcharter.html.

17   http://humanism.org.uk/humanism/.

18   http://www.education.gov.uk/schools/leadership/typesofschools/maintained/b00198369/voluntary-and-faith-schools.

19   April Guasp, *The experiences of gay young people in Britain's schools in 2012* (Stonewall, 2012), p. 6. It should be noted that the report also stated that "faith schools are still less likely than schools in general to take steps to prevent and respond to homophobic bullying".

20   Gerald Grace, 'Educational Studies and Faith-Based Schooling: Moving from Prejudice to Evidence-Based Argument', *British Journal of Educational Studies* 51(2): pp. 149–167, June 2003, p. 149.

facts and figures

Church involvement in education provision predates the existence of the modern state education system. The Church of England provided 17,000 public schools between 1811 and 1860 through the National Society, with the intention of providing education to the poor at a time when the government was unwilling, and perhaps unable to do so.[1]

The creation and expansion of non-religious state-maintained schools in 1870 was not intended to provide a radical alternative to traditional church schools. Rather, these schools were simply seen as building upon and expanding the work of traditional church schools.[2] Since the late nineteenth century, Church of England, Catholic, Jewish, Methodist, and Quaker schools have existed within the state-maintained sector. The founding of these schools reflected a need to address problems faced by the respective faith communities, including, "poverty, educational inequalities and the desire to use education as a route for socio-economic mobility".[3] They also sought to address "successive waves of immigration and efforts to promote integration".[4] Hence, the number of Roman Catholic schools grew to respond to the influx of working-class Irish immigrants between 1847 and 1906.[5] It is also revealing that the Catholic Education Service was formerly known as the Catholic Poor School Committee.[6]

The term 'faith school' refers to the ethos and governance of the school.

In 1902, the Education Act merged church and state-based school systems to establish free, compulsory Christian education. A further Education Act in 1944 introduced the dual system of education recognisable in England today: the co-existence of schools with and without a religious character in the state-maintained sector.[7]

In many ways, the lines between state-maintained and non-religious schools continue to be blurred. For instance, all state-maintained schools are legislatively required to have a daily act of collective worship. In schools without a religious character, this collective worship is not neutral, but must (by law) be "wholly, or mainly of a broadly Christian nature".[8] Within state-maintained faith schools, this collective worship may be carried out in accordance with the tenets and practices of its designated faith. Yet the term 'faith school' does not refer to the religious beliefs of its pupils. A state-maintained school may, by chance or geography, contain pupils all of one religion, but this would not be enough to qualify the school in question as a faith school. The term thus refers to the ethos and governance of the school. The pupils need not necessarily follow the religion of the school (state-maintained faith schools are required by law to admit pupils from all faiths and none if they cannot fill their quotas), but its lessons (despite following the National Curriculum in all but Religious Education and Citizenship) and its environment are shaped by the tenets and beliefs of a particular religious tradition. The precise nature of a state-maintained faith school is largely dependent upon its financial status and relationship to the state. If a school is *voluntary controlled* (VC), the primary responsibility for the school's admissions and staff lies with the local authority. If the school is *voluntary aided* (VA), the school has greater autonomy in these areas.

types of faith school

The term 'faith school' is relatively new, originating during Tony Blair's premiership. 'Faith school' can refer to schools with a religious character in either the state-maintained (non fee-paying) or independent (fee-paying) sectors.

Distinct from previous state-maintained schools with religious affiliation, 'church schools' had, until 1997, been invariably of Christian or Jewish origin. The use of the term 'faith schools' is indicative of a broader desire from other religious groups for their own specialist schools, and the willingness of the Labour government to encourage and support these schools on the grounds of justice and fairness.[9]

A maintained school is deemed by the Department of Education to have a religious character if it fulfils one of the following criteria:

- At least one member of the governing body is appointed as a foundation governor to represent the interests of a religion or a religious denomination.

- If the school should close, the premises will be disposed of in accordance with the requirement of the trust which may be for the benefit of one or more religions or religious foundations.

- The foundation which owns the site has made it available on the condition that the school provides education in accordance with the tenets of the faith.

Within the state-maintained sector, faith schools may be voluntary aided, voluntary controlled, foundation schools, academies, or free schools. Academies and free schools, in turn may not be registered as having a religious character but may still have a faith ethos. The table below, adapted from data gathered by the British Humanist Association, offers a snap shot of the main differences between state-maintained schools with a registered religious character.[10] The differences between voluntary aided and voluntary controlled schools, which form the main focus of our paper are discussed in greater detail below.

Type of school	Community schools	Voluntary Controlled schools	Voluntary Aided schools	Foundation schools	Academies and Free schools
Percentage of which are faith schools	0	97	99	5	17
Percentage of total faith schools	0	36	59	1	4
Funding	From local authority	From local authority	Local authority pays all running costs. Central government pays 90% of building costs. Religious authority pays remaining 10% of costs	From local authority	From central Government. Sponsor no longer required to invest any start-up capital costs
Fee-paying	No	No	No	No	No
Are admissions on the basis of faith permitted?	No.	About a quarter of authorities allow some faith-based selection	Only if over-subscribed	Only if over-subscribed	Only Free schools with a religious character allowed 50% of faith-based selectio
If occupational requirement is demonstrated, can a religious test be used to appoint, remunerate and promote staff?	No.	Only for 20% of teachers	Yes.	Only for 20% of teachers	Yes.

There is a further, crucial distinction to be made between voluntary aided and voluntary controlled faith schools. Both are state maintained, but their freedom and relative independence from the broader system is markedly different. When a 'faith school' is referred to in public debates, it generally refers to a voluntary aided school as it is these schools which have the greatest autonomy from the local authority (LA).

voluntary aided faith schools

- **Admissions**: the governing body of a voluntary aided (VA) faith school acts as the school's admissions authority (in place of the LA) and consequently may give priority in admissions to pupils of a specific faith. When a VA faith school is oversubscribed, it may admit 100% of its pupils from a specific faith. However, if a VA school is undersubscribed, it must admit pupils from all faiths and none. As with all maintained schools, a voluntary aided faith school must adhere to the Admissions Code and School Admissions Appeals Code.[11]

- **Employment**: a VA faith school may employ all teaching staff from a specific faith. It may also apply a faith test in the appointment of supplementary staff, where it can demonstrate a 'genuine occupational requirement'.

- **Funding**: a VA school may receive up to 100% of its capital funding at the discretion of the Secretary of State, although it is typical for the governors of the school to provide 10% of capital funds. The land and buildings of a VA school are typically owned by a charity or religious organisation, such as a church.

- **National Curriculum**: both VA and voluntary controlled (VC) schools must follow the National Curriculum. However, VA schools may teach Religious Education in accordance with their particular 'trust deed', or religious affiliation, unless parents request otherwise. These lessons are not subject to Ofsted inspection but must be inspected under the Education Act 2005 by a person chosen by the governing body after consultation with a person deemed appropriate by the appropriate religious authority.[12] A VA school may also decide how, and whether, it wishes to teach subjects which are not on the curriculum, such as Personal, Social and Health Education and Citizenship.[13]

voluntary controlled faith schools

- **Admissions**: in a VC school, the admissions policy is usually determined by the LA which may prioritise pupils of a particular faith, although this is not typical. If oversubscribed, then VC schools may prioritise up to 100% of places on faith-based criteria, and if undersubscribed, a VC school must admit pupils of all faiths and none. As with all maintained schools, VC schools must adhere to the Admissions Code and School Admissions Appeals Code.

- **Employment**: A VC school must adhere to the employment regulations set out by the LA but may discriminate on the basis of faith for up to 20% of staff (including head teachers).

- **Funding**: A VC school is funded wholly by the LA.

- **National Curriculum**: all VC schools must adhere to the National Curriculum in all areas, including Religious Education – unless parents request denominational Religious Education. As with VA schools, Religious Education is not subject to Ofsted inspection, but is subject to inspection under section 48 of the 2005 Education Act. For VC schools, an inspection is to be carried out by a person chosen by "the foundation governors after consultation with the appropriate religious authority".[14]

There are therefore significant differences between VA and VC faith schools – primarily in relation to the admission of pupils and employment of staff, both of which VA schools have far greater control over. All Catholic, Jewish, Hindu, Sikh, and Muslim schools are VA (with the exception of one Catholic foundation school) whilst Church of England and Methodist schools are a mixture of VA and VC.[15]

how many faith schools are there?

According to data from the Department for Education, one in three (34%) state-maintained schools in England are faith schools, or 6,750 schools out of a total of 19,783.[16] Of these state-maintained faith schools, about 99% are affiliated to the Christian faith: 68% to the Church of England, 30% to the Roman Catholic Church, and less than one per cent to Methodist and other Christian denominations. Compared to the 4,598 Church of England state-maintained faith schools, there are 41 Jewish schools, 12 Muslim schools, five Sikh schools and eight schools characterised as 'other'.[17]

conclusion

England's unique dual system of community and faith schools within the state-maintained sector reflects both the legacy of church involvement in schooling and the changing religious composition of society. Today, about a third of state-maintained schools are faith schools. The vast majority are voluntary schools associated with the Christian faith, with about 36% voluntary controlled and 59% voluntary aided.

chapter 1 – references

1   *Faith in the System: the Role of Schools with a Religious Character in English Education and Society* (Department for Children, Schools and Families, 2007), p. 1.

2   Julia Ipsgrave and Ursula McKenna: 'Diverse Experiences and Common Vision: English Students' Perspectives on Religion and Religious Education' in Throrsten Knauth, *Encountering Religious Pluralism in School and Society: a Qualitative Study of Teenage Perspectives in Europe* (Waxman, Munster: 2008), p. 113.

3   Rob Berkeley, *Right to Divide?: Faith Schools and Community Cohesion* (Runnymede, 2008), http://www.runnymedetrust.org/uploads/publications/pdfs/RightToDivide-2008.pdf p. 11.

4   Ibid.

5   Ibid.

6   Ibid, p. 12.

7   *Faith in the System*, p. 2.

8   Schools Standards and Framework Act 1998, Schedule 20, para. 3(2).

9   Robert Jackson, 'Should the State Fund Faith-Based Schools? A Review of the Arguments', *British Journal of Religious Education* 25(2) (2003): 89–102, p. 91.

10 These figures have been rounded to the nearest percent. http://www.humanism.org.uk/wp-content/uploads/schools-with-a-religious-character.pdf.

11 The Schools Admissions Code and the School Admissions Appeals Code are two key pieces of legislation applicable to the admissions authorities of all maintained schools, and Academies. The aim of the School Admissions Code legislation is to ensure that all school places for maintained schools and academies are allocated and offered in an open and fair way. This piece of legislation is to be read in conjunction with the School Admissions Appeals code, which ensures the independence of admission appeal panels, and to ensure that all appeals for maintained schools and Academies are conducted in a fair and transparent way (Correct according to the Department for Education, http://www.education.gov.uk/aboutdfe/statutory/g00213254/school-admissions-code-2012, http://www.education.gov.uk/aboutdfe/statutory/g00213244/school-admission-appeals-code-2012, accessed September 2013).

12 The Education Act, 2005. http://www.legislation.gov.uk/ukpga/2005/18/section/48.

13 Department for Education, 18 June 2012.

14 Education Act 2004, 48. http://www.legislation.gov.uk/ukpga/2005/18/section/48.

15 Department for Education, 19 June 2012.

16 http://www.education.gov.uk/schools/leadership/typesofschools/maintained/b00198369/voluntary-and-faith-schools.

17 http://humanism.org.uk/campaigns/schools-and-education/faith-schools/.

are faith schools divisive?

The Cantle Report found that the 2001 riots in the cities of Bradford, Burnley and Oldham were the outcome of "the 'parallel and polarised lives' of residents who were 'self-segregated' in neighbourhoods and schools".[1] Some argued that the report conflated cause and effect; by criticising victims of social exclusion for favouring 'divisive educational policies', it failed to consider how this could be an expression of other forms of social exclusion.[2] Nonetheless, the tragic events of 9/11 and 7/7 underscored the urgent need for multicultural societies to better balance diversity and cohesion. In this climate, faith schools came under attack. The state-maintained faith education sector, some claimed, both embodied and perpetuated social divisions. To the extent that faith and ethnicity are correlated, faith schools were seen as promoting social segregation on both grounds.[3] These schools were simultaneously represented as recruiting grounds for terrorists and religious extremists.[4] The UK government's response was to enact legislation, which placed a legal obligation on schools to promote both community cohesion and the wellbeing of students.[5] This legislation also conferred Ofsted with powers – repealed in 2011 – to inspect how effective schools were at "helping pupils empathise with others, value diversity and promote shared values".[6]

social cohesion in faith schools

The perception that faith schools *therefore* act as a cradle for social division and unrest, however, appears to be unfounded. Runnymede, a race equality think tank and member of the Accord coalition, found that despite common perceptions, the intake of faith schools *is* ethnically diverse.[7] The report suggested that despite faith schools being more "effective at educating for a single vision than at opening a dialogue about a shared vision", they had some success in providing opportunities "for young people of different backgrounds to mix in faith-based and secular spaces".[8] For example, the report highlighted for most ethnic minority groups, "Catholic schools, parishes and organisations provide a meeting place and important support in becoming fully integrated into society".[9] Further, Roman Catholic schools were found to have a much higher population of black Caribbean and black African young people than any other group of schools, but a lower population of pupils with an Asian background.[10] Similarly, in certain places, 60-90% of pupils in Church of England schools are Muslim.[11] Despite several good-practice examples, Runnymede found that faith schools generally failed to systematically articulate what a faith-based approach meant for diversity and equality.[12] They observed, with disappointment, that given faith schools' emphasis on:

> whole-child approaches, values and moral education, their teaching of race, gender and disability equality is similar to that offered by non-faith schools, and they are therefore no better placed to respond to the needs of young people.[13]

Consequently, they concluded that the experience of effective intervention by faith schools to promote race equality is as mixed as it is within the broader education system.

Church groups and religious organisations argue that faith schools play an important role in promoting social harmony. The Church of England and the Centre for Christian Education, for example, have separately conducted research examining Ofsted inspection findings on schools and social cohesion. The Church of England research revealed that although there was no difference between schools at primary level, faith schools at the secondary level fared better on average than schools without a religious character.[14] The Centre for Christian Education's findings were more emphatic. In the three year cycle between 2008 and 2011, it found that "Catholic schools [at the primary and secondary level were] more effective in promoting community cohesion, as defined by government, than other educational institutions".[15]

Other research appears to confirm this conclusion. The Catholic Education Service highlights the role of faith schools in encouraging participation of minority communities, irrespective of their faith or denomination, within mainstream society.[16] Runnymede agreed that "inequalities and the failure to tackle religious discrimination in non-faith schooling are significant drivers for faith school attendance".[17] A limited study exploring data from one academic year only appears to reinforce these choices. It found that students from minority ethnic communities and disadvantaged backgrounds in Catholic schools appear to be achieving "higher scores in National Curriculum tests and in the various measures of examination attainment favoured by government for comparing institutional performance" than their counterparts in non-faith schools.[18]

The Accord coalition and the Fair Admissions Campaign, while not engaging in the question of religious discrimination in non-faith schools, dispute the assertion that faith schools are better at promoting community cohesion. They suggest Ofsted's inspection criteria were limited and failed to consider "how representative schools were of their local communities in terms of religion or belief, ethnicity or socio-economic factors".[19] This argument is explored further in the next chapter.

social capital and models of integration

There is extensive research which establishes that school diversity has a positive impact on community cohesion and mutual understanding. Diverse ethnic composition at a school level promotes positive inter-group attitudes and more cross-group friendships.[20] The benefits of mixed primary schooling are found to extend into the early years of secondary school.[21] Further, there is "some evidence to suggest that parents learned to respect people from other backgrounds as a result of their children's experiences in mixed schools".[22]

That social harmony is a good is not in dispute. Instead, it is competing constructions of 'social capital' and models of integration that lie at the heart of this debate.[23] Social capital, although contested, refers to "the ability of actors to secure benefits by virtue of membership in social networks or other social structures".[24] At the heart of social capital theory is the assertion that "relationships matter".[25]

> In simple terms, [it] claims that a society with high levels of social capital is a cohesive, well-functioning society, with improving socially desirable outcomes, such as high educational achievement, and fewer negative ones, such as crime and social exclusion.[26]

Faith schools are keen to emphasise their historical role in promoting integration. Church of England schools have traditionally sought to cater to the needs of the poor and less privileged. Jewish and Catholic schools have played an important role in the successful integration of earlier minority faith immigrants. Today, Muslim schools seek to provide an environment for children and young people to develop the confidence to play a role in the wider community and to theologically explore their dual identities as Muslim and British.[27] To the extent that the Muslim model (and older models of Catholic and Jewish schools) counter the dominant model of the community school, they may be seen as prioritising "bonding social capital" or the development of a collective identity over "bridging social capital" or the development of connections between people who are different.[28] In this sense, they embody different positions on whether high bonding capital or high bridging capital is better for civil society. An alternative view expresses concern about a sole emphasis on high bonding capital. To mitigate the risk that religious identity might undermine community cohesion, some call for a framework for civic engagement, which also emphasises bridging capital.[29] However, it would be misleading to suggest that all faith schools champion a particular model of cohesion which prioritieses

Despite common perceptions, the intake of faith schools is ethnically diverse.

bonding rather than bridging social capital. Indeed, in the course of the twentieth and twenty-first centuries, England has seen faith and ethnic communities embrace different and changing visions of social capital and models of integration.

conclusion

The evidence suggests that faith schools in general do not promote social division on racial and ethnic lines. Faith schools are ethnically diverse spaces. They have drawn on the discourse of social capital to emphasise their commitment to immigrant social mobility. At worst, faith schools' efforts at promoting cohesion are as good as the broader education system.

chapter 2 – references

1   Claire Dwyer and Violetta Parutis, ' "Faith in the system?" State-funded faith schools in
    England and the contested parameters of community cohesion,' in *Transactions of the Institute
    of British Geographers*, 38: 267–284 (2013), p. 268. See also, http://tedcantle.co.uk/pdf/
    communitycohesion%20cantlereport.pdf.

2   J Mark Halstead and Terence McLaughlin 'Are Faith Schools Divisive?' in Gardner et al (eds.),
    Faith Schools: Consensus or Conflict? (Routledge, 2005) p. 64.

3   David Conway, Paper delivered to the London Society for the Study of Religion on 7 June 2011.

4   http://www.policyexchange.org.uk/images/publications/faith%20schools%20we%20can%20
    believe%20in%20-%20nov%2010.pdf.

5   Education and Inspections Act 2006, s. 38.

6   Andrew Morris, 'Some Social Benefits of English Catholic Schools', due for publication in
    International Studies in Catholic Education 5(2), October 2013.

7   Berkeley, Right to Divide op. cit., p. 41.

8   Ibid, p. 66.

9   Ibid, citing Catholic Bishops' Conference of England & Wales, and department for Christian
    Responsibility, p. 40.

10 Ibid, citing the CES, p. 41.

11 Ibid, citing the National Society, p. 41.

12 Ibid, p. 53.

13 Ibid, p. 68.

14 Strong Schools for Strong Communities: Reviewing the impact of Church of England schools in
    promoting community cohesion, (Church of England Archbishops' Council Education Division,
    2009) http://www.churchofengland.org/media/1204726/strong%20schools%20for%20
    strong%20communities%20-%20cofe%20report%20final.pdf.

15 Andrew Morris, 'Some Social Benefits of English Catholic Schools' op. cit.

16 Bernadette O'Keefe and Richard Zipfel. 'Ethnicity, identity and achievement in Catholic schools:
    supporting minority ethnic pupils in Catholic Secondary Schools', Catholic Education Service
    (2003), p. 46.

17 Berkeley, Right to Divide, pp. 7, 68.

18 Andrew Morris, 'Bridging Worlds: Ethnic Minority Pupils in Catholic Schools in England', *Journal
    of Belief and Values* 31: 203-213, (2010), p. 210

19 http://fairadmissions.org.uk/why-is-this-an-issue/faqs/

20 Rupert Brown, Adam Rutland and Charles Watters, *Identities in Transition: A Longtitudinal Study
    of Immigrant Children* (2008). Note this report advised against single faith schools based on the
    assumption that such schools are likely to be less ethnically diverse.

21   Irene Bruegel, *Social Capital, Diversity and Education Policy* (London South Bank University, August 2006) http://accordcoalition.org.uk/wp-content/uploads/2012/11/SCDiversityEdu28.8.06.pdf.

22   Ibid.

23   Dwyer and Parutis, "Faith in the System?" op. cit.

24   Portes, A. (1998). Social Capital: its origins and applications in modern society. Annual Review of Sociology, 24, 1-24, p.6, cited in Ann Elizabeth Casson p. 74.

25   Ann Elizabeth Casson, *Perceptions of Catholicity in a plural society*, (Institute of Education, University of Warwick, 2010), p. 66.

26   Eva Gamarnikow and Anthony Green, 'Keeping the faith with social capital: from Coleman to New Labour on social justice, religion and education' in Gardner, et al *Faith Schools: Consensus or Conflict,* op. cit., p. 93.

27   Berkeley, Right to Divide p. 34.

28   Dwyer and Parutis, "Faith in the System?" p. 274.

29   John Annette, 'Faith schools and communities: communitarianism, social capital and citizenship, in Gardner et al, *Faith Schools: Consensus or Conflict?* op. cit. p. 196.

are faith schools exclusive and elitist?

The assertion that faith schools are exclusive and elitist has at its core the assumption that faith-based pupil selection criteria have the effect of favouring the socio-economically privileged. As outlined in Chapter 1, faith schools (at the time, solely Church schools) began with a mission of ameliorating poverty and inequality by providing education for all. Their stated policies continue to reflect this commitment. However, it is often asserted that in practice faith-based schools do not reflect the socio-economic composition of their communities, educating fewer children from poorer backgrounds. This chapter has three purposes. Firstly, it provides an overview of the relevant legislation governing admissions. Secondly, it explores the claim that the admissions in faith schools contribute to a socio-economic bias. Finally, it asks whether there is an exclusive correlation between faith-based selection and socio-economic filtering.

the law governing admissions

There is legislation in force which prevents admission decisions that discriminate on the basis of socio-economic criteria. Prior to 2007, admission authorities were allowed to set admissions criteria that did not comply with the Code of Practice on School Admissions if they had good reason.[1] The 2007 Schools Admissions Code applied to admissions from September 2008, as a statutory requirement for all school admissions authorities. A further code, which came into effect in February 2009, continued to mandate statutory regulation in this vein. The 2007 Schools Admissions Code enforced several legal requirements with regard to the admissions policies used by state-maintained schools. The Code stipulated:

> In drawing up their admission arrangements, admission authorities must ensure that the practices and the criteria used to decide the allocation of school places:
>
> a) are clear in the sense of being free from doubt and easily understood…;
>
> b) are objective and based on known facts. Admission authorities and governing bodies must not make subjective decisions or use subjective criteria;

    c) are procedurally fair and are also equitable for all groups of children (including those with special educational needs, disabilities, those in public care, or who may be a young carer);

    d) enable parents' preferences for the schools of their choice to be met to the maximum extent possible;

    e) provide parents or carers with easy access to helpful admissions information…;

    f) comply with all relevant legislation, including…on equal opportunities…

Failure to comply with the mandatory provisions means that the body concerned is in breach of its statutory duty to act in accordance with the provisions in the Code, and could result in an objection being made to the Schools Adjudicator or a complaint being made to the Secretary of State for Children, Schools and Families.[2]

The primary importance of the Schools Admissions Code for faith schools, and all voluntary aided schools with responsibility over admissions, is in terms of the 'supplementary information forms'. As the name suggests, supplementary information forms may be supplied by such schools in addition to the Common Application Form provided by the local authority. In relation to these forms:

Admission authorities must not use supplementary application or information forms that ask:

    a) for any personal details about parents, such as criminal convictions or marital, occupational or financial status;

    b) for details about parents' achievements, educational background or whether their first language is English;

    c) for details about parents' or children's disabilities, special educational needs or medical conditions, unless this is in support of positive action…;

    d) about parents' or children's interests, hobbies or membership of societies (this does not apply to membership or participation in activities as part of religious observance or practice at schools designated as having a religious character).[3]

Therefore, schools are effectively prevented, by law, from discriminating against particular socio-economic groups, or from taking parental information into account when applying oversubscription criteria. Schools may not interview prospective pupils, parents or carers and they must not accept monetary donations. These things are illegal for all state-maintained schools, including faith schools.[4]

socio-economic bias?

Extensive research conducted prior to the introduction of this legislation made the case that there was "a direct correlation between the number of potentially selective admissions criteria that schools use, and the extent to which their intakes are advantaged".[5] A 2007 IPPR Report argued that there was no justification for schools to act as their own admissions authorities, other than to select students by ability or socio-economic background.[6] It demonstrated that schools that act as their own admission authorities were both "hugely over-represented in the top 200 comprehensive schools as measured by examination results" and "much more likely to be highly unrepresentative of their local areas than schools whose admissions are controlled by the local authority".[7]

The National Union of Teachers endorsed the recommendation of this report that "no school should be its own admissions authority."[8] The report, concluded that the current system of admissions is a direct cause of "segregation by social class and ability across our schools system" and recommended that all local authorities should "move towards a system of area-wide banding, where the objective of achieving a mixed ability intake of pupils at every school would sit alongside other factors such as parental preference and the distance from home to school".[9]

Rebecca Allen's doctoral research corroborated these findings.[10] Her work demonstrated that "own-admissions schools have intakes that are more advantaged than community schools, even when the characteristics of local neighbourhoods are taken into account".[11] This phenomenon is not restricted to any particular denomination of faith schools, but is a pattern common to all voluntary aided schools.[12] However, the Accord Coalition's reading of the IPPR report suggests that while all schools that act as their own admissions authorities are likely to be unrepresentative of their local areas, this is particularly pronounced in faith schools.[13]

Despite the introduction of the 2007 legislation, the data suggest there is some cause for concern that faith school admissions continue to perpetuate socio-economic divides. A 2012 *Guardian* report found that the vast majority of Catholic and Church of England schools continue to have a lower proportion of pupils eligible for free school meals than the average for the local authority area and amongst children in the same postcode. The *Guardian* reported:

Some 73% of Catholic primaries and 72% of Catholic secondaries have a lower proportion of pupils eligible for free school meals than the average for the local authority. It is the same for CofE primary and secondary schools. Some 74% of these primaries and 65.5% of secondaries have a smaller proportion of pupils eligible for free school meals than is average for the local authority. In contrast, non-religious schools tend to reflect their neighbourhoods. Half (51%) of non-religious primaries and 45% of non-religious secondaries have a smaller proportion of pupils eligible for free school meals than is representative for their local authority.

Faith schools fared no better when examined at a more local level. We compared the proportion of poor pupils in each postcode with the proportion of poor pupils in faith schools and non-faith schools studying in that postcode. The data show 76% of Catholic primaries and 65% of Catholic secondaries have a smaller proportion of pupils eligible for free school meals than is representative of their postcode. This is the case for 63.5% of CofE primaries and 40% of CofE secondaries. Non-religious primaries and secondaries are far more likely to mirror the proportion of poor pupils in their postcode – just 47% of non-faith primaries and 29% of non-faith secondaries take a smaller proportion of free school meals than is representative for their postcode.[14]

> "Own-admissions schools have intakes that are more advantaged than community schools."

Drawing on Department of Education performance data, the Fair Admissions Campaign also argues that faith-based selection criteria result in socio-economic sorting. Their research found that Catholic primaries and secondaries in England have on average 26% and 20% fewer pupils, respectively, requiring free school meals than their post codes, while Voluntary Aided Church of England schools have 17% and 8% fewer. Schools without a religious character have 17% more at primary level and 26% more at secondary level.[15]

The use of free school meals eligibility as a proxy for whether the school's intake reflects the socio-economic make-up of its community is something of a blunt instrument. The Catholic Education Service, for example, suggests that fewer eligible children might claim free school meals because of the associated stigma. They also assert that their catchment areas are wider than the postcode or local authority where their schools are situated. Similarly, the Catholic Education Service contests the claim that Catholic schools are unrepresentative: separate figures from the DfE showed 18.6% of pupils at Catholic primary schools live in the 10% most deprived areas of England, compared with only 14.3% of primary school pupils nationally. Some 17% of pupils at Catholic schools lived in the 10% most deprived areas compared to 12% of pupils nationally.[16] Claiming that the local authorities controlled the admissions for more than half its schools, the Church of England challenged the assertion that their schools were unrepresentative of the local communities and that admissions were failing to mirror local diversity.[17] Despite this, the balance of the limited and contested evidence appears to point to some degree of socio-economic sorting.

causation

The numerous, sometimes conflicting theories which attempt to explain the perceived socio-economic sorting at oversubscribed faith schools suggest there are complex and multiple causal factors. One commentator, for instance, argues that socio-economic sorting is inevitably bound to systemic issues like 'location disadvantage'. He argues that house price premiums in residential areas linked to the catchment areas of high-performing state schools serve to exclude many middle- and low-income households. Unless the argument is made that all fee-paying independent schools should be abolished and access to high-demand housing made more equitable, then a focus on faith schools as creating 'education apartheid' limits the state's role to preventing social separation on the basis of religion but not doing so on the basis of parents' economic (and indeed social and cultural) capital.[18]

For academic Geoffrey Walford, diversity of school choice will always come at the cost of equity. He suggests freedom of choice advances an "individualistic and inequitable education system".[19] Indeed, as many disillusioned parents have found, once popular schools are oversubscribed, it is the schools that select children rather than parents having a 'choice' of school. Within each area there is a likelihood that a hierarchy of schools will develop, and there is growing evidence that various privileged groups are better able than others to influence the selection of their children by those schools at the top of the hierarchy. Those with most concern about the education of their children are able to 'play the system' such that their children have a greater chance of being selected by the prestigious schools.[20]

Rebecca Allen and Anne West conducted research which demonstrates that "parents reporting a religious affiliation are more likely to be better educated, have a higher occupational class and a higher household income" and that "higher-income religious families are more likely to have a child at a faith school than lower-income religious families".[21] Earlier research conducted by the IPPR supports this claim. The research found that families for which the mother had a degree or higher qualification are three times more likely to say that they knew how popular schools allocate places, and twice as likely to apply to a school outside the local authority.[22] In contrast, parents from low socio-economic backgrounds "are more likely to consider their child's friendship groups and proximity to the school as more important than its performance table position".[23] It is important to emphasise two things. First, the research does not point to a deliberate policy of socio-economic discrimination in faith schools. What is causing the perceived socio-economic sorting is unclear, but few suggest that faith schools admission policies are deliberately designed to that effect. Second, to the extent that a school's perceived success is often bound to academic attainment, there are fewer incentives for oversubscribed schools to expand school places or radically alter existing admission policies.[24]

The primary mechanism which may be facilitating this sorting appears to be the use of supplementary information forms (SIFs).[25] In 2009, an London School of Economics report found that SIFs were sometimes used to request information that was either unrelated to the school's admission criteria or was impermissible under the School Admissions Code.[26] This information could have been used to select students on the basis of class. In addition, SIFs sometime feature questions permitted by the code, which nonetheless gather information about socio-economic status. Some examples include information about the child and parents' language skills, the language spoken at home and previous schools attended. The use of open-ended questions and long questionnaires can disadvantage people from lower socio-economic backgrounds. However, in the absence of data linking patterns of applications with patterns of offers, no conclusive link can be drawn between admissions criteria, and practices and school composition.[27]

In practice, complaints about a lack of clarity around admissions criteria seem to be fairly rare. Speaking to the House of Commons Education Select Committee on Wednesday, 2nd February 2011, Dr. Ian Craig, head of the Office of the Schools Adjudicator (OSA), sought to clarify the media interpretation of a recent OSA report, revealing that just 45 of the 151 cases reported to the OSA regarding admissions in 2010 were related to faith schools who were their own admissions authorities.[28] Twenty-three of these 45 were submitted with regard to SIFs, and 12 were submitted in regard to the 'clarity and complexity' of faith school criteria. This amounted, as Damian Hinds MP made clear in the discussion, to "12 or 23 out of 6753 religious schools in this country".[29]

The ability of oversubscribed faith schools to prioritise students from their faith communities is often cited as the causal factor for faith schools' less representative socio-economic make up. Some suggest that parents from more privileged backgrounds seek to enrol their children in high performing, oversubscribed faith schools by feigning religiosity. It has been suggested that because they have greater resources at their disposal that they are better able to manipulate existing faith-based selection criteria.[30] We have not found any concrete evidence to support this idea.

However, it has been suggested that faith-based selection criteria often work to exclude devout families from immigrant or lower socio-economic backgrounds.[31] This is supported by Allen and West's research, which finds that poorer religious families are less represented at oversubscribed faith schools.[32] This might occur for two reasons. First, supplementary information forms gather information on church attendance and may sometimes require a reference from a priest. However, parents who are new to the country or working several jobs may not have established patterns of church attendance. Additionally, they are less likely to be involved in their church community.[33] Second, complex application processes and the composition of oversubscribed schools sometimes act as 'social clues' which have the effect of deterring less privileged families.[34]

While there is evidence linking selection criteria with advantaged intakes, it is unclear whether faith-based selection is the sole determinant. The Fair Admissions Campaign is seeking to conduct a mapping exercise to establish the extent of religious selection. While this will be helpful, there is a need for greater research establishing a causal link between faith-based selection and socio-economic privilege. As previously mentioned, Accord's analysis of a 2007 IPPR report did make the case that VA faith schools were ten times more likely to be highly unrepresentative of their surrounding area than faith schools where the local authority acted as the admission authority. However, it also concluded that non-religious state schools which acted as their own admission authorities were six times more likely to be highly unrepresentative of their surrounding area than schools for whom the local authority is the admission authority.[35] This research suggests that faith-based selection is not the sole cause of socio-economic sorting. This effect appears to be more widespread and linked to the existence of schools which act as their own admissions authority.

> *The use of long questionnaires can disadvantage people from lower socio-economic backgrounds.*

conclusion

The research thus far, although neither complete nor conclusive, points to some degree of indirect socio-economic sorting in schools which act as their own admission authorities. Whether faith-based selection can be isolated as the sole determinant, however, is not firmly established. While there may be good reasons to challenge faith-based selection, it would not solve the wider problem of socio-economic filtering which occurs at all oversubscribed schools.

chapter 3 – references

1   Anne West, Eleanor Barham and Audrey Hind, *Secondary school admissions in England: Policy and practice* (London School of Economics and Political Science, 2009), p. 9.

2   Ibid.

3   Ibid., p. 26.

4   Ibid. (para 1.71).

5   Rebecca Allen, 'Diversity of Schools: Faith Schools', *Minutes of Evidence taken before the Children, Schools and Families Committee* HC 311 – iii (House of Commons, Wednesday, 12 March 2008).

6   Summary of Sarah Tough and Richard Brooks, *School Admissions Report: Fair choice for parents and pupils* (IPPR, 2007). http://www.ippr.org/images/media/files/publication/2011/05/schooladmissions_1582.pdf as cited in http://accordcoalition.org.uk/wp-content/.uploads/2013/02/Databank-of-Independent-Evidence-on-Faith-Schools-April-2013.pdf.

7   Tough and Brooks, *School Admissions Report* p. 16.

8   National Union of Teachers, *In Good Faith: the report of the Executive Task Group on Faith Schools* (2008) http://www.teachers.org.uk/files/In%20Good%20Faith%2028pp%20.pdf, 4.

9   Tough and Brooks, *School Admissions* Report, p. 4.

10   Rebecca Allen, *Choice-based secondary school admissions in England: social stratification and the distribution of educational outcomes,* PhD thesis (Institute of Education: University of London, 2008).

11   Ibid, p. 115.

12   Rebecca Allen, Professor Mark Halstead, Professor Audrey Osler and Professor Anne West, The Right Reverend Stephen Venner, The Right Reverend Patrick O'Donoghue and Peter Irvine. 'Diversity of Schools: Faith Schools', Minutes of Evidence.

13   http://accordcoalition.org.uk/wp-content/uploads/2013/02/Databank-of-Independent-Evidence-on-Faith-Schools-April-2013.pdf.

14   http://www.guardian.co.uk/education/2012/mar/05/church-schools-shun-poorest-pupils.

15   http://fairadmissions.org.uk/why-is-this-an-issue/ (Accessed 21 August 2013).

16   http://www.guardian.co.uk/education/2012/mar/05/church-schools-shun-poorest-pupils.

17   Ibid.

18   John Flint, 'Faith-based schools: institutionalizing parallel lives?' in Adam Dinham, Robert Furbey and Vivien Lowndes, *Faith in the Public Realm: Controversies, policies and practices* (The Policy Press, 2009), p. 177.

19   Geoffrey Walford, *Educational Politics:Pressure Groups and Faith-Based Schools* (Aldershot, 1995), p. 124.

20   Ibid, p. 120.

21 Rebecca Allen and Anne West, 'Why do faith secondary schools have advantaged intakes? The relative importance of neighbourhood characteristics, social background and religious identification among parents', *British Educational Research Journal* 37(4): 691–712, (2011) p. 691.

22 Tough and Brooks, *School Admissions Report*, p. 17.

23 Ibid.

24 Ibid, pp. 6–7.

25 West et al, *Secondary school admissions in England*.

26 Ibid.

27 Ibid, p. 37.

28 Damian Hinds MP, 'Select Committee Questions Media Reporting of Church Schools' Admissions Criteria' (4 February 2011). Accessed online at http://www.damianhinds.com/Content%20-%20 PDF%20Docs%20for%20web%20site/PR%20Faith%20Schools.pdf.

29 Ibid.

30 http://fairadmissions.org.uk/why-is-this-an-issue/faqs/.

31 *Unlocking the gates: Giving disadvantaged children a fairer deal in school admissions* (Barnardo's, 2010).

32 Allen and West, 'Why do faith secondary schools have advantaged intakes?'.

33 Dr Craig commenting on Office of the School Adjudicator Report, 2010 http://www.telegraph. co.uk/education/educationnews/8102227/Faith-schools-skewing-admissions-rules.html.

34 Allen and West, 'Why do faith secondary schools have advantaged intakes?', p. 708.

35 http://accordcoalition.org.uk/wp-content/uploads/2013/02/Databank-of-Independent-Evidence-on-Faith-Schools-April-2013.pdf.

4

is there a faith school effect?

One of the most popular arguments in favour of state-maintained faith schools is that these schools achieve better academic results than community, or non-religious state schools. It is to this argument from attainment – the ostensible ability of faith schools to achieve higher levels of pupil attainment by means of their superior 'ethos' – that Tony Blair turned to justify his encouragement of the increase in the numbers of state-funded faith schools in England and Wales. The Labour government Green Paper, *Schools Building on Success* (2001), cited the "good record" held by these schools in "delivering a high quality of education", and this association between faith schools and greater academic attainment has continued to influence government policy ever since.[1] Against this, faith school critics claim that the admissions policies of these schools (referring here in particular to voluntary aided faith schools) allow these schools to handpick students by ability and socio-economic position under the guise of religious faith, and that this process accounts for any and all levels of heightened academic attainment. This chapter examines two questions: Do faith schools promote higher academic achievement? And if so, what are the causal factors?

higher academic achievement

A recent investigation carried out by *The Daily Telegraph* used data provided by the Department for Education to illustrate that 60% of 'top-scoring' primary schools in England, schools in which all pupils achieved the expected attainment levels in English and Maths, were faith schools.[2] Of the 898 state-maintained primary schools in England which achieved government targets for Key Stage Two (KS2) examinations across the board – all pupils achieving a Level 4 in the KS2 National Curriculum Tests (SATs) – 64% were faith schools, despite only constituting around 35% of primary schools overall.

At the top end of the scale, the dominance of faith schools in the league table is even clearer: of those schools which dramatically exceeded government targets for KS2 in 2012, with 75% or more of all pupils attaining a Level 5 in their KS2 assessments, 70% (48 schools) were faith-based. A 2008 report confirmed that in primary education, taking account of the prior attainment levels of pupils and allowing for other factors known to influence pupil attainment, such as ethnicity, sex and socio-economic position, faith schools do have higher levels of pupil progress than non-faith.[3]

It appears that the academic effect of faith-based primary schools is strongest for children with special educational needs: a 2005 study found whilst pupils at faith-based primary schools had an average academic advantage of one years over their counterparts at non-faith schools, this rose to 1.5 years for the academically weakest quarter of pupils. Examination results of pupils at non-faith-based primary schools were three times poorer than those at faith-based primary schools.[4] These data point towards a level of greater academic attainment in primary level faith schools, and are supported by a number of further studies.[5]

This picture of higher academic attainment seems to translate into secondary education, though not at the same magnitude. Data released by the Department for Education in February 2013 revealed that of all the state-maintained secondary schools in England where 50% or more of pupils achieved the government target of five A* to C grade GCSEs (regardless of whether these schools were selective in admissions in terms of religion or academic background, i.e. whether these schools set entrance examinations) just under a third of these schools (32%) were faith-based, where faith schools are around 20% of the total. Moreover, of those schools which dramatically exceeded the government target, with 80% or more of their pupils attaining five A* to C grade GCSEs, over half (53%) were faith schools.[6] A series of studies carried out by Andrew Morris between 1993 and 2005 illustrates that students in Catholic secondary schools tend to fare better in GCSE examinations – but notes that this effect does not continue to A-level.[7] Both of these points are backed up by a 2006 report produced by the Catholic Education Service.[8]

causation

Faith school critics argue that any positive differences between the academic achievements of faith schools and other state-maintained schools are directly attributable to the admission policies of faith schools, and thus to the previous attainment levels and the contextual socio-economic make up of their pupils. This claim is corroborated, at least in part, by government-sponsored research. A report published by the Centre for the Economics of Education – an independent research centre founded by the Department for Education and Skills – sought to compare the achievement of pupils at faith and non-faith-based state-maintained schools at the end of their primary education (aged 11). This study estimated that there is only a "small advantage" (approximately a 1% increase on age-12 examination results) from attending a faith-based primary school, and surmised that the so-called 'faith school effect' can be largely attributed to differences "between pupils who attend these schools and those who do not".[9] Interestingly, this study found that all faith-based primary schools (both voluntary aided and voluntary controlled), and all primary schools without a religious character but with a degree of autonomy from their local authority (e.g., control over admissions policies) start from an academic advantage when compared to non-autonomous state-maintained schools. Pupils arrive at these schools with a 1.2 to 1.7 point head start on their contemporaries (where one point is equal to one school term).[10] Again, this suggests that improved academic attainment is not due to a faith school effect, but to autonomy over selection criteria.

While the authors of the 2006 report suggested that any academic benefit of attending a faith-based primary school can be primarily attributed to its VA status[11], the report found 'no evidence' that pupils who attended a VC faith-based primary school outperform pupils from non faith-based state primaries at age 11 examinations.[12]

A 2005 analysis of statistical evidence also suggests that not only is the difference in attainment between faith-based and other state-maintained schools 'extremely small', but that in cases where faith schools do achieve "good 'raw' results" – in this case referring particularly to the quality of the results of Church of England schools – this is generally attributable to the "nature and quality of their intake."[13] A succession of studies carried out in relation to faith-based primary schools in England in 2009 suggest that any increase in academic attainment can be primarily attributed to "prior attainment", "background", "parental self-selection", and the "selection methods used by some faith schools".[14] This report also found that while "non-faith schools perform better in certain categories, faith schools do better in others and there is no clear difference in some."[15] Higher levels of academic attainment in faith-based primary schools, it seems, cannot be solely attributed to the faith-based nature of the school itself.

> *Higher levels of academic attainment in faith-based primary schools cannot be solely attributed to the faith-based nature of the school itself.*

The Accord Coalition also asserts that better exam results in faith schools are due to the profile of their pupil intake.[16] They conducted research to test the claim that students in faith schools fared better academically than students at non-faith schools. They compared faith school performance in exam result league tables and Contextual Value Added score (CVA) league tables. The CVA is regarded as the fairest government indicator of school performance. The measure adjusts the impact of external factors like "pupil mobility, ethnicity and deprivation on school attainment".[17] This comparison revealed that faith schools perform better overall in exam result league tables than CVA league tables. This seems to support their claim that superior academic results are the result of student selection rather than the 'faith' status of the school.

Andrew Morris however disputes the assertion that there is a link between higher academic achievement and student selection. He states that his analysis "provides firm evidence that (for the particular cohort he examined) the higher attainment and greater progress of pupils attending Catholic schools is not explained by socio-economic factors or pupil characteristics".[18] However, he goes on to argue, while it is certainly the case that different statistical approaches would result in some variation in the detail of our findings, the extent of the Catholic differential could be in either direction. They may find a narrower performance gap. On the other hand, they could show even stronger evidence than we have done for the existence of a 'Catholic school effect'.[19]

Nonetheless, there is some evidence that the "values, attitudes and practices seemingly inherent in the traditional confessional model of Catholic school can provide a particularly supportive environment for high academic attainment, especially by socially disadvantaged pupils".[20] Data presented in a small-scale study suggested that "the Catholic sector schools seem able to generate and sustain a positive school culture that can mitigate the effects of deprivation more easily than the generality of other schools".[21] These findings call for more extensive research into the impact of ethos on academic attainment.

> "non-faith schools perform better in certain categories, faith schools do better in others and there is no clear difference in some."

conclusion

Reports of higher academic attainment in faith schools frequently make the headlines. The research seems to support the claim that students in faith schools, generally do fare better academically than their counterparts in non-faith schools. At the moment, the body of evidence appears to suggest this is probably primarily the outcome of selection processes. It is possible that faith schools could "do well because the families represented are a part of a recognisable community, and that as a consequence there would be shared values, a high degree of parental support and good home-school relations".[22] However, this hypothesis has not been tested in any of the research we have reviewed. Further, the impact of ethos on academic attainment has not been systematically explored. The research also points to the possibility that faith schools may have a more positive effect on students from deprived backgrounds, although more research on 'ethos' is again required to substantiate this claim.

chapter 4 – references

1   http://www.archive.official-documents.co.uk/document/cm50/5050/5050.pdf.

2   Sam Marsden, 'Primary School league tables 2012: Faith Schools account for six out of ten top scoring Primaries', *The Daily Telegraph* (14 December 2012).

3   Tilaye Yeshanew, Ian Schagen and Suzanne Evans, 'Faith Schools and Pupils' Progress through Primary Education', *Educational Studies* 34 (2008), pp. 511–526.

4   Sig Prais, 'The Superior Educational Attainments of Pupils in Religious Foundation Schools in England', *National Institute Economic Review* 193 (2005): pp. 102–105.

5   Yeshanew et al, 'Faith Schools and Pupils' Progress, Andrew Morris. 'Parents, Pupils and their Catholic Schools: evidence from School Inspections in England 2000-2005', *International Studies in Catholic Education* (2010), pp. 80–94; Andrew Morris and Ray Godfrey. 'Statistical Survey of the Attainment of Pupils in Catholic Schools in England with particular reference to Secondary Schools operating under the Trust Deed of the Archdiocese of Birmingham', National Institute for Christian Education Research (2006), pp. 1–50.

6   Data provided by the Department for Education [accessed 20 February 2013]. Data tables available at: http://www.education.gov.uk/cgi-bin/schools/performance/group.pl?qtype=NAT&superview=sec&view=aat&set=1&sort=&ord=&tab=149&no=999.

7   Andrew Morris, 'Catholic and other Secondary Schools: an analysis of OFSTED Inspection Reports, 1993 – 1995, *Educational Research* 40 (1998), pp. 181–190; Andrew Morris, 'So Far, So Good: Levels of academic achievement in Catholic Schools', *Oxford Review of Education* 31 (2005), p. 311–330; Andrew Morris, 'Contextualising Catholic School performance in England', *Oxford Review of Education* 35 (2009), pp. 725–741; Andrew Morris and Ray Godfrey, 'Statistical Survey of the Attainment of Pupils in Catholic Schools in England with particular reference to Secondary Schools operating under the Trust Deed of the Archdiocese of Birmingham', *National Institute for Christian Education Research* (2006), pp. 1–50; Andrew Morris, 'Parents, Pupils and their Catholic Schools: evidence from school inspections in England 2000-2005, *International Studies in Catholic Education* (2010), pp. 80–94.

8   Catholic Education Service, *Quality and Performance: a survey of Education in Catholic Schools* (2006), pp. 1–44.

9   Stephen Gibbons and Olmo Silva. *Faith Primary Schools: Better Schools or Better Pupils?* CEEDP 72 (London: Centre for the Economics of Education, 2006).

10 Ibid, p. 18.

11 Ibid, p. 17.

12 Ibid, p. 20.

13 Schagen I and Schagen S 'The impact of faith schools on pupil performance' in Roy Gardner, Jo Cairns and Denis Lawton (eds) *Faith Schools: Consensus or Conflict?* (New York: Routledge, 2005), p. 210.

14 *Faith Schools: Admissions and Performance* (House of Commons Library: 2009).

15   Ibid.

16   http://accordcoalition.org.uk/wp-content/uploads/2013/02/Databank-of-Independent-Evidence-on-Faith-Schools-April-2013.pdf.

17   Ibid.

18   Andrew Morris and Ray Godfrey, 'A Statistical Survey of Attainment in Catholic Schools in England with Particular Reference to Secondary Schools Operating Under the Trust Deed of the Archdiocese of Birmingham' (Archdiocese of Birmingham, 2006).

19   Ibid, p. 32.

20   Andrew Morris, Academic Standards in Catholic Schools in England: Indications of Causality, *London Review of Education* 3(1): 81-99, (2005), p. 94 .

21   Andrew Morris, 'The Academic Attainment of Disadvantaged Pupils: Some Avenues of Inquiry'. Unpublished paper.

22   Schagen and Schagen, 'The impact of faith schools on pupil performance', p. 211.

5

do faith schools offer a distinctive education experience?

Critics of faith schools suggest that these schools do not serve a genuine religious function. Instead, they argue that parents' decisions to send their children to faith schools are informed primarily by the schools' academic performance. A 2010 YouGov/ITV Daybreak poll, appears to support this claim. It revealed that just 9% of parents consider the religion of the school to be one of their top three factors when choosing schools.[1] Factors such as the school's performance, how easy it was to get into, the area in which it is situated, the preference of the child, the facilities, class sizes and curriculum offered were ranked ahead of the school's religious affiliation. Such research however fails to grapple in a meaningful and nuanced way with the enduring appeal of faith schools. In particular, do faith schools offer a distinctive education experience? Is there something about a faith school's ethos, which promotes higher academic attainment and the development of character (or virtue)?[2]

There does not appear to be a common language amongst researchers or research participants for talking about values, character development, spirituality or ethos; nor are there agreed definitions for these concepts.[3] What is the difference, for instance, between a school's culture, climate and ethos?[4] Further, is 'ethos' confined to the classroom or school, or is it embodied in a broader philosophy of education? These questions point to the difficulties associated with defining, quantifying and therefore studying 'ethos'.

Although ill-defined, Andrew Morris suggests that pupils have some awareness of 'ethos'. Interviewing students who moved from a Catholic school to a secular sixth-form college, Morris noted that these pupils highlighted the difference in ethos, paying tribute to the 'secure' atmosphere of the Catholic school and mentioning its 'aura' – noting that a "very strong Christian outlook on life comes through."[5]

academic attainment

There is some research, which suggests that schools with a strong sense of identity or ethos perform better academically.[6] As previously outlined, Andrew Morris' research suggests that higher academic performance is linked to a school's ethos rather than other socio-economic determinants. Some commentators offer reasons why ethos may influence academic attainment. These include:

- A religious stance that is shared, celebrated and motivates the school community to respect and honour the innate abilities of self and others;

- A greater sense of vocational commitment on the part of teachers to sustain a faith ethos;

- Greater parental involvement and commitment to the school;

- An emphasis on the pastoral activities of the school with a marked focus on building a community with high expectations of behaviour and attendance;

- An emphasis on a wide range of pedagogical methods and less emphasis on wholesale 'child centred' approaches and a stronger atmosphere of order;

- Greater emphasis on academic as opposed to vocational courses, particularly a strong focus on religious education and the humanities;

- An atmosphere of success and belonging with strong parental support – on average, providing a more homogenous school system of norms and values.[7]

In the absence of a definition or method of quantifying ethos, however, much more research is required before these claims can be substantiated.

character development

The idea that there is a connection between educational ethos and character development dates back to Aristotle.[8] Although there is no systematic study of ethos in character development, some research suggests that faith schools might be able to support character development. Theos' *Mapping the Field* review found that pupils at church-maintained schools and independent Christian schools showed a more positive attitude towards religion and better spiritual health than pupils in other schools.[9] The Learning for Life project on character education, which is funded by the Templeton Foundation and administered by Canterbury Christ Church University, also found that students lacked a formal language to express concepts of values and virtues.[10] They found that 'the most important pedagogical strategy for character formation in schools is teachers modelling values. Students see schools as places that help to shape their values, but not through assemblies, tutor time or in non-examinable subjects'.[11] That faith schools have the potential to meet these needs in a unique way ought not to be understated. Trevor Cooling, for instance, challenges the assumption that education is a worldview-neutral activity.[12] He underscores how faith schools can offer a foundation for character education beyond RE classes, for example, in subjects like history, literature, biology, and mathematics. His thesis rests on the claim that "what teachers teach and the way they teach it is heavily coloured by who they are and what they understand as being of value".[13]

conclusion

It is clear that the actual impact of ethos in faith schools is under-explored. As a result, it is impossible to offer even a tentative answer to the question posed by this chapter. It is hoped that these gaps will be remedied in part by the findings of Trevor Cooling's two year project investigating "the impact of a distinctively Christian education". The project due to be delivered in August 2014, will investigate the impact of secondary schools' implementation of a distinctively Christian ethos in their approaches to teaching and learning.

chapter 5 – references

1   YouGov/ITV Daybreak Survey Results (September 2010) Accessed online at: http://cdn.yougov. com/today_uk_import/YG-Archives-Life-YouGov-DaybreakReligion-130910.pdf .

2   Terence McLaughlin, 'The Educative Importance of Ethos', *British Journal of Educational Studies* 53(3), 306-325, (2005).

3   Elizabeth Green, *Mapping the Field* (Theos, 2009).

4   Derek Glover and Marianne Coleman, 'School Culture, Climate and Ethos: interchangeable or distinctive concepts?', *Journal of In-service Education*, 31(2), 251–271, (2005).

5   Andrew Morris. 'The Catholic School Ethos: its effect on post-16 Student Academic Achievement', Educational Studies 21 (1995), pp. 78–79.

6   McLaughlin, 'The Educative Importance of Ethos', p. 306

7   J Arthur and R.C. Godfrey, *Statistical Survey of the Attainment and Achievement of Pupils in Church of England Schools*; Andrew Morris, 'Same Mission, Same Methods, Same Results? Academic and Religious Outcomes from Different Models of Catholic Schooling', *British Journal of Educational Studies* 45 (1997) pp. 378–391; Andrew Morris, 'The Catholic School Ethos: its effect on post-16 Student Academic Achievement', *Educational Studies* 21(1) (1995): pp. 67–83; Andrew Morris, 'Academic standards in Catholic Schools in England: Indications of Causality', *London Review of Education* 3 (2005): pp. 81–99.

8   McLaughlin, 'The Educative Importance of Ethos', p. 306.

9   Elizabeth Green, *Mapping the Field* (Theos, 2009).

10   http://www.learningforlife.org.uk/research/research-projects/character-education-the-formation-of-virtues-and-dispositions-in-16-19-year-olds-with-particular-reference-to-the-religious-and-spiritual/.

11   Ibid.

12   Trevor Cooling, *Doing God in Education* (Theos, 2010).

13   Ibid, p. 8.

conclusions and recommendations

This report has tried to offer a summary and analysis of the evidence on 'faith schools' in England. It has asked two interrelated questions: 'What do state-maintained "faith schools" offer students?' and 'How do state-maintained "faith schools" impact society?' These are explored through four different issues: potential divisiveness in relation to race and ethnicity; potential socio-economic sorting; the effect of faith schools on pupil outcomes; and faith schools' ability to deliver a distinctive education experience. Despite the certainty of many commentators on these questions, we have come up with no conclusive answer to any of the four. This is partly due to the need for further research, but also may reflect the diversity of even those 'faith schools' we have included in this report. As noted, speaking about these schools as a monolithic block is necessarily misleading, and the distinction between faith schools and community schools is less clear-cut than often perceived.

With these caveats, this survey of the existing evidence points to the following conclusions:

- Faith schools' contribution to community cohesion in relation to race, ethnicity and minority religious communities, despite some dire public warnings, does not seem to be problematic. The research we have reviewed suggests that faith schools do not promote social division along racial or ethnic lines. While some research suggests that faith schools may have actually had a positive impact on community cohesion, at worst their efforts would appear to be on par with the broader education system.

- Our review of the existing research confirms that there is some evidence of indirect socio-economic sorting in schools which act as their own admission authorities, irrespective of their faith status. Using the contested measure of pupils' eligibility for free school meals, faith schools (particularly voluntary aided schools) are less representative of the socio-economic composition of their local authority and postcode compared to community schools. While the use of faith-based selection criteria in oversubscribed schools may indirectly privilege pupils from higher socio-economic backgrounds, there is no evidence that this is the intention of schools. Neither is its eradication likely to be a panacea for the broader, deeper and more complex socio-economic context of English society of which faith schools are a small part.

• There is some research which indicates that faith schools have particular strengths in meeting the needs of primary children with special educational needs. In addition, there is some evidence of higher academic attainment in faith schools, particularly at the primary school level. In the absence of research which examines the role of a faith 'ethos', the balance of evidence suggests this is the outcome of pupil selection processes rather than the 'faith' status of the school.

• Whether faith schools offer a distinctive education experience remains the most difficult question to answer. Ethos is a difficult concept to define and quantify. Consequently, the claim that a school's ethos might contribute to academic attainment or character development in a way that is distinct from schools without a religious character is hard to verify.

It is hoped that this report will be of use for those wanting a balanced summary of the existing evidence on these questions, so the authors have refrained from offering opinion or recommendations up to this point, seeking simply to offer a resource. However, in light of these conclusions the report concludes with some tentative recommendations.

recommendations

The research around faith schools, despite some excellent work, is as yet relatively sparse and inconclusive, although one would not always know this from the tone of the debate. This shows how ideologically-loaded the issue has become, acting as a battleground on which to fight larger battles about the role of religion in an increasingly plural society.

• We recommend that all those engaged in the debate acknowledge the partiality and contested nature of many of the conclusions and seek to make conversations more constructive.

• In particular, participants in the debate should be more open about the values underpinning it. At base, this is not a debate that can be decided on evidence alone, but is also about the kind of society we want to live in. Differing conceptions of pluralism, secularism and the primacy of equality over other moral concerns are often the true points of tension, rather than any one group having a unique concern for quality education or the well-being of pupils. Being clearer about where the points of tension really are might help make the debate more honest.

- As it stands, the evidence that the higher academic attainment of faith schools is due to something other than pupil selection criteria is weak. Therefore, for supporters of faith schools, we recommend moving away from a justification on the basis of academic outcomes and instead developing a stronger understanding and articulation of the value of an education in a school with a religious character, possibly in relation to ethos, a more holistic approach and development of character. More research into this will be required.

- For Christian schools in particular, there seem to be good reasons to reassess policies around pupil selection. The most pressing concern should be to ensure that applicants from less privileged backgrounds are fairly represented in the school's intake. Secondly, some schools may wish to explore ways to maintain their religious character whilst broadening their selection basis because of their historic ethic of hospitality and concern for the poorest in society.

responses

Simon Barrow, Ekklesia and the Accord Coalition

In averting to the way debates about religion in the public sphere influence thinking about education, *More than an Educated Guess* asks how we envision common spaces like schools in our society. "Are they 'neutral' spaces that require us to disregard our religious, philosophical and cultural identities? Or can they be spaces where we come together in difference *and* equality?"

The way these questions are formulated could lead us to suppose that non-partisan approaches to schooling must somehow be sterilising of identities, that identities are more received than developed, or that difference and equality might require (rather than need to negotiate with) the prescriptions of denominationally-based schooling.

As in other areas cited, the issues do not have to be construed in this way. While entrenched or ideological positions are bound to exist in any public policy deliberation, the encouraging news is that the ground is gradually shifting in the debate about schools of a religious character. The case for reform is being articulated more broadly than ever before – not in opposition to diversity, but precisely in order to ensure it.

That is why the Runnymede Trust, in its groundbreaking report *Right to Divide? Faith Schools and Community Cohesion*, argued that in order that "faith should continue to play an important role in our education system" selection on the basis of religious affiliation should be ended, children should have a greater say in how they are educated, RE should be part of a core national curriculum, and faith schools should serve the most disadvantaged and value all young people – a shared ethos to which people of all faiths and none can contribute.

The trajectory of *More than an Educated Guess* seems less persuaded of the need for this shift. It rightly speaks of a desire to "clear the ground" and to consider "all available and relevant research" in assessing the impact of "state maintained" (in fact state-funded) religious foundation schools. Yet serious questions will inevitably be raised about its selection, comprehension, interpretation, evaluation and presentation of research data and findings – as well as the account given of several organisations involved in the current debate.

For example, it assesses positively the Church of England report *Strong schools for strong communities*, which Parliamentary Under Secretary of State for Schools Lord Nash cited (22 July 2013) as demonstrating, on the basis of Ofsted data, that in the secondary sector "faith schools contributed more highly to community cohesion than community schools." But it does not relate this to the Education Act 2011 actually removing Ofsted's requirement to inspect the contribution made by schools to community cohesion, or to its previous inspection taking no account of a school's admissions policies, assemblies or provision of Religious Education – all vitally important areas when considering the impact of publicly funded faith schools on society and students.

Questions are raised against a "reading of the IPPR report" (*School Admissions: Fair choice for parents and pupils*) which "suggests that while all schools that act as their own admissions authorities are likely to be unrepresentative of their local areas, this is particularly pronounced in faith schools." Yet this is the actual finding of IPPR's research, which unambiguously states that "Faith schools which are their own admission authorities are ten times more likely to be highly unrepresentative of their surrounding area than faith schools where the local authority is the admission authority", while "Non-religious schools which are their own admissions authorities are six times more likely to be highly unrepresentative of their surrounding area than community schools for whom the local authority is the admission authority."

Equally, it is not the case that the Accord Coalition and the Fair Admissions Campaign argue for just one model of inclusive education – their diverse members promote a range of practical reforms and derive inspiration for their values from different sources, religious and non-religious. Nor is it the case that they do so "without regard to religion or belief" – both use this term specifically to argue against *excluding* pupils and staff on grounds of religion or belief. This is entirely different and indicates respect rather than disregard for such differences.

There are also some surprising omissions. There is no reference to the widely discussed data showing that faith schools take fewer children with Special Educational Needs than other schools.

These and other important questions raised by the approach, method and findings of *More than an Educated Guess* illustrate the vital need to continue the conversation about how faith schools can contribute to education that truly serves the needs of the whole community – not least those marginalised by the increasing segmentation of our schooling.

The Right Reverend Malcolm Mcmahon OP, Chairman of the Catholic Education Service

In a public sphere where there is a fair amount of heat in the debate surrounding schools with a religious character, this report attempts to provide a balanced overview of the current research, which is much needed. It is refreshingly professional in its discussion of the complex issues surrounding faith schools.

We very much welcome the report's conclusion of the need for substantial additional research in this field. We also welcome the recommendation that all those involved in the debate seek to make conversations more constructive. As a contribution to this process, the Catholic Education Service (CES) intends to respond in a more detailed way following the publication of the report.

One particular area where further research is needed is the question of whether schools with a religious character, and especially Catholic schools, are less socially mixed. As an education provider with a particular mission to the poor, we find that the measure of Free School Meal take-up does not accurately represent our school communities. We know from the Income Deprivation Affecting Children Index (IDAC Index) that Catholic schools serve poorer communities than other schools (20% of pupils at Catholic maintained secondary schools live in the most deprived areas compared with 17% of pupils nationally), but this isn't always indicated in the uptake of Free School Meals in those same schools.

Although we appreciate that policy makers (particularly in the Department for Education) perceive Free School Meals data to be the least inaccurate indicator, it clearly conflicts with other available data. This conflict needs to be explained. There could be a range of reasons why eligible pupils in Catholic schools aren't claiming Free Schools Meals. Research which is currently being carried out by the CES highlights that pupils aren't claiming due to immigration status, a lack of recourse to pupil funds, cultural differences as well as the fact that some local authorities already provide Free School Meals to all pupils, so parents see no reason to claim.

We believe it would be helpful if the government and commentators would look at a range of indicators rather than just one, to get a more accurate and rounded picture. We would like to see, for instance, research on how much difference different types of school make to those pupils with the most challenging backgrounds. The Catholic Church has always set itself the mission to make the greatest difference to those who are poorest – in the broadest sense of the word. We need to challenge ourselves to ensure we continue to live up to that mission.

A large part of the history of English Catholicism over the last two hundred years has been a story of immigration. The Catholic community here has been strengthened by these waves of immigration with huge numbers of Irish in the nineteenth century through to more recent times with large numbers of Eastern European, African and South American immigrants. This cultural and ethnic diversity in our churches is even more marked in our Catholic schools which have higher proportions of pupils from ethnic minorities than the national averages.

One of the celebrated strengths of our English education system is that it has never been a 'one size fits all' system. The former Education Minister, Lord Hill of Oareford described it as "a patchwork quilt of provision." We celebrate the diversity which has been reflected in English education law from the very beginnings of state funded education.

A golden thread which has run through education policy over the last century is the one of parental choice, and it is in this context that having a diverse educational system is a strength rather than a weakness. A wide range of education provision to suit the needs of local communities is essential to the continuing success of English education and Catholic schools play an important part in this rich tapestry.

We welcome the recommendation that a stronger understanding of the place of values and ethos in education needs to be developed. Nevertheless, we also place an emphasis on Catholic schools performing well. Canon Law 806 §2 states that schools have a duty to ensure that "academic standards, [are] at least as outstanding as that in other schools in the area." This duty is shown in the success of pupils at Catholic schools in all stages, with Catholic schools outperforming the national average at SAT level and in GCSEs.

The Catholic Church owns over 2,100 schools in England; educating over 808,000 pupils, and employing over 45,500 teachers. This is all part of our contribution to civil society and to the Common Good.

We thank Theos for highlighting the important role that Church schools and other schools with religious character play in contributing to the common good of society as a whole and we look forward to the future research which will support this.

Right Reverend John Pritchard, Bishop of Oxford, Chair of Church of England Board of Education and National Society

I welcome this report and its attempt to draw together some of the evidence about schools with a religious character (which the report refers to as faith schools). The report argues against drawing simplistic conclusions and we echo its call for further research in a number of areas. It also recognises that 'faith schools' are diverse in nature, so we must be careful not to make sweeping generalisations about such a complex sector.

The report warns of the danger of making schools, and the education of our children, a battleground for a discussion about the role of religion in a plural society. Campaigns led by the British Humanist Association, the National Secular Society and Accord continually seek to question the legitimacy of faith schools and their existence within this country's education system, which inevitably leads to a defence from the churches and, all too quickly, schools do find themselves at the centre of a debate which should properly be focused elsewhere. Shifting this debate away from its simplistic focus on schools would leave educationalists free to examine the role faith-based schools play in developing character and securing educational achievement, as well as being more able to make an honest assessment of why such schools remain so popular.

The report asks whether faith schools are divisive and elitist and whether their ethos has any effect on achievement. Our own recent reports (*Church School of the Future* and *A DBE for the Future*) enable me to frame my response using rather more positive language, referring to our schools as being effective, distinctive and inclusive: positive terms which are actually borne out by the substance of the Theos report.

How we measure the effectiveness of an education and of our schools is clearly an area which needs a great deal more research. We choose to focus overtly and transparently on ethos and the values underpinned by the Christian narrative because we believe they lead to the development of character and virtues which will serve children well through their adult lives. This may, or may not, have a significant impact on their academic achievement (and my expectation is that the research will demonstrate that it does) but, whilst we are 100% committed to the need for our schools to enable children to achieve their very best academically, we do not think that this is the sole purpose of education. In calling for further research, I would also welcome some more longitudinal studies which assess the effect of ethos- and virtue-based education on: a child's development into adulthood; the family; the workplace; and what is broadly defined as social capital. Our Church schools' distinctive approach stems from the absolute belief that such things really matter for the good of society, these are far greater goals than the position of the school in this year's performance tables.

Since the Dearing report (2001), the Church of England has emphasised that our schools are inclusive as well as effective and distinctive, and I am pleased to see that this report recognises two very important facts. The first is that faith schools contribute successfully to community cohesion; they are culturally diverse and there is no evidence that there is any social division on racial or ethnic grounds.

This distinctive and inclusive approach naturally leads to an examination of admissions and so the second important fact acknowledged in the Theos report is that faith schools do not intentionally filter or skew admissions in a way which is designed to manipulate the system.

The report rightly recognises the complexity of the situation and cautions against drawing simplistic conclusions, but affirms that faith schools' admissions policies are clear, transparent and fair. Attendance of a church is the only basis upon which objective assessment can be made, but this is an activity entirely open to all irrespective of wealth or background. Nevertheless, we are still left with some challenging questions about how we can ensure that pupils from less privileged backgrounds are fairly represented in the school's intake. But, as the report makes clear, this is a problem throughout any system which espouses parental choice, it is not peculiar to faith schools. Any over-subscribed school faces the same issues, not least because of the link between the popularity of a school and the value of housing in its catchment area.

One conclusion to all of this might be that, rather than continually adopting the 'battleground' approach, which often leads to a reticence on the part of local authorities to expand faith school provision, a better way would be to celebrate the quality, popularity and success of faith schools and seek to expand them. This way the problems of oversubscription and resulting admissions criteria would be greatly reduced.

Such an approach would refocus the debate to make it more about the philosophy of education and the place of ethos, values, virtue, character and spirituality in the development of a successful school system. It may not attract the sensational headlines of some of the more familiar debates, but I suggest it would serve our children well.

bibliography

Accord Coalition, http://accordcoalition.org.uk/

Allen, Rebecca and West, Anne, 'Why do faith secondary schools have advantaged intakes? The relative importance of neighbourhood characteristics, social background and religious identification among parents', *British Educational Research Journal* 37(4): pp. 691–712, (2011).

Allen, Rebecca, *Choice-based secondary school admissions in England: social stratification and the distribution of educational outcomes.* PhD thesis, (Institute of Education: University of London, 2008).

Allen, Rebecca, Mark Halstead, Audrey Osler, Ann West, Stephen Venner, Patrick O'Donoghue and Peter Irvie, 'Diversity of Schools: Faith Schools', *Minutes of Evidence taken before the Children, Schools and Families Committee* HC 311 – iii (House of Commons, Wednesday, 12 March 2008).

Annette, John 'Faith schools and communities: communitarianism, social capital and citizenship', in *Faith Schools: Consensus or Conflict?*, edited by Roy Gardner, (Routledge, 2005).

Arthur, J and Godfrey, R.C, *Statistical Survey of the Attainment and Achievement of Pupils in Church of England Schools*; Andrew Morris, 'Same Mission, Same Methods, Same Results? Accademic and Religious Outcomes from Different Models of Catholic Schooling', *British Journal of Educational Studies* 45, (1997).

Arthur, J. 'Parental Involvement in Catholic Schools: a case of Increasing Conflict', *British Journal of Educational Studies* 42 (1994), pp. 174–190.

Barker, Rachel and Anderson, John, 'Segregation or cohesion: Church of England Schools in Bradford', in *Faith Schools: Consensus or Conflict?*, edited by Roy Gardner, (Routledge, 2005).

Barnardo's Policy and Research Unit, *Unlocking the gates: Giving disadvantaged children a fairer deal in school admissions* (Barnardo's, 2010).

Berkeley, Rob, *Right to Divide?: Faith Schools and Community Cohesion* (Runnymede, 2008).

British Humanist Association, https://humanism.org.uk/

Brown, Rupert, Adam Rutland and Charles Watters *Identities in Transition: A Longtitudinal Study of Immigrant Children*, (2008).

Bruegel, Irene, *Social Capital, Diversity and Education Policy*, (London South Bank University, August 2006) http://accordcoalition.org.uk/wp-content/uploads/2012/11/SCDiversityEdu28.8.06.pdf.

Burtonwood, Neil, *Cultural Diversity, Liberal Pluralism and Schools: Isaiah Berlin and Education* (Routledge International Studies in the Philosophy of Education, 2006).

Cairns, Jo, *Faith Schools and Society: Civilizing the debate* (Continuum, 2009).

Casson, Ann Elizabeth, *Perceptions of Catholicity in a plural society: an ethnographic case study of Catholic secondary schools in England*, PhD thesis (Institute of Education, University of Warwick, 2010).

Catholic Education Service, *Christ at the Centre* (Catholic Truth Society, 2013).

Catholic Education Service, *Quality and Performance: a survey of Education in Catholic Schools*, (2006).

Cooling, Trevor, *Doing God in Education*, (Theos, 2010).

Conway, David, 'Faith Schools: Enrichment or Division?', Paper delivered to the London Society for the Study of Religion, 7 June 2011, http://www.civitas.org.uk/pdf/Conway_FaithSchools.pdf.

Department for Children, Schools and Families, *Faith in the System: the Role of Schools with a Religious Character in English Education and Society* (Department for Children, Schools and Families, 2007).

Department for Education and Employment, *Schools Building on Success* (DfEE, 2001), http://www.archive.official-documents.co.uk/document/cm50/5050/5050.pdf.

Dinham, Adam, Robert Furbey and Vivien Lowndes, *Faith in the Public Realm: Controversies, policies and practices* (The Policy Press, 2009).

Donald, Alice, *Religion or belief, equality and human rights in England and Wales*, (Equality and Human Rights Commission Research Report 84, 2012).

Dwyer, Claire, and Violetta Parutis, '"Faith in the system" State-funded faith schools in England and the contested parameters of community cohesion' *Transactions of the Institute of British Geographers*, 38: 267–284, (2013).

Fair Admissions Campaign http://fairadmissions.org.uk/about/

Francis, Leslie J, Mandy Robbins and Jeff Astley, *Religion, Education and Adolescence* (University of Wales Press, 2005).

Gardner, Roy, Jo Cairns and Denis Lawton (eds.), *Faith Schools: Consensus or Conflict*, (Routledge, 2005).

Gibbons, Stephen and Olmo Silva *Faith Primary Schools: Better Schools or Better Pupils?* CEEDP 72 (London: Centre for the Economics of Education, 2006).

Glover, Derek and Marianne Coleman, 'School Culture, Climate and Ethos: interchangeable or distinctive concepts?', *Journal of In-service Education*, 31(2), 251–271, (2005).

Grace, Gerald, 'Educational Studies and Faith-Based Schooling: Moving from Prejudice to Evidence-Based Argument', *British Journal of Educational Studies* 51(2): 149-167, (June 2003).

Green, Elizabeth, *Mapping the Field*, (Theos, 2009).

Guasp, April, *The experiences of gay young people in Britain's young people in Britain's schools in 2012* (Stonewall, 2012).

Hart, Stuart, Cynthia Price Cohen, Martha Farrell Erickson and Malfrid Flekkoy, *Children's Rights in Education* (Jessica Kingsley Publishers, 2001).

Hinds MP, Damian, 'Select Committee Questions Media Reporting of Church Schools' Admissions Criteria' (4 February 2011). http://www.damianhinds.com/Content%20-%20 PDF%20Docs%20for%20web%20site/PR%20Faith%20Schools.pdf.

Jackson, Robert, 'Should the State Fund Faith-Based Schools? A Review of the Arguments', *British Journal of Religious Education* 25(2) 89-102 (2003).

Joint Committee on Human Rights, *Legislative Scrutiny: Equality Bill (second report); Fourteenth Report of Session* (House of Lords, House of Commons: 2010).

Knauth, Thorsten, *Encountering Religious Pluralism in School and Society: a Qualitative Study of Teenage Perspectives in Europe* (Waxman, Munster, 2008).

Learning for Life, http://www.learningforlife.org.uk/

Lord Lester of Herne Hill QC and David Pannick QC, *Human Rights Law and Practice*, (Butterworths, 2004).

Marsden, Sam, 'Primary School league tables 2012: Faith Schools account for six out of ten top scoring Primaries', *The Daily Telegraph* (14 December 2012).

Morris, Andrew, 'Parents, Pupils and their Catholic Schools: evidence from school inspections in England 2000-2005', *International Studies in Catholic Education* (2010).

Morris, Andrew, 'Bridging Worlds: Ethnic Minority Pupils in Catholic Schools in England', *Journal of Belief and Values* 31: 203–213, (2010).

Morris, Andrew, 'Contextualising Catholic School performance in England', *Oxford Review of Education* 35 725–741 (2009).

Morris, Andrew and Ray Godfrey, 'A Statistical Survey of Attainment in Catholic Schools in England with Particular Reference to Secondary Schools Operating Under the Trust Deed of the Archdiocese of Birmingham', (Archdiocese of Birmingham, 2006).

Morris, Andrew, 'So Far, So Good: Levels of academic achievement in Catholic Schools', *Oxford Review of Education* 31 311–330 (2005).

Morris, Andrew, 'Academic standards in Catholic Schools in England: Indications of Causality', *London Review of Education* 3 81–99 (2005).

Morris, Andrew, 'Same Mission, Same Methods, Same Results? Academic and Religious Outcomes from Different Models of Catholic Schooling', *British Journal of Educational Studies* 45 378–391 (1997).

Morris, Andrew, 'The Catholic School Ethos: its effect on post-16 Student Academic Achievement', *Educational Studies* 21(1) 67–83 (1995).

Morris, Andrew, 'The Academic Attainment of Disadvantaged Pupils: Some Avenues of Inquiry', unpublished paper.

Morris, Andrew, 'Some Social Benefits of English Catholic Schools', due for publication in *International Studies in Catholic Education 5*(2), (October 2013).

McLaughlin, Terence, 'The Educative Importance of Ethos', *British Journal of Educational Studies* 53(3), 306–325, (2005).

National Secular Society, http://www.secularism.org.uk/

National Union of Teachers, *In Good Faith: the report of the Executive Task Group on Faith Schools* (2008) http://www.teachers.org.uk/files/In%20Good%20Faith%2028pp%20.pdf

O'Keefe, Bernadette and Richard Zipfel *Ethnicity, identity and achievement in Catholic schools: supporting minority ethnic pupils in Catholic Secondary Schools*, (Catholic Education Service, 2003).

Parker-Jenkins, Marie, Dimitra Hartas and Barrie A Irving (eds.), *In Good Faith: Schools, Religion and Public Funding* (Ashgate, 2005).

Prais, Sig, 'The Superior Educational Attainments of Pupils in Religious Foundation Schools in England', *National Institute Economic Review* 193 102–105 (2005).

Shepherd, Peter, *Values for Church schools*, (Church House Publishing, 1998).

The Church of England, *Church School of the Future Review*, (Church of England Archbishops Council Education Division, 2012).

The Church of England, *Strong Schools for Strong Communities: Reviewing the impact of Church of England schools in promoting community cohesion*, (Church of England Archbishops' Council Education Division, 2009).

The Department of Education, http://www.education.gov.uk/

Tough, Sarah and Richard Brooks, *School Admissions Report: Fair choice for parents and pupils* (IPPR, 2007).

Vickers, Lucy, 'Religion and Belief Discrimination and the Employment of Teachers in Faith Schools', *Religion and Human Rights* 4: 137–156, (2009).

Walford, Geoffrey, *Educational Politics: Pressure Groups and Faith-Based Schools* (Aldershot, 1995).

West, Anne, Eleanor Barham and Audrey Hind, *Secondary school admissions in England: Policy and practice*, (London School of Economics and Political Science, 2009).

Worsley, Howard J ed., *Anglican Church School Education Moving Beyond the First Two Hundred Years*, (Bloomsbury, 2013).

Yeshanew, Tilaye, Ian Schagen and Suzanne Evans, 'Faith Schools and Pupils' progress through Primary Education', *Educational Studies* 34 (511–526).

YouGov/ITV Daybreak Survey Results (September 2010) http://cdn.yougov.com/today_uk_import/YG-Archives-Life-YouGov-DaybreakReligion-130910.pdf.

BROKEN WINGS

LOVE, LIES & FAIRY TALES

BROKEN WINGS

LOVE, LIES & FAIRY TALES

Mandy Morrissey

ISBN: 9781689640855

Published by Mandy Morrissey
ahmorrissey@outlook.com

To my family and close friends
We got there in the end!

For my beautiful boys
Harry, Olly & Danny.
Love you always.

MANDY MORRISSEY

One

DREGS

E ver get the feeling you're one breath away from your last? That someone out there wants you dead with an overdue squeeze of the larynx? Or a cowardly blunt blow to the back of the head?

Well, I hadn't. Well not until today. Well, actually, not until ten minutes ago!

I didn't see it coming, why would I...but they did. They wanted me dead, that I was certain. Don't ask me who, how many, or even how I knew. I just did.

It was a feeling like no other. A strange, mysterious, 'screw with your head' type feeling. Sixth sense? Maybe.

You can't quite put your finger on it, but you know it's there. You can smell it. Yet you ignore the warning shot as life's a game and you fancy your chances — well, you could say I fancied mine.

I'm not saying today was my day to die or if I would indeed die at all, but something was coming for me...one way or another. I could almost taste it.

This feeling in particular came out of nowhere, smacking me straight in the face like a hefty saturated nappy sack! But hey, here I was, kidding myself that I was ok. Doing what I always did — filing it away with no shits given.

With my back to the crowd, all eyes were on me — I was a sitting duck, no wonder I was drenched in an anxious layer of unexpected sweat. Seated at the front, I should have known

1

better. I was practically begging to be singled out. Though frankly, right now, I had bigger worries than a potential case of badly timed paranoia! What could be bigger than that, right? Well, in actual fact, today was the very first day of the rest of my life!

Two years of studying, twenty-four months of wild partying, seven hundred and thirty days of making lifelong friendships — and it was all about to end in less than twenty paltry minutes! I was on the verge of entering adulthood on my own two feet, with my college years patiently waiting to signal their retirement with a concluding ring of a tedious ear-splitting bell. I was scared, nervous, a little apprehensive, but most of all I had no idea what path I was likely to venture on. All I knew was that if the journey was anything like my life to date, then I was in for a long and bumpy ride.

Mrs. Chan, the Head of College, was stood proudly on the main assembly stage as she delivered the final sentiments of her tearful and awfully drawn out speech to us — her attentive students.

"There are no words left for me to say…apart from thank you — thank you from the bottom of my heart for your hard work, effort, grit and determination over these past two years. The future is yours for the taking, welcome all opportunities with the friendliest of handshakes, and learn from your mistakes. Better yourselves!

"Bla, bla, bla! Wrap it up already will you, Chan," I grumbled, rolling my daddy long-leg lashes towards my face-framing bangs.

She was milking this moment for all it was worth, and boy was it long-winded! Wasn't she in the slightest aware that some of us actually had lives to live!

"I wish each and every one of you all the success and happiness you truly deserve. For the last time, students of Eldercrest, please be dismissed!"

"Finally!" I mumbled.

With those concluding words, an out of tune chorus of

whooping, cheering and hollering filled the hall with furor. Our echoes bolted through the gap in the assembly double doors, surging through the corridors and spilling into the breakout areas.

Everyone, well everyone apart from me had someone to congratulate, shake hands with, hug or kiss. They all had somebody to cherish this memorable occasion with — apart from me, the miserable loner in the corner. Hoping not to be noticed, I hugged my well-worn study books closely against my chest and nimbly shuffled past the throng of jubilant bodies as they rejoiced in merriment.

So...I lied, I lied about the whole lifelong friendship thingy and then the little bit about the wild nights of partying. I was, however, completely telling the truth about the studying part, but I guess that's just because I didn't have the other two to distract me with.

Don't get me wrong, I wasn't a complete recluse. I had friends, in fact I had many friends, just not ones I could say were close enough to be lifelong, y'know? I knew them to say hello to or to chat about the weather with, but not one of them could I say, I actually felt comfortable enough to divulge my most intimate of feelings to. So, really, was it any wonder my lonely existence had driven me to conjure up these particularly rash and wacky thoughts of doom.

I was a private girl, a quiet girl. I didn't buy into the whole girly girl image. Sleepovers, hair rollers, tubs of sugary sweet ice-cream and unlimited gossip were not my thing. I was more your average tomboy — confident yet reserved. I knew my own mind and didn't rely on the acceptance of others to fit in. So, to be hit with a last-minute strain of trepidation from my peers was most bizarre!

You see, Eldercrest College was the kind of place, that if you didn't fit the mould, then you wouldn't fit in with the college. There were three types of people who meandered through those clinical concrete halls, and they were all pigeon-holed into groups, dependent on their social status.

These consisted of the 'Trends', the 'So-So's and the 'Basics'.

I was none of the above, just a little bit of all three. I didn't have a place. I wasn't given a name. I fell by the wayside, drifting my way through each learning day like superfluous belly fluff.

I knew the odd person from each group, and unfortunately for me, this was to be my downfall. See, when pledging your allegiance to your chosen group, you promised not to associate with any other member of an opposing clan. It was a massive no-no in the eyes of each cult to socialise with the enemy. So how could I be categorised and agree to such discriminating terms when I had interaction with several diverse individuals?

I had to make a decision, and it was to be a simple one. I would create a group of my very own and name it 'Me', population one!

It was hard to be accepted fully by any gang, especially when you were the one that had chosen to be on the outside looking in.

"Greetings there, Alanna, I do deem that a congratulation is in order for the vanquishing of your diploma. I also note that prescribing an overdose of yours truly as your study partner was key to your success — no need to thank me, my dear. Now come here, my forbidden princess and allow me to say farewell to you properly," snorted Gilbert Bagley.

Seems I wasn't as invisible as I might have liked and unluckily for me, I had found myself in the company of 'Ogle Eyes Gilbs'.

Clumsily, he pawed excessively at my hand. The residue of his clammy and moist palm lingered on my fingers, as years of escaping his clutches climaxed into this one clasping of skin-on-skin. I endeavoured to loosen my grip, to free myself from the undue dewiness of his hold, but he was determined to savour this moment for as long as it was humanly possible.

"Oh erm, thank you, Gilby. Y'know, it goes without saying that the same goes for you too... Don't be a stranger, and keep in touch from time to time, won't you?"

This was also a lie. An empty offer. I had no desire to meet up with Gilbert, and once my foot had crossed the territorial lines of the college gates, then that would be that. Our paths would never purposely cross again. However, whilst still on the premises, I felt compelled to continue with the formalities — it seemed the right thing to do.

Gilbert was only a small lad, 5ft 4inches to be precise, but what he lacked in height, he certainly made up for in gumption. He was a proud upstanding member of the 'Basics', but as a result of his loyalty, he would be constantly ridiculed on his appearance by his arch-rivals — the 'Trends'.

He had a shrewd tongue, biting back with vigor at any crude comment directed his way. Known for his trademark blonde, circa 1990s curtain hairstyle, he was hardly your chic geek, but he couldn't care less. He wore his trousers buckled up high to his chest with his mismatched colour socks peeking out from underneath his ankle grazing leg holes.

Unflattering chequered shirts and bright oversized sleeveless sweaters were a staple in his wardrobe. He was also never seen without his thick round bottle-lensed glasses, which came in a fetching tortoiseshell frame. When incensed, Gilbert could often be seen repositioning his spectacles onto the bridge of his nose.

He was a ball of nervous energy but staggeringly intelligent with a love for anything scientific, technical or statistical — flourishing at any task he set his mind too. Many of our snack breaks were spent together discussing the big bang theory, the meaning of life and the many ways in which we could put the world to rights! Our discussions were more likened to a debate, but I liked that about him, he had his beliefs, as did I.

The only negative I could say about Gilbert was his wandering eye, hence the nickname 'Ogle Eyes Gilbs'. Mid conversation you could guarantee without fail that his glance would head south, engulfing his vision with the female form. His breath would become heavy, his sentences strung out as he teetered to concentrate on anything other than the two obstacles in his direct line of view, and we weren't talking eye-balls here!

"Move aside, Bagley, let me give my girl here a hug," insisted Mackenzie.

Gilbert, unimpressed by the unwanted intrusion, did as he was told as per the unwritten ruling of the pecking order. Registering yourself as a 'Basic' would ultimately rank you at the bottom of the chain and without question, answerable to those above you. The 'Trends' dominated the hierarchy and answered to no one bar the college tutors. The 'So-Sos' occupied the post in between, and as you can probably guess were considered socially superior to the 'Basics' but inferior to the 'Trends'. As for me, I was at rock bottom. I was considered to be the 'dregs'. I was no better than the unwanted loose tea found in the bottom of your teacup — inconvenient and a nuisance.

With a fraudulent unzipped smile and a weak thumbs-up, Gilbert went on his way; shaking hands with his fellow minded friends until reaching the exit via the double swing doors. Taking his final steps, he disappeared through.

Mackenzie 'Mack' Malloy, the leader of the 'So-So's' had seized his opportunity to say goodbye and wasted no time in spewing his advice. "Well, this is it, we only went and smashed it, A-Bomb!" he boomed whilst embracing me in the warmest of bear hugs. "Now remember to always be true to your fine self! If that heart of yours says jump, then you jump — you hear me! Your head doesn't always know what's good for you!" he instructed with a motivating prod to the chest.

Mack was never one to be short of a few thought provoking words, and for the majority of the time he made a lot of sense — dress sense, however, was not his forte and could only be described as alternative! He was known for his traits of quirkiness, and his fascination for pushing boundaries came as second nature to him. Mack thrived on the reception of his peers, dressing in outlandish and eye-catching clothing in order to extract their much-anticipated reactions. Often, he would arrive to class in pristine dickey bow ties, vibrant shell suits, sequined skin-tight trousers, sweltering PVC jackets and so on. He was not afraid to express emotion through his garments and virtually most of the time his ensembles did the talking. From month to month his hair would transform, never remaining the same for too long. As for today, he was sporting a shaved back and sides with a tight curly perm on top.

Mack wasn't quite cool enough to join the 'Trends' and far from nerdy to fit in with the 'Basics'. The 'So-So's' were the perfect medium for him.

Mack also wasn't one to follow the crowd, he had his own agenda and his own convictions in life. An avid supporter of the underdog, he would spend countless hours chained to a tree, brandishing protest plaques or peacefully marching through the streets. He was well-known for advocating the afflicted and abused — if he felt the cause was just.

Our first encounter and the onset to our friendship ignited little over three years ago, way before we had enrolled in college. My nan had enlisted a handful of protestors to line the outskirts of Eldercrest Woods whilst chained together by a 40mm wide steel chain. The mission was to sabotage the impending deforestation in objection to the proposed construction of three, ten-storey high flats. As a lover of nature and all that dwelled within her, I was naturally dead set against the destruction of our treasured woodlands and would do anything I could to help. Mack was equally, if not more enthusiastic to assist than me, and it was linked together over that honking sweat fest of a weekend that our bond was first fused.

I was genuinely sad to wave Mack off, more so than Gilbert. Deep down I knew that this would be the last I would see of him. A social butterfly, he had a world to explore, people to meet and endless causes to fight.

Now lastly, we had my least favourite of the groups — the 'Trends', otherwise known as the popular, cool kids, whose majority were recognisable by their resting bitch faces and soul-sapping dispositions. Fortunately, I had a close contact within the group, meaning that although I was not accepted, I was rarely troubled. A small mercy, allowing me to see through my college years with little hassle.

One wrong look, slip-up or crossed word could mark you, lampooning your entire existence for the remainder of your college years or for however long you could endure. This group was brutal, condemning you for the slightest of margins!

From day one, each group would mark their territory, refusing to cross lines unless it was to goad their opposition. Uncomfortable stares and smarmy smirks would regularly be exchanged within the corridors with little hesitation from group to group. Then there were the classes themselves! Your fellow students would be determined by the subjects you chose.

Choose wisely and you would be assigned a class with like-minded people, remaining relatively unscathed. However, choose poorly and you could guarantee a class overrun with antagonistic imbeciles.

The 'Basics' were pretty much harmless and would situate themselves at the very front of class. You would find their noses deeply ingrained within their books. The 'So-So's' would casually slot within the middle section. They were mildly friendly and usually tapping pencils against desks to the sound of their own exclusive beat. The 'Trends' could be found at the back of the room, overseeing proceedings whilst contemptuously swinging on the hind legs of their chairs.

Myself?

I would take whatever seat was left and pray I would make it through another day in peace. It was fair to say that college was not for the faint-hearted, but somehow, I had managed to survive the turbulence...until now.

∞∞∞

Most of my year had by now vacated the premises. The laughing, the crying, the hooting was all but a distant memory, and like them, it was time to leave too. Begin my new life, secure an admin job, own a home, maybe even find myself a boyfriend — get married — adopt a dog — have kids! Yes, I was a little ahead of myself, but there was no harm in dreaming, and one day I hoped to have all those things and more.

Although...deep down I knew the secretarial life was not for me. No, what I really wanted was to become a conservation volunteer. Protecting endangered species and rehabilitating poached wildlife was my big dream. I wanted to make a difference, play a part — give to those who were most vulnerable — those that were despicably targeted and affected by the evil of mankind. Just the thought alone of those vile scum, was all the encouragement I would ever need, for me to one day sign myself up.

Taking time to reflect on what had been and what was yet to come, I began the slow amble through the whist corridor towards the inevitable swing double doors. When unexpectedly from out of the storeroom to my right, came my reason for abiding the last two alienating of years.

And their name?

Well, it was Kalen Snow, and he was the most handsome, heaven-sent man I had ever had the pleasure to lay eyes on.

With skin the paleness of a silkworm and cheeks dusted with the balletic petal of a light pink Rose, he reminded me of one of those nostalgic wintery mornings. His enthralling eyes instantly melted the crispness of the deep frost with a dramatic kaleidoscope of colour. They were like the vivid green flesh of a lime, speckled with flecks of twenty-four carat gold and encompassed within the sear of a single coffee bean. His mousy brown hair teased me with its lustrous well-kept glow, whilst his 'barely there' smile summoned me in with curiosity. This boy was too good to be true, and he was staring right at me.

"Pull it together, Allie," I muttered warily underneath my fractured breath.

The last thing I wanted to do was to appear desperate, but try as I might, I couldn't resist but prolong my stare back. Though, the chances were, he wasn't even considering me!

Perhaps he was searching for a tutor, or maybe his attention was caught by the overfilled notice board behind me? Well, whatever it was, it was in my direction and he was heading the same way.

Tied low against my neck, I nervously coiled the sleek loose tail of nutmeg repeatedly around the uncontrollable shudder of my index finger. My upper lip — a rounded cupid bow, twitched with excitable unease as the breath of my desire became detectable.

This was it, regardless of his intentions, I had to grab the opportunity with both hands and say, 'hi!'. Hmmm, maybe just a smile would suffice, or how about I throw in a cheeky wink? Perhaps a seductive lick of the lips was the way forward?

No, no, no!

I was overthinking things far too much. I needed to remain calm and simply go with the flow. Although, this was a pretty big deal right here — in fact, it was my one and only chance to say something to the boy I had become infatuated with. I would never get this moment again. I had to make it count.

'Hello...?', hmmmm seemed a little too formal, slightly mundane.

'Howdy...?', oh no, definitely random, heading towards weird!

I should play the situation down, y'know, keep it casual with a playful 'hi', but then again, if I enter in with a strong 'hey', shows I'm approachable, yet not overly keen.

"Alanna? It is, Alanna…isn't it?" came his silkily spoken words.

He sounded just like I'd always imagined he would.

I was buzzing! Kalen Snow knew my name, not just my forename but my surname too — this was surreal!

"Hello, you," I dreamily whispered underneath my breath.

"Sorry, what was that?" came his unenthusiastic reply.

"Oh erm…er, that's me, but call me Allie," I stammered — not as breezy as I had originally hoped!

Unable to comprehend that it was actually me he was talking to — I had to take a second look around, but put it this way, I would be anyone he wanted me to be at this precise moment in time.

Kalen was in his early twenties, an unflappable, remote type of character and definitely much more of a man than a boy. Never one to cause a scene, he much preferred to fade into the background, similar you could say to me. Though as reticent as he tried to behave, I still noticed him. How could I not? Although sadly, when I did notice, it was much too late. In fact, when he first caught my eye, I only had three measly months remaining on my Secretarial Diploma. I knew then that my time admiring him from afar would soon run out. I only wished I'd clocked him sooner!

Kalen was not a student, he was employed as the college janitor, a part time post; meaning every break and free period from Monday to Wednesday was utilised by me to productively stalk the corridors for my enigmatic deer. Any other day and you wouldn't see my tracks for dust, but I was besotted and found that deception was absolute key in luring said prey from its place of concealment.

The trap was simple! It involved a can of bubbling fizz and his immaculate sterile floor. Within moments of the syrupy liquid lashing his pristine stage, he would arrive, fluently weaving his way through a cluster of salivating females. His grubby grey worn out boiler suit gleamed through the gaps of heaving bodies like flashes of glimmering light, bursting through the swaying leaves of a palm tree.

It was immature of me I know, but it was completely harmless and my only opportunity to feel him close by. I was far too shy to actually speak to him, so instead I would take the odd sneaky peak as he rubbed his dishevelled mop into the sticky stain. Some days I would be so close that his wet bundle of yarn would tickle against my boots. I only wished it was his large meaty palms rather than his limp sagging mop!

Kalen never complained or happened to question the continuous pools of candied liquid, opting to vigorously clean the affected area and hastily move on. A perfectionist, he would take great care in disinfecting, ensuring the area was spotless, better than new.

Kalen was a professional, he was rarely seen engaging with the students, and that included any drawn-out eye contact. Even on the odd occasion when I entered his vision, he would blankly respond with a frigid stare. I guess I had spilt one too many cans of fizzy pop for his liking, but then again, he always had this unintentional habit of making me feel awkward. Sad thing is, I always went back for more. Another puddle here, an extra puddle there. I suppose you could say I was deserving of his neglect. Anyway, there really was no need for me to dwell on these little minor negatives, because now at last, I had his full attention.

Kalen was looking me square in the face — my breathing became shallow, my heart felt like it was about to stall as I desperately waited to hear more.

"Sorry to throw this on you, but if you hadn't already guessed, I'm sort of new to the area. I don't really know much about the place or many people for that matter. I was wondering...now that you have all this free time, would you mind showing me around?" he politely asked. "Plus, maybe now that you have my attention, you will stop making a mess of my unblemished corridors," he added, with half a smile and a nod of the head in the direction of the partially drunken coke can in my hand.

There was no point in me attempting to hide the evidence, not that I had any intention of wasting this particular one. However, it seems the game had been up a long time ago, and if the can wasn't a big enough giveaway than my infrared cheeks sure were. The effort to obtain my weekly fix of Kalen was a poor one, but it had worked time and time again. I just wished I'd been a little subtler!

"Of course, I will!" I blurted. I hated to appear keen, but I simply couldn't control my excitement towards his proposal.

"I would formally introduce myself to you, Alanna, but I'm guessing you probably already know my name..."

Well, this moment was increasing with embarrassment by the second. I smiled bashfully, hoping he didn't want me to answer that. I also noticed he had declined to shorten my name. I didn't mind though; he was finally talking to me — he could call me whatever he bloody well liked!

"I know a charming little restaurant. My treat in return for your enlightenment of the local area. Pick you up at 8pm sharp. Be ready and waiting for me!"

"Sounds perfect!"

'PERFECT!', did I have to come across so ardent! It wasn't exactly a date, just a meeting for two to discuss the local area...with a little food thrown in. It was hardly a candlelit dinner, followed by a hand in hand stroll, ending in the most dramatic kiss imaginable! No, not even I was going to allow myself to get carried away by this little scenario...although, it did feel promising!

With arrangements formed, he grabbed his well-worn mop, his crusty bucket and headed off into the corridor. Never one to waste an opportunity to admire him, I watched him adoringly, step by step, until he was completely out of sight.

"You can keep your scrubby little paws off him, Pickering, you know he's out of bounds," screeched a high-pitched female voice. "He isn't interested in little girls, he prefers a woman, a woman who knows how to treat a man — I would know after all. Best you keep on walking!"

This gobby yap belonged to twenty-year-old Coral Stone, a buxom scarlet-haired floozy. With her pinched in waist, sharp facial features and brilliant caterpillar green eyes, she didn't half attain a strong presence. Idolised by oodles of concupiscent boys and despised by a ton of resentful girls — she hands down stole the crown for queen of the 'Trends'.

Although, she did have some girlfriends, that's if you can call them actual friends. These girls were known as 'Stonie's Phonies', and they were fake with a capital 'F', tolerating Coral's indescribable ways for popularity purposes only.

The 'Phonies' were made up of Lacey, Ella, and Dee; three vain, self-centred, wicked tongued girls. Similar in looks, they dressed to impress the opposite sex, prospering on attention, be it good or bad. They hung on to every word muttered by Coral, refusing to never defy her as their leader. These girls were part of her chosen clique, completing errands and acting as their master's eyes and ears. Coral named it; they would do it — they were totally spell-bound by her. In return, they were given the power of celebrity status. The boys loved them, and they loved the boys. These girls were as genuine as Coral's over-inflated breasts!

In my opinion, this tart was the worst transfer Eldercrest College had ever seen. Not only did she roll up nine months late into a two-year course but the instant she laid her eyes on Kalen, she claimed him. Everyone within the college walls knew that Kalen was the property of Coral, therefore he was off limits, even if he had other ideas on the matter.

Often, she could be found in a darkened area of the corridor, collaring Kalen up against the confectionary vending machine. Time and time again, she would pretend the machine had swallowed her money, but in reality, we all knew what she was up to. Heck, I couldn't talk, after all, I had been playing my own little game with him.

Slamming Kalen up against the flimsy glass, his broad shoulders would penetrate the fiddly buttons as she whispered sensually into his ear. She never did walk away with a bar of chocolate or her lodged money for that matter!

No one could confirm fully if they were in a relationship or just dabbling with one another, but there was definitely 'something' going on between them.

I didn't know too much about Coral, but what I did know was that she was not the sort of girl you wanted to mess with. A gym enthusiast, she would train at least three times a week. Kickboxing was her specialty, and there was no way I wanted her practicing on me!

Y'know, I wouldn't be surprised if old scabby knickers here was the 'feeling' behind my earlier episode of dread, and as short-lived as it was, I refused to be intimidated by 'it' or her!

"Oh, ignore her, Allie, the girl is all talk, no action!" chipped in a protective voice.

I knew straight away that this reassuring tone belonged to Mollie White, a childhood friend from years gone by, and although she was the closest of all my 'friends', I still found it difficult to completely open up to her. In truth, we rarely spent any quality time together, which was of course more down to me than it was to her, but regardless, she always had my back, as did I with her.

As it happened, we were born on the same day, in the same hospital, within the same hour. From that moment on our mums laid the groundwork, forging a close relationship over detailed birthing pain and endless nights of sleep deprivation! Birthdays, Christmases and special occasions were celebrated together, so it would come as no surprise that we spent the majority of our childhood growing up together. College, however, was the blade that changed all that, severing our ties and the reason for our parting ways.

Unlike me, Mollie straightaway found her feet within her group. She was pretty, smart, confident and could handle herself. She had the whole package. She wasn't your stereotypical 'Trend', and luckily for me, she was the reason I was tolerated by so many of her peers. Coral, on the other hand, was a spiteful individual, manipulating her way into the group with false promises, dirty lies and a plastic image. Evidently, Mollie was not a fan of Coral, but like it or not, she accepted the person she was, choosing to overlook, rather than fight against her. They did not socialise, but to keep up appearances, they continued to acknowledge one another.

As it goes, Mollie happened to be strolling behind Coral, with her lengthy blowout threads of ombré bouncing across her poised back at the precise moment that the unprovoked attack was launched. She too was on her way out of the building but had been held back by the amount of well-wishes she had received.

"Allie, you know 'airbags' here is just jealous of what she can't have, and it seems to me, she really, really wants something or shall we say somebody that wants you!" teased Mollie.

Coral's face shrivelled like the bitterness of a sucked lemon at the public display of loyalty shown towards me by Mollie. She was clearly aghast but fully aware she could not compete with the likes of her. The 'Phonies' were also close to Mollie. They had no bad feeling towards her and would not pick sides, and dear old Coral was well aware of this.

"What she has! Hah! Don't make me choke! She has nothing I want or need. It's a meaningless date, if you can even call it that!" she bit.

I raised an eyebrow towards Mollie who was revelling in delight at Coral's unrest.

"Kalen would have asked me, but as you know, I'm as new to this area as he is. I can hardly give him the grand tour, but understand this, I will help him in other ways that you can't!" she slyly jabbed back.

Having said her slutty piece, she snapped her fingers and one by one her 'Phonies' stepped in line behind her. United, they each flicked out a glossy preened leg and proceeded to strut down the corridor and out of the virtually vacated building. I cannot tell you how relieved I was to visibly capture their departure, and I can assure you, their combined glare of loathing would not be missed.

"Brush it off, Allie. This right here is the start of your new life, and it's very unlikely you will ever see that snide cow again. It's over! Time to start living. Be you and enjoy life without Stone breathing down your neck. Oh, and in case you've forgot, you have a date — a date with thee Kalen Snow! Now go home and glam yourself up already..." declared an over delighted Mollie.

Her voice trailed off as she followed suit, leaving me and my triumphant smile to bask in this moment of glory alone... although, I wasn't exactly alone...was I?

"Be careful, won't you...a wish as dreamy as Kalen, isn't a wish you're necessarily going to want to come true," came the echo of a singular foreboding threat.

Two

FIRST & LAST

The small hand was firmly gripped onto the seventh hour, refusing to let go, whilst the big hand precariously danced on the fifty-eighth minute, inevitably teasing me into a state of unease.

Embarrassingly, I had found myself standing impatiently in the very core of my bedroom, glaring back and forth from window to watch. With a front facing room, I overlooked the charcoal pebble-strewn driveway of the family home. If anyone came knocking, I would clearly be able to see and hear them. It was always a godsend when avoiding uninvited, not to mention, unwanted visitors.

Well, fifty-ninth minute and still no sign of him. Kalen may be a thing of beauty, but he was definitely no timekeeper. I mockingly chuckled at the thought of myself standing in full view of my window with sheer desperation in my eyes. If only he could see me...I'm sure he would run a mile!

As the big hand hit the sixtieth minute, I peered outside and prepared myself for a surge of disappointment. The thought of anyone standing me up would be hard to bear, but if Kalen was to deliver me this insensitive blow, then it would be like taking a blunt bullet to the heart.

"You're here!" I gasped, unexpectedly, as I caught sight of the two dazzling emerald greens staring back up at me.

Casually, he raised his arm to signal a warm, yet extremely sexy hello. He was leant up against the body of his car, legs loosely crossed with one hand penetrating a singular faded jean pocket — he was effortlessly edible to the eye.

His soft lips immediately took a direct hold of me as I watched them caress the succulent ruby red cherry that they were feasting into. My eyes were unable to remove their focus from his moist mouth as he licked the juices clean off. I couldn't take my gaze off of him, and god, did he know it!

He was exactly on time, not a minute early nor a minute late. How he had driven unnoticed down that noisy pebbled path of ours, I do not know. Not only was it an achievement but it was also unheard of! I had been on guard for longer than I would like to admit and hand on heart, I can certify that I had not heard a peep from outside. There was no visible movement, no notification of sound and there was definitely no sharp crunch of a cumbersome set of wheels treading the gravel below.

Even Jed, the family German Shepherd was oblivious to Kalen's presence. It appeared he was not so proficient at picking up on my dates after all. Saying that, Jed was not as young as he used to be. He was eight in human years, making him fifty-six in canine.

When we took him in, he was a bag of bones, scared and timid. Mum had found him tied to a rusty old lamp post, left to rot, neglected and unloved. He was fourteen months old, still only a puppy, yet the poor thing had been exposed to so much cruelty already.

However, today was a different story. He was strong, confident, too confident you could say and a very much-loved member of our family.

What once was a glossy ice-chocolate, jet black and acorn coat, was now a shabby speckled grey mane. He was a little older, a little wiser and his discoloured teeth had seen better days. His pungent breath was known to clear a room, but I still loved him just as much, if not more than I did that very first day I laid eyes on him.

Jed was still very much the man of the house, strutting

from room to room, observing his domain. His bushy tail, although aged, was proudly hoisted high into the air. His creamy ash brown eyes were not as vigilant as they once were but continued to survey every slight movement and location of sound.

If Jed didn't like you, then believe me, you would be the first to know. If there was a knock at the door, Jed knew about it before you did. He didn't care who you were, as to him you were an intruder, and intruders must be destroyed.

You see, Jed was never one to miss the action, as he was always the first one to know about it...well, that was until today!

I threw Kalen a wide smile, flirtatiously waving back at him with a nervous flicker of several of my shuddering fingers. Flustered by his presence, I tiptoed to my bedroom door and poked my head through. As anticipated, Jed was stationed on the landing at the top of the stairs. Sound asleep, his back legs were robustly twitching to alternating beats. No doubt he was dreaming of skipping through freshly watered blades of mint-green meadows in search of sprightly bunnies to chase.

Frustratingly, Jed had a gift of always managing to find the most awkward of places to lie in. I swear this was a strategical move of his, but he would have to try a hell of a lot harder if he wanted to scupper my evening with Kalen! Not even Coral was capable of executing that! I was pretty certain the jealous viper was responsible for sneaking her way back into college in a maggoty attempt to warn me off her crush. No chance! She wasn't fooling anyone with her pathetic spooky threats, especially not me with those hateful, snaky games of hers.

Teeteringly, I raised my left leg over his sprawled-out chest and gently lowered myself on to the adjoining step. Gingerly lifting my right leg over, I avoided touching a single strand of coarse hair on his body. Nimbly, I landed step after step, successfully managing to creep down each and every one, and without so much as a flinch from the old boy, or so I naively thought....

I was almost there, with only the base step to hit, when there it was, with a grin that could have won Miss World and potentially the answer to world peace.

"Mum!" I gasped. Jed I expected but not mum....

Her eyes were intoxicated with jubilation as she proudly greeted me at the footing of the staircase with my cream cardigan in hand.

"Make sure you're back in before 11.30pm, young lady!" came her ecstatic squeal.

She added a waggle of her index finger and dropped in a saucy smile as she rejoiced in foiling my plan. I bashfully nodded and accepted her order whilst gently snatching my crumpled garment from beneath her clasp.

Reluctant to make further eye contact, I scurried through the double doors to the porch behind her and straight out the front door. I was adamant I would avoid an inquisition about tonight's schedule!

Now, I know it may not sound like it, but I have dabbled in the odd date y'know, although I've never actually had any input into them or in fact consented to them. I personally have never asked a boy out on a date nor have I actually been asked out — orchestrated as a blind date with no warning was the usual set-up.

Mum had an unhealthy obsession with my love life, unable to fathom out why I had a lack of interest in the opposite sex. It's not that I wasn't interested, it's just I never wanted or had the urge to spend countless of hours mooning over someone that didn't bring me to my knees with that one look. I was more into my education, preferring to study, read and learn rather than waste time pursuing a boy that probably hadn't even heard of me. Well, that was until I laid eyes on Kalen, no one had ever enticed me in like he had.

∞∞∞

I first caught sight of Kalen opposite the sports field, pruning the overgrown shrubbery that backed onto the college walls. It was a humid, sweltering day. Too hot to be pounding the track, but nevertheless, I was committed. Keen to maintain some level of fitness, I would frequent the running track at least once a week, and this day was no different.

It happened to be his shears sparkling in the glorious sun that not only caught the blistering rays of light but my attention too. I'm not exaggerating when I say I almost tripped over my own feet at the sight of him.

Taking a break from the overbearing heat, he wiped his brow with the back of his hand, shears in tow, narrowly skimming the side of his delectable flushed cheeks. His free hand rested casually onto his waist as he took a minute or two to relax. He was dripping with globules of slippery sweat but not the greasy kind. This was the type of perspiration that trickled from the brow like a diamond droplet.

His overalls were loosely tied around his waist, revealing a tight white T-shirt soiled with freshly cut grass stains, and his skin was smeared with perfectly placed black mud. He was filthily delicious, and it was in this moment that my knees first buckled — I was hooked!

I never spoke to Mum about Kalen for fear she would intervene, ruining any small chance I might have with him. She wasn't afraid to get involved, and in the past, had rendered her fair share of meddling.

Mum once set me up on a date with Billy Rayner. We were both nearing the tender age of sixteen. He was all bones with scraggly ash-blonde hair that he would tie into a ratty shoulder length ponytail. He would dress in nothing but the drabbest of oversized business suits that had somehow escaped the sealed closet of the 1980s! I suppose he was cute in his own way, but he wasn't my type, we didn't have that spark.

He was shy, ever so shy, to the point where we ended up spending the bulk of our date in silence. Now I wasn't the liveliest of girls, but I did have a sparkle. I just chose when and whom to show it to, and Billy was definitely not chosen!

This boy was afraid of everything! He had a fear of flying, water, trees, fire, spiders, clouds, thunder...and even baked beans! He couldn't bare the parched texture of the beans against his sensitive tongue or the aftertaste of its tangy amber mucus as it inhabited his mouth.

Billy had taken me to one of those all-you-can-eat buffet type restaurants, which lasted all of thirty-three minutes! It wasn't my idea of the perfect first date, but thirty odd minutes was more than ample. As expected, the night was over before it even had a chance to get going, and I couldn't have been happier.

After one serving of wilted salad, overcooked spuds and scraps of gristle — Billy called it a night, insisting he would drop me off home. In fact, he walked me all the way to my porch door, much to my disapproval. You see although Billy was timid, he bent the rules when it came to kissing girls. He decided that this right here would be his window of opportunity for a little tongue-twister sandwich, and his modesty was most definitely not going to knock him off his stride.

Fumblingly, he leant in, his lips were swamped with stringy saliva and tightly pursed together with the accompaniment of left-over breadcrumbs. With his eyes cinched shut, his gangly arms lunged towards me, pulling me in against his skeletal frame.

Urgh! Just the thought alone sends shivers down my spine. I remember thinking that this was it, this meaningless, soggy, flaccid peck was going to be my first kiss, the kiss I would remember for all my life!

For me, my first kiss meant more to me than it probably did for most. I believed that in the midst of kissing my true love, my heart would feel like it was about to beat its very last beat. My first kiss would also be my last kiss with that one person. I did not want to kiss a thousand warted toads to find my prince. I didn't have the time or the lip balm to invest into it! I wanted to be sure I had found my one and only, and once we kissed, we would seal our love forever. Corny, right?

I believed in love at first smooch. I only had one chance to get it right and consequently had been saving myself for that very reason. I never envisaged that it would be with someone I didn't love or even remotely like but none of that mattered, it was all too late. Billy Rayner of all people was to be my first, and my reason for finding the one was about to disperse into this very moment of unwelcome tonsil bashing.

"Ahhhhhhh," a blood curdling scream poured from Billy's wide opened mouth, directly into my screwed-up face.

Billy had caught sight of Jed's huge padded paws as they thudded up against the porch glass window. Protectively, he had heard the awkward commotion from outside the house and was on hand to welcome Billy, much to Billy's disappointment. Thankfully, Jed had been on form and with perfect timing, he had unintentionally managed to block Billy from stealing my first kiss from me.

With its snarling bared teeth and enormous presence growing before him, it's no wonder Billy bolted. In his haste, he rather rudely forgot to thank me for my company or even say goodbye!

Unfazed by his impertinence, I expelled a bulky sigh of relief as I unlocked the front door and retreated to the safety of my home. Patting Jed's shaggy crown, I made sure he knew he was my hero.

"Good lad, but please make sure you don't do that to 'the one' when he comes along...if he comes along!" I whined.

Funnily enough, I never saw Billy again — turns out he had a fear of dogs too!

∞∞∞

My mum Elizabeth, 'Betty' to her family and friends, had met Billy's mum at Eldercrest's local pub, 'The Old Crow'. Everyone that frequented the local knew everyone else, and everyone who went there was from the village. The pub was famed for its close-knit environment, with everyone knowing one another's business. If you wanted to keep your private life private, then this was not the pub for you.

Mum happened to visit the pub on a weekly basis, she was one of the better-known regulars and notorious for drinking the pub bone dry. She even had her own bar stool!

In happier times, Mum was booked as the resident singer, talented and beautiful, she could hold the attention of a room just by being in it. It wasn't until a few years later that Mum decided to dust off her vocal cords and pick up where she had left off.

It happened to be on one lazy Wednesday evening that Mum boisterously burst through the living room door with some cold home truths for me. She was in her usual sloshed, might I hasten to add irritating state when she aggressively informed me that I needed to explore life, make some friends but most of all...meet a boy!

"H — h — heeeeey! life is too ssshort, Allie, yeeeer wasting the best yearsss of yeer life, stuuuck in 'ere, doing god knowsss what yooou doooo in that roooom of yers," she slurred with an encore of odorous vodka hiccups.

This was not the first time I had received this monotonous lecture. Although inebriated, I knew what she meant, and what she was trying to articulate was that not everyone is given the gift to fully live their lives. I should stop wasting precious time and make the most of what I have been given, for one day without warning, it could all be taken away.

You see, earlier that evening, Mum had been gassing to Gabby Rayner, Billy's mum, after a boozy night out in 'The Old Crow' — you can probably see where this one is going!

Well...they had decided to take it upon themselves to tinker with the love lives of their sweet and innocent spawn i.e. Billy and I. A plan that was fuelled with copious amounts of Gin and toasted with Vodka had been concocted for us to date with or without our consent, mine being the latter. Conniving, they had set the whole thing up with an eager Billy obliging to their sneaky plan.

The first I knew about their dealings was when Billy unexpectedly arrived on my doorstep one light evening in late spring. He was dressed in his trademark goose grey three-piece suit, that was two sizes too big for him. Underneath his oversized jacket were a neatly buttoned white shirt, silver waistcoat and dusky grey bow tie. His jittery palms clutched a sagging cerise Rose that he extended towards me as if he was prematurely asking for forgiveness. His face was petrified with rejection. I didn't have the heart to shoo him away, especially as he had worked so hard to pluck up the courage to stand in front of me, which was no easy feat! Any other day and I would have gently let him down, but the problem I had, was that I was caught off guard. I had no back-up plan or any advanced warning of the evenings unfolding events. Plus, there was no time to even consider a sharpish getaway, Mum had made sure of that by shoving me out the front door and flicking across the locks.

So, bearing the above in mind, it's pretty easy to understand the uncontrollable joy Mum felt when she realised her passive daughter had a bona fide date with a real-life boy.

Oh, and this time, she finally had no menacing part to play in it. For the first time in a long time, she felt relieved. She didn't have to worry about me spending all my time alone. I was getting out there and creating a life for myself. I didn't dare tell her I was acting as a tour guide rather than a date, but what she didn't know, wouldn't hurt her — would it?

She was ecstatic that I was integrating with the male species. I hadn't seen her this happy since the time I won the Eldercrest Infants egg and spoon race, aged five. She excessively clapped and hollered as I dived over the finish line with eggshell intact.

Mum was a competitive soul, an athlete in her youth, she used to run for Eldercrest's Cross Country Running Team. Physically talented, she was fierce competition on the track, contending in adult championships, marathons and triathlons, but that all came to an abrupt end when she started to hit the bottle.

It had been twelve years since I charged through the taut red tape of that finish line and twelve long years since I had seen her smile again — just like she had done that day. I had almost forgotten how beautiful she was, and on that basis alone, I wasn't going to ruin this milestone for a silly minor detail!

Clutching my shoulder bag as a security blanket, I traipsed over towards Kalen. Not wanting to appear overly keen, I took my time and played the situation down, although my version of cool left a lot to be desired.

"Hi, Alanna," purred Kalen with those soft appetising lips of his. "8pm as promised, and you should know I always keep to my promises. I just hope I don't disappoint," he cheekily added.

"Oh no. You don't disappoint. At all!" I whispered, not wanting him to hear me gush.

"Hope you don't mind but I brought this old thing with me, not mine, happens to belong to a friend. Janitor work doesn't pay all that well, but we needed a ride…" he sighed.

The car in question was an electric blue sporty little number with butterfly doors, the type that opened vertically and out. Of course I didn't mind, it was a stallion of a motor!

Listless, I nodded back, pretending not to be impressed by the effort he had gone to.

"It will do...so erm, where we going?" I responded with a nonchalant tone.

"There's this little place, it's located on the crest of Hawks Hill. Apparently, they are renowned for their desserts, and all you girls like a sweet treat, don't you!" he beamed with a twinkle in his eye.

He looked extremely smug. It was as if he had uncovered the key to unlocking every woman's heart, but it wasn't for me, unimpressed, my lock began to jam. Not wanting to ruin his grand plans but dessert really wasn't a deal breaker. I was more your savoury toothed kind of girl, loving nothing more than munching into a family size bag of salted crisps. Give me that over a bar of chocolate any day of the week! Still...this was Kalen we were talking about; he didn't need to impersonate a locksmith to unpick me — I was already open.

Three

TRIPLE VISION

As gracious as Kalen was to open the passenger door for me, he abstained from actually helping me enter underneath those big theatrical doors of his! It seems he preferred to watch, rather than offer me a helping hand as I slid crudely onto his smart leather bucket seats.

Fitted out in a baggy black midi slip dress, I was hardly dressed appropriately to navigate myself around such a car. I had topped off my minimalistic look with a pair of white converse trainers and my longline cardigan. Kalen, on the other hand, was in complete contrast to me.

He wore a bright sky-blue crew neck T-shirt with white skinny jeans and grey lace-up hi top trainers. He accessorised his eye-popping look with a woven multi-coloured wristband. He was alive with colour, very different to the grungy grey Kalen I knew from college, and as he slipped the car into first gear, I decided that this 'right here' would be an opportune moment to break the ice.

"Tell me... how many shades away are you from landing your very own pot of gold?" I snorted.

I couldn't help but giggle at my lighthearted jest. Kalen, however, didn't find my banter as funny and immediately took offence. Looking me up and down, he wasted no time in absorbing my choice of outfit.

"No point in looking drab and dreary is there! Who wants to 'just' blend in when you are blessed with the freedom to stand out!" he retorted.

Ouch! He was definitely a biter and a little more sensitive than I originally thought. Mortified, I rigidly tugged my cardigan across my body and bashfully peered down to inspect my lack of vibrancy to his. He seemed as unimpressed with my clothing as he did with me as a person. This was not starting off as well as I had hoped it would — a definite blip in my efforts to woo him, but it wasn't over. I would absolutely try harder from now on.

Ruffled by my comments, Kalen slammed his foot hard on the accelerator. Wheels spinning, he sped off the drive, kicking up an insignificant twister of gravel and dust in his wake.

"Five minutes max!" he shouted, with the noise of the engine battling to overpower his voice.

He drove fast, dangerously fast, soaring through the winding tree lined lanes and gripping to the track with the finesse of a butterfly. His display of inconsiderate recklessness did nothing for my nerves — choosing now to be as good a time as any to show. This might I add, was primarily caused from the diabolical speed in which we were travelling in.

Panicking, I latched my hand onto the side of the seat nearest to the passenger window. Refusing to show I was scared, I gamely rested my free hand upon my lap to mask my fear. I would not allow myself to come across boring or wimpish, it wasn't an attractive quality, and let's face it, his first impressions of me so far were lacking somewhat.

Several more trees had now flown by, blurring into an explosion of mint chocolate spread when Hawks Hill suddenly came into view. It was a beast of a hill and resembled more of a rocky mountain than the grassy knoll I had envisaged.

"Hold on tight!" Kalen rejoiced.

The engine roared as the vehicle rocketed up the incredibly steep mound, clamping itself to the road as it coiled up towards a milky cloud scattering of squidgy-centred meringues.

The hill itself mimicked the distinctive image of an extravagant wedding cake that was oozing with gooey layers of creamy filled caramel. Three distinct tiers created the curvature of the dirt track, which pleasingly whirled itself around to the pinnacle of the hill within a ribbon of silky ganache.

Crunchy truffle formed rocks laced the walls with their nutty coffee-coloured misshapen spheres, whilst spindly tassels of bottle-green ivy cascaded their wandering licorice threads over the cliffs edge.

To finish, superbly placed heather flourished from its earthy bed, veiling the hill in a buttercream sea of florid mauve — the perfect decadent frosting.

I was speechless. I had no words to say, well, none that would do it the justice it deserved anyway. Put it this way, I had never been surrounded by so much beauty before, and as a result I had hardly noticed we'd arrived at our destination.

To be truthful, as beautiful as it was, I was secretly relieved to have finally come to a standstill. I wasn't the best for travelling at high speeds and could have done without all this excitement, especially before teatime!

Ramming the car door wide open, I gawkily heaved myself from out of the seat I had become so firmly accustomed to. Patting down my dress, I swiftly composed myself as I rambled over towards the fringe of the hill. I could sense Kalen's eyes burrowing into my flesh as he exited the car and followed my every move on foot.

"It's stunning here, Kalen," I gushed in awe.

We were on the summit of the hill with a view to die for — it was breathtaking. With a panoramic perspective, the hill overlooked Eldercrest, you could see for mile upon mile — no wonder my breath had been stolen!

In all my years within this small village, I had never been

here before, in fact, I had never known it existed. Then again, I never had anyone special to dine with, so I guess it seemed pointless ever venturing this far out.

"Ready, Alanna?" Kalen called.

He had a real knack for purring my name. His sensuous voice instantly ricocheting tingles of pleasure throughout my spine.

"Oh yes! More than ready..." I jubilantly replied as I turned to face him.

Kalen though, seemed utterly disinterested in my response and incapable of picking up on any of my signals. He appeared to be exhausted, lacked any sort of enthusiasm and to be candid, I was starting to question my presence here at all. Maybe this wasn't such a good idea, especially as my company didn't appear to be appreciated or any longer required!

Agitated by my suspicions, I marched moodily towards the restaurant, which was aptly named 'Hawkers Cavern'.

The cavern was the focal point, the cake topper if you will. Neatly positioned on the tip of the hill, it casted a solitude figure as it sat on its lonesome. Kalen was quick to inform me that this old 18th century building had been respectfully converted into a quaint rustic restaurant, and over the years, had become smothered in the same leafy green foliage that adorned the hill.

Keen to eat, Kalen, urged me to step through the large shabby oak plank door, where we were instantly accosted by a pleasantly warm and welcoming member of staff.

"Good evening to you both, and welcome to 'Hawkers Cavern'. My name is Basil, and I am the Maître d' of this fine establishment. Table for two?" he prompted.

"Please!" I insisted.

There was no point in looking at Kalen to take control of

the situation, he seemed to be dithering further and further into his own little world.

"Will this table be suitable for ma'am?" questioned Basil.

With virile copper hair, potent green eyes, pasty skin and a splashing of honey-yellow freckles — he was certainly striking to look at. Oddly, I felt as though I had seen his face before, as though we had already met....

I should mention that Basil had a broad Glaswegian accent and would most definitely not be easy to forget, particularly around Eldercrest, a sleepy village in the south of England.

"Yes, sublime, thank you," I replied with enthusiasm for the both of us.

We had a small rounded corner table by the window which was concave in shape and accessorised with external open wooden shutters. I was delighted to be allocated a seat with a view, especially one with a backdrop as stunning as this!

Inside the restaurant, aged wooden oak beams supported the rustic stone walls and slightly threadbare thatched roofing. Solid ivory wax candles, the height and width of a wild boar stood to attention within every darkened corner of the room. A musty odour, peculiar in scent wafted throughout the four walls, sticking to the back of my throat with unfaltering pluck. Potted Bay Trees dusted with twinkly fairy lights were perfectly positioned throughout the cavern, thriving within their dwellings and adding to the romantic ambience.

Our area in particular was dimly lit by a crackling fireplace that burned slowly, releasing the sweet smell of burnt orange peel. This place definitely had a touch of the olde-worlde about it — it was quite the find, and it would have been the most ideal lovey-dovey of settings, if it hadn't had been for the company I was keeping!

"Hello there, my names Morris, and I'll be your Waiter for this evening. Whatever you want, we've got it, and if we haven't, I'll get it," said the assertive young chap now standing in front of us.

Morris, unlike Basil, was not from Scotland, he seemed to have some dodgy makeshift cockney accent but uncannily looked just like his colleague — same skin tone, eyes, hair colouring and teeth! Now these teeth were big, like the type of teeth you could adopt to gnaw through a plank of plywood with. If it wasn't for the accents, I could have sworn they were related!

I shrugged the thought to the back of my mind and allowed Morris to push the menu of bountiful selections into the palm of my hand. Though, the same could not be said for Kalen as he curtly stopped Morris within his tracks.

"Sir, your —," stumbled Morris — unable to release the weighty menu from his clasp.

"A triple chocolate cookie fudge cake, followed by a walnut honey drizzled salad. Oh, and as for drinks, make mine a chocolate and vanilla milkshake with extra toffee sauce and a splash of your finest blackberry syrup, please!" demanded an inpatient Kalen.

Clearly, he had no need for options as he was already and waiting for his order to be taken.

"Hungry are we, sir?" teased a slightly baffled Morris.

"Place the order!" snapped Kalen, rudely.

"Why, certainly, sir," came the reply with an added roll of the eyes. "To recap, we have one tasty little walnut salad for mains and a rather dirty triple chocolate cookie fudge cake for dessert."

"No, no, no! The dessert followed by the salad! It's quite simple, MORRIS!" ranted Kalen, who appeared to be quite irked by the confusion manifested from what he thought was an easy enough request to make.

I must admit, I was almost as confused as Morris, but this was no joke, it was dessert before mains.

"And for, madam?" probed a bemused Morris.

With one hand resting apathetically on his waist, I could tell Morris was less than impressed with Kalen's behaviour. I had no inkling of what to order! I hadn't the time to open the menu, let alone peruse the fulsome number of pages awaiting to be turned.

Kalen, however, must have visited the cavern plenty of times before. He didn't need to look at the menu to know what he wanted.

"Sorry, Alanna, I can see how ungentlemanly this must look to you. I do apologise, but when I know what I want, I don't see the point in wasting time looking at another option," he suggestively put forward.

Oh, if only he felt for me like he did for his food, then I would be one very satisfied girl right now.

"I know what pleases me, and I don't need to flick a plastic sheet to confirm. Take your time and choose…please," he insisted.

Feeling pressured, I fumblingly opened the menu and randomly picked the first meal I could lay my eyes on.

"Erm, no it's fine…I will have the steak and ale pie, eh… lemon cheesecake and let me see…ah, a diet coke, please," I spluttered as I flipped the pages. "Oh, and do you serve chips with the mains?"

"Chips, nah…no chips," responded Morris in a gruff brusque tone.

"Could you perhaps request them for me?" I pushed.

"Madam. We don't do chips. Not in the likes of here. If you want your greasy fries, may I suggest you go elsewhere!" he replied snootily.

Rude! So much for getting me whatever I wanted, eh!

Oh, and get this, it wasn't just Morris who was miffed by my request, as Kalen, once again, snubbed his nose up at my choices.

"Problem?" I queried.

"Nope, no problem, well, that is unless you think eating a friend of Bambi is acceptable? Oh, and don't get me started on all this diet nonsense, low fat this and low fat that. Absolute garbage!" he blurted.

Shocked by his unwarranted outburst, I refused to answer and allowed the awkward strain of silence to filter through the room. It was probably at this point I began to realise that Kalen and myself were not as compatible as I had originally hoped.

However, they do say opposites attract, and I was very willing to learn, even compromise to his way of thinking. His stand-offish nature was after all what had attracted me to him. Every time he deviated from the norm, he inadvertently made me yearn for him more. Unorthodox, opinionated and stubborn personalities were apparently a huge turn on for me!

Morris and his cocksure attitude had by now swivelled on the spot, swiftly marching off towards the rear of the cavern and vanishing through a chunky set of slatted saloon doors.

I presumed these doors led to the kitchen where the hot-headed chef was waiting in anticipation for our titillating order.

Though, it turns out, I didn't have to wait too long to find out if my assumption was correct as the doors flew open just as quickly as they had shut.

"They don't hang about do they!" I gasped.

"About time!" tutted Kalen in disagreement.

He aimed his impatience towards Earl, the Barman, who had come scuttling over in place of Morris.

Goddammit! I could kick myself! Being the nosy cow that I was, I had been given the opportunity to grab a sneaky glimpse of the activity unfolding in the closed room behind Earl, but in doing so, had failed rather miserably! The speed in which the doors swung open and shut were mind-bogglingly quick. Prohibiting me from seeing much at all, apart from a weird electric flash of fiery white light as the doors came to a swift halt.

"Did you see that?"

"See what?" queried Kalen.

"The light! The flash of light from the kitchen!" I blurted, puzzled.

"Alanna, calm down, the chef was probably flambéing your cow!" he spat.

Well that was a tad much! But not wanting to argue, I let his comment slide. Besides, I was more preoccupied with this little niggly feeling I had — a feeling that something was just a tiny bit off about this place. The staff for one, were fairly odd, and what on earth was that freakish zip of light all about? Stranger still, I noticed there was no bar in the immediate restaurant!

Why so low-key?

I could only assume the manager preferred a minimalistic look...food and drinks prepared outback and out of view of the paying customer, but it was all still a bit weird — a bit 'secretive'.

I could ponder all night — easily, but I was most likely overacting, and it was best all round if I reverted back to the situation in hand, which involved a twitchy Earl, standing before us with a juddering tray of beverages.

Kalen, wasting no time, snatched the rich chocolatey milkshake from off the silver platter. Without a word, he slurped it down whole. There was no alarming gasp or any frantic effort to surface for air. Instead, he busily sucked the dense shake through the slender straw, only stopping once he had guzzled every last droplet.

"Mmmmm, mmmm, mmm, that was delicious and exactly what was called for!" he applauded with a grateful rub of the tummy.

Fulfilled from his liquid marathon mission, he proudly licked his tacky lips, making sure not to have left a single morsel. Taken aback by his aberrant behaviour, I unthinkingly found myself staring at him. This had not gone unnoticed and quickly he too became conscience-stricken of his actions.

"Excuse me, I was parched!" he stated. "Oh, and as you can probably tell I have a major sweet tooth, it sometimes gets the better of me!" he nervously laughed.

Earl, who was still in the process of serving, pretended not to notice Kalen's gluttonous chops as he daintily poured my diet coke into a frozen tinted tumbler. The glass released a delicate yet gratifying crack as the fizzy fluid smashed against its arctic lining, subsequently muting out Kalen's awkward titter.

∞∞∞

No sooner had Earl left then did Morris arrive in his place, although you wouldn't have noticed the difference, as they too looked pretty much identical to one another. Basil of course making it a hat-trick!

Now Earl was squat and stockier than both Basil and Morris who were both poker-stick thin. Earl didn't feature the same teeth, but he did sport the same compelling bottle-green eyes and a very prominent beaklike nose! He was also a little on the shy side, refusing to mutter a single word, preferring to be seen and not heard.

Another point worth noting was that Basil, Morris and Earl were the only staff members on shift, which probably meant that this was a family run business. It would sure explain the doppelgängers!

"Madam, your meat pie, and for you, sir...the dessert!" sniffed Morris.

He pulled an expression of bewilderment as he smacked the contrasting meals heavy-handedly onto the table.

The pie smelt mouth-wateringly good, the pastry wafer thin and golden, the mash potatoes smooth and creamy. I lavished my dinner in a thick helping of juicy gravy and seasoned with a dusting of salt. I could not wait to tuck in and by the looks of it neither could Kalen. He had already demolished half his cake and was proceeding to indulge into a heaped spoon of velvety chocolate, gooey, pudginess. Buttery crumbs from the cookies flaked on to his plate, and he made sure to devour each and every one. He daren't waste a single piece.

Again, I caught myself gaping at him. I was fascinated by his quirky little habits, and yet again he caught me openly gawking at him. Kalen had by now professedly sensed I required an explanation and began to unravel the real reason behind his strange eating habits.

"I know it's not the norm, evidently it's unconventional to you — I get that. Thing is, Alanna, I didn't have the most traditional of upbringings. Abandoned at a very young age, I was left to fend for myself. I taught myself the way of the world and how to survive. I did what I wanted, when I wanted, and no one with any real control could stop me. If I wanted a slice of carrot cake for breakfast, a palatable three course banquet for lunch and a stodgy bowl of porridge for dinner — then so be it. The way we live our life is an individual choice and is ours for the taking. The way I live is the choice I made, and I guess a decision that has stuck with me ever since," declared Kalen.

My heart compressed with sadness for him. I had no idea he was abandoned and at such an impressionable age too. I wanted to hold him, to remove the aching pain that had burdened him for all these years. Where were his parents? Did they die? Had they given him up? Who took care of him? Surely someone must have?

I had so many intrusive questions to ask, but it really was far too early for me to pry, and who exactly was I to question the way he went about his personal life. I knew this was not the time. I had to place my thinking aside and turn my attention back to the here and now. Besides, it appeared that Kalen had already ceased the conversation for me, refusing to divulge any further. The matter was now closed, but if given half the chance, I hoped he would let me readdress this topic at a later date.

∞∞∞

Kalen's eyes were no longer with me. They had swayed over towards Basil who was lurking at the entrance of the cavern. He had been there intermittently throughout the night, waiting to greet the next set of hungry diners. Strangely though, no other customers did arrive — it was just Kalen and I. Come to think of it, the restaurant was eerily quiet and had been from the second we arrived.

There was no noisy natter from bustling tables or irritating lip smacking from customers that were incapable of chewing their food quietly. We were the restaurants only priority, and it seemed that Kalen was growing increasingly agitated by the fact that Basil had not clocked his pressing need! The vast amount of eyeballing and lip-scrunching thrown from Kalen was well-noted by me as he poorly attempted to telepathically summon Basil.

"Urgh, finally!" grunted Kalen as Basil knowingly nodded in the direction of his disgruntled customer.

Morris, immediately bolted through the saloon doors, allowing the stained wood to neglectfully smack back against the brick walls. With full tilt, he sashayed over to our table with Kalen's mains and my dessert poised upon the top of his fingertips. Skillfully, he positioned the dishes down onto our table and from underneath our noses, snatched away our dirty plates, including my uneaten helping of mash.

Morris proceeded to hotfoot it back through the saloon doors and out of view.

Seriously, how inpatient could one person possibly be. The reason for Kalen's thorny and unnecessary stares were down to his greedy gut! You would think I would be shocked by his etiquette but from what I had witnessed so far, I wasn't the least bit surprised.

Kalen probed his dish with an immaculately polished

knife, flicking his crunchy walnuts from side-to-side. He scraped a heaped mountain of lettuce onto his fork and rammed it into his open mouth. Tutting in detest, he tossed another one of 'those' looks to Basil who at this point was ready and waiting for the next demanding request from his needy customer.

Again, without any words exchanged, Basil nodded and instantly Morris hurtled through the stable doors with a bottle of golden syrup held proudly within his fist.

Like a hawk, Kalen nabbed the bottle of gummy sweet gloop from the grip of our attentive waiter and dribbled it over every inch of his greens. He made sure to smother his walnuts with an extra double coating!

"Too bland?" I inquired with a touch of scrutiny.

How anyone could devour a bowl of lettuce and syrup was beyond me, but what was more intriguing was that Basil knew exactly what Kalen wanted without him having to say a single word.

"Alanna, walnuts and maple syrup complement one another, everyone knows that," pronounced Kalen.

"Do they? I never knew...what if you wanted something else. It was a bit presumptuous of him, wasn't it?" I queried.

"Good guess I suppose!" replied Kalen in a cheery manner.

His once cranky demeanour had now been lifted by the quick fix of a sugar rush.

"Maybe..." I concluded as I delved my spoon into the appetising cheesecake that was screaming to be engulfed.

Flavoured beads of lemon zest exploded upon the crown of my tongue, sending my taste buds into a soured frenzy of exultation. Kalen's eyes widened as he generously wet his lips on viewing the creamy goo foam within the flesh of my mouth. He had outright food envy and feeling less than impressed with his choice of salad, spent the remainder of the evening eyeing up my scrumptious cheesecake. I knew men were known for loving their food, but Kalen took it to a whole new level. I had to take action and distract his attention away from the lure of a dessert, so I decided it was time to bring up the real reason for why I was here.

"Come on then, Kalen. You wanted to know about the area, didn't you?"

Part of me hoped this was all just a ploy to invite me out on a date, but Kalen quickly dashed any hopes of such a wish.

"Yes, that's right!" he joyfully replied.

True to his word, he was more interested in the local area than he was of me.

"As you know, Alanna, I'm pretty much new to Elder-crest, and I'm dying to get up close...and very personal with my surroundings — do you know what I mean?" he chimed.

Actually, no, I didn't know, as every now and again Kalen would make me feel as if he was flirting, like he was trying to tell me how he really felt. Then without warning, he would snatch those blissful thoughts from out of my mind and re-place them with the stone-cold misery of reality.

"I don't know of many people around here, but what I do know is that I love all things related to nature. Nothing quite beats exploring the beauty of the world we live in, and I want to be able to scout it out and see what Eldercrest has to offer. Plus, I'm an avid photographer and would love to capture some snaps of the local wildlife, it's a little hobby of mine," he added.

How wrong was I! I had judged him all too soon, pigeon-holing him just like the college had tried but failed to do with me. I incorrectly assumed he wanted information on where the grotty drunken hotspots were. I had wild visions of him partying away in the liveliest pubs and clubs with a bottle of Moët in tow, surrounded by a flock of scantily clad trollops.

I had him down wrong, totally wrong. The person who I thought wanted to be where everyone else was, actually loved being alone. He was an adventurer, an outdoorsy spirit, prefer-ring to spend quality time in the open, not stuck in a stuffy room with a hundred-other people, bopping to the same beat with a stomach full of festering lager.

"Oh, right, well...where do I start!" I stumbled, delighted by his unexpected yet very appealing revelation. You know, maybe we weren't so dissimilar after all....

"WAIT!" he shouted, interrupting me.

"What?" I quizzed worriedly.

"C...can I trust you?" he blurted.

Where had that come from? He had hardly given me a chance to bequeath my expertise before ambushing me with this not so pressing life or death question!

"I need to know," he pushed.

"Completely," I urged.

With lowered brows, he continued. "There are these things, dark deep things. Things you don't know about me, things that are not so easy to say."

"Whatever it is, whatever these 'things' are, you can tell me," I spurred.

"Promise?" he pressed.

"Forever," I replied.

"In that case, there is something you should know," he whispered.

Four

FORBIDDEN

Eldercrest had always been referred to as this sleepy, quiet, keep yourself to yourself kind of village...that is bar those that were commonplace within the local pub!

"From what I've heard, this area dates back to the 17th-century, and rumour has it, it was renowned for its plague of witch activity!"

For the first time, Kalen's eyes sparkled with exuberance as he listened attentively within my company. It was like a match had been lit, burning bright — he had come alive! His facial expressions were animated, and his body presence stemming in stature as his energy levels bloomed before me. Deep down I hoped his sudden flare of interest was linked to me, but, if we were being sensible, it was probably down to the mass sugar intake he had just inhaled!

With his torso facing inwards towards me, his attention had been grasped.

The possibilities of the dark arts taking place within our little community had clearly tickled his fancy, and with his focus secured, it was the perfect time to flip the subject.

"Kalen — what was it you needed to tell me?"

"Maybe later," he replied.

"You said that five minutes ago! I thought it was urgent?"

"It can wait," he smiled, shrugging off my request.

Could it? It seemed pretty important if you asked me.

"Alanna. Tell me about Eldercrest first. Please."

Fine but how much 'later' was later? I didn't want to pester, but he had sown a massive seed of intrigue that needed uprooting!

"Alanna!" he groaned.

Fine! Later it was.

Kalen gently cradled his chin with his left hand, allowing his fingertips to laze against his rosy cheek. His pupils fixated on the steady movement of my lips as I continued to spout the gossip learnt through years of overheard conversations.

"There are tons of tales associated with the black magic of Eldercrest Woods that often circulate from time to time. I'm surprised you haven't heard them?" I questioned.

Kalen irrevocably shook his head and urged me to continue.

"Well, the most notorious tale was of Cornelius Wentworth, a young twenty-something knight of the King who had captured the heart of a poor domestic servant named Blythe Fairfax.

Their love was a forbidden one which was ruled solely by their class. If made public, the family and acquaintances of Cornelius would most definitely have disapproved of his relationship with that of a mere servant girl. As a result, they would have disallowed such an affair to continue for fear of shaming the family name.

'Apparently', Blythe was a single child who lived in her master's attic with her mother, father and a handful of other servants. The number of servants a master had in those days was a sign of their social status, and with twenty on his books, Blythe's master was ranking mighty high on the ladder of distinction.

The pay was absolutely pitiful for having to rise each day at the crack of dawn in order to tend to a never-ending list of household chores. But nevertheless, it was a job and a warm roof over her head.

Most days Blythe would find herself up to her eyeballs

in soiled laundry, copious amounts of dusting and a steady stream of urine bespattered chamber pots.

The one saving grace for Blythe was the quantity of domestic servants present at her master's abode. It allowed her to sneak off unnoticed for an hour or two, and it was in one of these hours that she met her true love," I excitingly spilled.

Kalen was snared! Not wanting to lose this new-found connection—I continued.

"Cornelius was a gallant knight and was hardly ever seen without his trusted black stead named Humphrey. He was well respected in his field for his seamless combat ability and technique, never hesitating to charge into battle and protect his King when ordered."

"Impressive!" chimed Kalen.

"Indeed, but it's not hard to see that Cornelius and Blythe were worlds apart. They only happened to stumble across one another by pure chance."

"Doesn't mean to say they couldn't have worked," he rhetorically added.

"Well, let me finish and then you'll know," I playfully quipped. "The day in question was no different to any other. Cornelius and Humphrey were out hacking against the periphery of Eldercrest Woods. They were riding in single formation alongside their fellowmen — with Cornelius heading up the rear of the unit. When without warning an unfamiliar loud rumpus spooked Humphrey, recklessly careering him off track and into the heart of the woods. No one and I mean no one was permitted to enter into these woods without first seeking authorisation from the hierarchy. The area was prohibited by order of the King, and only his most audacious of knights were granted access on command or via a request to enter. It was only the brave or the downright stupid that would travel in there otherwise!" I revealed.

"Why?" demanded Kalen.

"Isn't it obvious?" I snorted. "You were either a witch... or the witch's prisoner! Once in those woods, you belonged to her, that's after she had hunted you down of course!"

Kalen appeared rattled by my preposterous claim, and sensing his perplexity, I swiftly persisted with the story for fear of losing his interest.

"It transpired that the absence of Cornelius had gone totally unnoticed by his fellow men. Their horses had too been unnerved by what some say was the sound of a deathly female scream. Distracted, they had not noticed the disappearance of one of their own."

Kalen was hooked. I had him. Now all I needed to do was to reel him in!

"Unconcerned by Humphrey's route deviation, the King's knights obliviously charged off down the path in which they had been travelling on. They were gone, and to Cornelius' dismay he was all alone in the one place that made the hairs on the back of his neck stand on end...though on the flip side, he met his Blythe!"

"In the 'woods', you say?" he interrupted.

Ignoring another interruption — I continued. "Blythe didn't care for grand stories of broomsticks and black cats or indeed for the orders of the King — often taking herself off into the woods illegitimately. This was the only place she was able to gather her thoughts and escape the hustle and bustle of her everyday mundane duties.

As this was restricted land, Blythe never saw another soul. So, for her it was quite an unexpected occurrence when (from the distance) she witnessed a robust nag, charging directly towards the wholesome Apple tree she was daydreaming upon.

Humphrey irrepressibly zig-zagged towards Blythe's static body, swerving the fruit tree and only narrowly missing a collision of disastrous proportions.

The force from his stern hoofs attempting to alter direction was, however, unavoidable, sending a wave of vibrations throughout the woods. Consequently, shaking Blythe from off the crook of the tree branch that she was nestled into."

"Dead?" he asked, straight-faced.

"Not yet," I answered.

Blythe had actually tumbled towards the dirt track below inside a hailstorm of unrestrained waxy red apples. Luckily for her, she landed straight into the oncoming lap of Cornelius who was erratically passing underneath at that exact moment in time.

"He, the unintentional hero had saved her," I gushed, to the delight of Kalen. "Blythe gazed into Cornelius' eyes and he into hers, and from that petrifying moment on, they were enamoured. She was his damsel in distress and he, her knight in shining armour. For them, class didn't play a part, and they ventured into a whirlwind romance."

"Don't stop, Alanna! Whatever happened to them? I must know!" pleaded Kalen as I paused to take a breather.

"Ok, ok!" I reassured before continuing my tale of ta-booed love. "Both Cornelius and Blythe would regularly sneak away from their evening duties and meet up within the pro-hibited woods under the cover of darkness. It would not have boded well for either of them if their relatives and peers had been made aware of their rendezvousing—so they hid. No one would dare risk being met by the so-called witch that wan-dered the woods, but for these two lovers, they had no alterna-tive option."

Kalen seemed utterly smitten with my little tale, though I wasn't sure if the next part would go down as well....

"So, you know I said only the brave and stupid ventured into these woods? Well, I forgot to include snitches into that list too! You see, Kalen, there was this young knight named Tobias Bassingborne who was eager to please. He wasn't shy in causing havoc, and unfortunately for Cornelius, he had no-ticed his unusual nighttime habits."

It happened to be on one cold winters evening that To-bias took it upon himself to follow Cornelius into the woods. Unafraid and evidently a fan of rule-breaking himself, he con-tinued without deliberation. He was discreet to the point he was invisible, hiding behind trees, crawling on all fours and doing whatever he needed to do to remain incognito. Once Cornelius had tiptoed to a standstill, Tobias dashed, hiding himself behind the same Apple tree that had played a vital role in Cornelius and Blythe's first encounter.

It was also here that he watched in utter disbelief as Blythe emerged from out of the bushes and into view. The frolicking that then commenced confirmed to Tobias that Cornelius was, in fact, pursuing relations with a witch. As no respectable knight of the King would even conceive of cavorting with what appeared to be a simple servant girl and in the woods of all places.

He was adamant that witchcraft was at play here, and this unproven hunch of his was enough for him to raise the alarm bells and betray one of his own.

On returning later that evening to the King's castle, Cornelius caught wind of Tobias' accusations. He immediately knew that any mention of witchcraft would not be taken lightly.

Worrying of his love's impending fate, Cornelius took the heart-wrenching decision to vanish, and within the early hours of the morning — vanish he did. He left no trace of himself, in the belief that this would be the best solution for them both.

The next day, Blythe unsuspecting to the unfolding events, went to meet Cornelius as she usually did, but instead of being held by the man of her dreams, she was confronted by ten of the King's gnarliest knights.

They were burly, affronted and seething with rage. Primarily, they had been disgruntled by the allegations against Cornelius and his 'al fresco' liaisons with a 'so-called' witch. But now, they were in uproar over his uncharacteristic disappearance, and had therefore, registered him dead.

With no explanation for Cornelius' disappearance, all fingers pointed to Blythe. As beautiful as she was, they could not believe that Cornelius would enter into this relationship when he knew full well the consequences that be.

Blythe unable to prove her innocence, and with no endorsement from Cornelius — was found guilty of witchcraft
and of the murder of her lover. She was sentenced to death via
public hanging.

Kalen was aghast, "that's dreadful!", he whimpered.

"Oh, you don't really believe all that bilge, do you? It's
an old fairy tale, probably made up by the parents of unruly
kids to stop them from causing mischief in those woods!" I
chuckled.

"Hmmm, maybe," he dubiously replied.

As upsetting as the tale was, I didn't believe the content
for a second. Witches, goblins, fairies alike, were a load of old
drivel in my eyes. They were made-up to scaremonger little
children into behaving.

Don't get me wrong, I found the woods a little intimidating, but I tried to put any negative thoughts to the back of my
mind. The same couldn't be said for Kalen. What I thought was
a harmless little story, seemed to have struck a delicate chord
with him. My words of reason didn't appear to reassure him
either. He was definitely more sensitive than I had given him
credit for. Although a little concerned I had upset him, I was
still delighted I had stolen his attention, even if it was only for
my lavish yarn spinning!

"Fiction or not, if you do decide to venture into those
woods, you won't be disappointed!" I chirped.

It was the truth. Eldercrest Woods had the most eye-
watering of sceneries, with an abundance of flowers and riveting wildlife, you could easily lose yourself in all its glory. With
a skinny turquoise stream trailing through the thrive of greenery — it was the perfect home to an array of native amphibians
and a handful of peculiar-looking swamp creatures!

"Oh, and the best part? There's not one witch to be
found!" I declared with a cheeky giggle.

With a wary smile, Kalen interrupted, "I adore her."

"Huh?" I grunted.

"Her...you know...nature, Alanna. She's a gift and one we should cherish. There really is no feeling more compelling than walking barefoot through dewy grass on a raw spring morning. Oh... and her scent! The scent from a succulent sweet flower...it never fails to pull me in or to awaken the senses!" he cooed.

I was shocked that someone so vague, so tense, so distant...so very different could be absorbed by the simplistic beauty of nature.

∞∞∞

"Finished, madam?" queried Morris as he interrupted my thoughts.

"Oh...yes, I'm absolutely bloated, I couldn't eat another bite!" I appreciatively puffed.

I glanced at Kalen's plate, which was, of course, empty, but instead of rubbing his belly in synchronised gratitude, he was firmly fixated on the leftovers of my cheesecake. To tell you the truth, if pushed, I could have gobbled down the remains of my dessert, but I sensed Kalen craved mine more than I did, so I played the situation out.

Meticulously, I scooped a helping of the sumptuous cake onto my fork. Then teasingly tipped the silver upside down; the contents scrambling across the plate like an overloaded avalanche. I was about to repeat my torturous display, when as expected, he bit. Greedily, stabbing his fork into a clump of the zingy lemon frosting, mindful not to leave any of the buttery biscuit base behind.

"Finished now!" he chortled, handing over the plate to Morris.

I couldn't help but giggle with him. He was definitely not one to shy away when it came to eating the sweet stuff. This was the first time I had seen Kalen genuinely laugh — a real belly laugh, and it was well worth the wait. He was gorgeous.

"You know, you really should laugh more often, it's so contagious, you brighten up the room," I spurted.

Kalen smiled coyly, acknowledging my sincere compliment but resisting to comment. The ice was slowly melting, and at last, I was breaking through his reinforced barriers.

We spent the rest of the evening getting to know one another. His favourite flower was a blue Myosotis Sylvatica, commonly known as the Forget-me-not. Mine — the Snow Drop, which Kalen pointed out was otherwise known as Galanthus Nivalis.

His favourite colour was debatable, he didn't just like one shade, he liked them all. If it was bright and bold, he more than likely adored it. I, on the other hand, preferred my shades dark, dull and moody.

We did, however, both agree that there was no better smell than the perfumed notes that lingered in the air before and after a heavy rain pour in the much-awaited summer months.

Real progress had been made. I was pinpointing his likes and dislikes, and he was beginning to open up to me in ways I could never have imagined. I didn't want this night to end, but regrettably, it did. Closing time had come and gone, and it was Basil that eventually kicked us out for overstaying our welcome.

"Come on, Alanna, I'm sure the staff would like to return home to their families, as no doubt do you — I'll drive you home," instructed Kalen in a gentle but firm tone.

Actually, if I had my way, I would have contently sat with him until the early hours of the morning or at least until our tongues stopped wagging! Kalen was right though — it was late, and I'm sure Basil and his team had seen quite enough of me pining over my companion for one night.

"Basil, thank you for your fab service, I've had such a lovely evening! I don't suppose Earl and Morris are available? I would love to thank them personally and wish them a good night."

Basil seemed a little taken aback by my request. Sheepishly he looked over his shoulder in a pathetic and slothful attempt to search for them.

"Thank you for your kind words, ma'am, but...erm no... they are a little tied up in the backroom at the moment. I'll be sure to pass on your compliments," he circumspectly replied.

"Oh, right...no problem...well, hopefully we will be back again soon to see you and your brothers. They are your brothers, aren't they?" I delved.

"No, ma'am, they are not. We are not related, and you're also not the first person to say that either," chuckled Basil nervously — and with that, he ushered us out the door and on our way.

"Well, that was strange!" I mumbled to Kalen.

Kalen, however, wasn't the least bit bothered about Basil's reaction, simply shrugging off his behaviour as if it were irrelevant. They really did look the spitting image of one another, and a straightforward no would have sufficed, but instead, I was met with an uncalled-for response as the cavern door was pretty much slammed in my face! Odd fella, I thought, though I wasn't going to dwell on the subject. The night was almost over, and I wanted to savour every last enjoyable second I had left with Kalen.

Reluctantly, I sloped myself back into the seat of the car, but this time as the doors closed, I knew the return trip would be different. This time I could practically feel the touchable warmth exuding from his body into mine.

"Here we are," Kalen announced, pulling lightly onto the drive.

With the journey quickly disappearing into the thick of the night, I hadn't had the time to acknowledge any of the ride. I was far too busy fantasising about him, about what he was thinking and about all the things he wanted to do with me — or more importantly to me!

The overwhelming surge of unbridled lust rained over me, leaving my palms hot and sticky from the sweet stream of slippery sweat that perspired from them. My body throbbed, aching to be touched and teased in ways that only Kalen would know how.

You see in-between the growling revs, I had caught Kalen briefly glancing at me, no words said, just a look. He was mulling something over. What it was? I wasn't exactly sure, but just the thought alone was enough to set my giddy heart racing.

It was only when those smoky rubber wheels of his wound to a standstill, then did my mind and body begin to rest as he unknowingly threw me back into the soberness of reality.

Breathless from the steamy heat, I couldn't believe I had allowed myself to get so carried away. I only hoped he hadn't noticed, I prayed he hadn't. It was so unlike me to lose sight of my inhibitions, but this was Kalen we were talking about, he had this effect on me. He was like a habit. A dirty one. One I couldn't kick, but I couldn't help myself—I didn't want to.

My reluctance was in full swing as I opened the car door and begrudgingly stepped out.

Kalen didn't budge, he was rooted to the driver's seat. I figured that there wasn't going to be the obligatory walk to the front door, and therefore a goodnight kiss had been unquestionably ruled out.

This came as somewhat of a disappointment to me, especially after the heated thoughts I'd been having. I felt something for this boy, and with my beliefs put to one side, I would have risked it all for him to have at least tried.

I didn't want this to be the end for us, but unfortunately, all the signs were there, screaming at me, telling me that this was most likely going to be the last time I was to see him. He clearly wasn't making any type of attempt to prolong the night, so it was up to me to draw these seconds out for as long as I possibly could. I knew what I had to do!

"TART!"

"Strawberry tart!"

"Fancy a tart!" I blathered.

Oh great! I had gone with the first thing that had popped into my head and it happened to be that well-known conversation starter known as the 'tart'.

Seriously! 'Tart' of all things! I was babbling at him, I must have looked ridiculous, gaga even! I had to compose myself, rectify my outburst, that's if I wanted him to believe I was a normal down to earth girl with her sanity intact.

"Erm sorry, Kalen. What I meant to say was — would you like to pop into mine for a bit? The evening is young, and we still have so much more to talk about. How does that sound with a strawberry tart and a cup of coffee thrown in for free?"

I didn't want to bribe him in with food but seeing as he loved a dessert…I figured it would be worth a sneaky try!

"Alanna, I would love to," his eyes kindling at the thought of more sugar. But all the same, he still declined my offer.

"I best not, another time perhaps, and besides, your mum wanted you home by 11:30pm, and I'm pretty sure that didn't include me as well!!"

"But…but I haven't even told you about this heavenly little spot that I like to visit! You have to see it; I just know you would love it!" I was clutching at straws here.

"Another time, hey," he gently enforced.

Another time! Did he genuinely want to see me again? Or was this his gentle way of brushing me off with a poor excuse, with no actual intention of stepping foot on my doorstep ever again!

And hang on, how did he know I was meant to be home before midnight? It must have been a bloody good guess unless he had supersonic hearing! I bet that meddling mother of mine had gotten to him before I had!

"Will I actually see you again?" I nervously asked. I didn't want to sound desperate, but I needed to know.

"Perhaps," he smiled with a wink before slicing the stallion into first gear and speeding off into the night.

Five

SLIPPERY FEELINGS

The morning after my 'date' with Kalen had arrived, it was dark and drizzly, and I was wide awake. Wasting no time, I threw back the layers of sheets and jumped out of my snug bed, ready for the day ahead. Mum would tell you that I was by no means a morning person. In fact, if I had the option to hibernate, then there would be no question of what I would be doing right now! This morning though was different. I felt different.

Unable to sleep, I was full of anticipation and wanted to be awake to experience whatever it was that was intending to head my way, and you can probably guess what it was I wanted.

Boy did I hope he would arrive on my doorstep, eager to see me with a spontaneous plan, headlining the two of us and only us. If by chance he did come knocking, I wanted to be ready and waiting, not lounging around in yesterday's creased nightwear!

Now I was quite aware that Kalen wasn't as interested in me as I would've hoped, but with time and a touch of non-creepy pursuing, I knew I could change all that. I now also had the advantage of knowing what made him tick, maybe, just maybe I could make him want me like I wanted him.

After last night, I knew I had fallen for him. More than I thought I possibly could have — and in such a short space of time too.

My heart was thumping with the strongest of feelings, those fuzzy, heated, feel good feelings — you know the ones. The ones I didn't think I could harbour in this bitter heart of mine. The more signs of rejection he showed me — the more I craved him, and if I wanted him to be mine, then I knew I had to wait.

Kalen never gave me an exact time or date that he would visit, actually he never promised he would visit me at all. If I recall, he chucked me a slightly vague 'perhaps'. Still, I didn't care, I was adamant that he would return, he had to — we had so much more to talk about.

∞∞∞

Warmly wrapped, I rushed out the front door like a kid on Christmas day and headed towards the old Cedar tree — located to the side of the house. Its thick regal branches entwined their way around the front of our humble abode, perfectly perching themselves in front of my bedroom window and in line with the porch roof.

From one of the sturdier branches hung a delightfully white shabby chic, two-seater swing chair. It was charmingly aesthetic in appearance and home to a multitude of cherished childhood memories. Without fail, the seat would always remind me of those lazy summer days, where I would spend countless hours daydreaming of magical tales and happy ever afters.

Dad had spent several palm blistering weeks handcrafting the seat as a fifth birthday gift to me — his baby girl. I can remember how chuffed he was with himself when he finally revealed his handy work from underneath a dusty old cream sheet. Through the years, wear and tear had taken its toll on its once youthful self, but I still loved it as much now as I did back then.

I nuzzled myself into one corner of the knackered old

seat, and just like so many times before, I began to daydream, but this time, I was cast as the lead role in my very own saucy tale.

Seconds ticked by, then minutes, followed by hours — it was becoming quite apparent that Kalen wasn't going to show, but nonetheless, I stubbornly refused to leave my self-appointed post. Only a burgundy fleece blanket straddled my frame, keeping the bite from the abnormal chilly July breeze off my skin.

Another hour passed and still no Kalen. Nor did he appear the hour after that or even the days that proceeded, but each day without fail I would do as I had done previously and wait. I treated each day as if it was the very first day after our 'date', and I would wait and wait and wait. It was only when the weather completely turned that enough was enough, and I admitted defeat. There was only so much oppressiveness a girl in lust could take, and I had unequivocally reached my limit. With a heavy heart, I hotfooted it towards the house, the pathetic blanket dragging onto the pebble spewed drive behind me.

I took one last peek at the seat and smiled. I smiled at the thought of all those wild fantasies I had conjured up with Kalen, but that's just it, they were fantasies, and I had finally succumbed to my monotonous reality.

Time passed as quickly as it had done on that wooden seat. We were now a little shy of two months, and between the days leading up to the present, I often wondered if I would ever see Kalen again. I did my best to function day to day like any other normal human being, but he was always on my mind. No day would go by that I didn't think of him. Stupidly, I had invested way too many feelings into someone that had proved he didn't reciprocate my affections, otherwise he would be with me right now.

As much as I tried to erase him from my mind. I couldn't. I refused to give up on him, and I was unable to forget him. I was desperate not to ache this way. I yearned to start living a normal life, free from emptiness, free from pain.

If I wasn't moping in bed, I would be out walking Jed, manically trying to decipher what to do with my life from here on out. I didn't have a job. I had no money, and I was yet to volunteer. Oh no, I was far too busy weeping over Kalen to have made that a priority. Some days I didn't even attempt to encourage myself to leave my bedroom. Whole mornings, afternoons and days would be wasted by myself blubbering into a crumpled up, snotty wet hanky whilst sprawled out in yesterday's clothes.

I was well aware I needed to pull myself together. Sitting around whimpering over someone that never committed themselves to me in the first place was not the most sensible of ideas, but today was not one of those days, so back to bed I went.

∞∞∞∞

"Aaallanaaaaa," came the prolonged ghostly whisper.

"Huh?" I stammered, as I woke from my slumber with a jolt. It was gone midnight, and I had woken up in a state of distress upon hearing the call of my name mellowly echoing through the silence of my bedroom.

Frightened, my body lay rigid underneath the bed sheets. My eyes wide open, staring at the bleak ceiling above as I gathered my bearings. Did I actually hear that? I must have been dreaming. I mean it sounded like someone was...was in my room...?

"Alanna!" sharply sounded the phantom voice.

"What the!" I spluttered.

There was no mistaking it this time. My name was loudly

and strictly hollered from within the four walls of my bedroom. Rubbing my eyes to focus, I sleepily scanned the room, checking all corners for a sighting, but there was no one there. Though I was absolutely certain I had heard my name called.

I had to be brave and investigate, so slowly I crept from out of my bed and tiptoed to the window in search of the reason for all this unsettling commotion. It was early, ridiculously early, but someone was and had been trying to summon my attention, and I needed to find out who.

"Morning, sleepyhead!" boomed the not so spooky voice.

"Shhhhhh, my mums asleep!" I giggled.

Was I dreaming? I had to be! He had been silent for all those weeks and now out of the blue, here he was, materialising on my doorstep at stupid o'clock in the morning!

Ignoring my polite request, he proceeded to yell up towards me, "I couldn't sleep, I've been thinking...."

Couldn't sleep! I've been lingering around here like a crusty old cold sore for months on end, but all of a sudden, he can't sleep so decides to show up! These were his terms, they were hardly fair or particularly normal, but as I was beginning to realise, neither was Kalen.

As much as I wanted to feel anger, or to be annoyed, I couldn't, I was secretly over the moon just to hear his voice again.

"Shushhhh, Kalen! You have to keep it down, you'll wake Mum... or worse — you'll wake Jed!" I worryingly whispered.

With weeks of silence, I had come to the conclusion that Kalen was long gone, that he had selfishly taken what he wanted from me and left. I never thought I would see him again, so why was he back after all this time? He was alive with elation, his body buzzing and overcome with enthusiasm, but surely this wasn't all for me?

"Let's talk!" he boomed.

If that hadn't woken Mum up, then I'm certain it would have stirred Jed. This was no use, I would have to clamber down the escape tree. It was the only way to go undetected.

Avidly, I scuttled over to the back of my bedroom door and yanked my aubergine cotton dressing gown from off its brass hook. With little time to spare, I hastily looked at my reflection in the wall mirror and gasped, "awful, absolutely awful."

With dark circles under my eyes, I looked an absolute state. Oh, and don't even mention the strands of hair ruffled and tussled all over the place. My interrupted snooze and weeks of sulking were definitely to blame here. Anyway, there was no time to sort out the imperfections on my face or slick down the scruffs of hair. Kalen was about to see what I looked like in the morning — if I liked it or not!

Had I expected our first time to be like this?

No!

Actually, I had imagined myself drowsily stirring with flawless peachy skin, freshly combed hair and minty fresh breath!

"Ohhh get on with it," I grumbled.

"Get on with what...?" loudly questioned Kalen.

"Woah!!" I wailed in shock.

Kalen brazen as you like was boldly stood upon the meaty branch outside my window. He had one arm firmly leaning against the outside wall, whilst his inquisitive head poked through the open window.

The branch was substantial in size and was more than capable of holding one or two persons weight. It was a god-send in my younger years for making the odd sneaky getaway without Mum knowing.

Although the breakouts were quick, the branch didn't come without its hazards. It should have probably been slapped with a health and safety warning!

Often, I found myself slipping off the sides in icy, wet and windy weather, but luckily, I never broke a single bone.

"Sorry, I scared you, didn't I?" soothed a worried Kalen.

"No, it's fine, you just caught me off guard, that's all. One minute you're stood outside on my drive, next thing you're perched outside my window ledge...looking in on me! I wasn't expecting to see you. I jumped, but it's fine. I'm fine," I frantically spouted.

"I'm sorry, Alanna. Maybe I should have waited, but I was concerned. You shouldn't be climbing out of windows and shimmying down rickety old trees. It's too dangerous for you, and I daren't see you harm yourself for the likes of me. It was much safer for me to climb, trust me!" affirmed Kalen.

"How do you know I was even contemplating that route?" I asked intrigued.

"A hunch I guess," he retorted.

That was all very sweet, but I didn't need him to hold my hand. I had mounted that bark more times than I could count, but I had to give it to him, he was fast! He had managed to scale that tree within seconds of me leaving to grab my dressing gown.

At least now I knew he cared...well at least a little bit. This was definitely slow but optimistic progress.

Fidgeting with the wide cord on my gown, I plodded over to the window. I didn't want to inappropriately expose myself, so made sure to knot it not once but twice. Feeling uncomfortable as well as unattractive, this was probably the worst scenario I could have found myself in. I just hoped I wasn't as off-putting to look at as I felt.

Timidly, I peered out the window and up towards Kalen. The branch was balanced just below the window frame, which meant Kalen was positioned to look straight down at me. His eyes were bigger and brighter than normal. His cheeks were flushed pink and his arms appeared more muscular than I once remembered. Slightly flustered from rushing to reach me, he looked sexier than ever — sweat dripping and all!

"Alanna, I wanted you to know...I've been thinking... thinking about you nonstop and what we spoke about that night. You mentioned you had a place that you go to, that's special to you and that I would love it as much as you do. You have me intrigued, and If I'm honest, I want to feel the way that you do about it!" he enthused.

"Oh Kalen, I don't know. I would love to show you but now, really?" I exclaimed.

"Take me there?" he asked. "It's just so bland around here in the village, there's no beauty, no excitement and I'm in need of some real excitement right now. I'm willing to try something new, are you?" he suggestively hinted.

Well, that was an offer I couldn't refuse! I'm not sure if it was intentional, but I felt like he was luring me in with the pretence that a little bit of fun could be had if I obliged to what he wanted.

I want to stand here and openly tell you I was better than that, better than to cave into the offer of a little bit of mischief. That before I made any rash decisions, I would sleep on it. I want to tell you that I 'ummed' and 'ahhhed' over my conclusion. That I made him grovel for my time, but the truth is, I've never been good at lying. So, I'll tell you straight...five seconds was all it took for me to say 'yes'. I wasn't daft, I knew Kalen was using my emotions against me to get his own way, but what can I say, I was a sucker for a little romance.

You're probably shaking your head at me right now, but you have to put yourself in my shoes. Imagine the boy or girl of your dreams pleading for your help. You have this one and only opportunity to make an impact, spending a few priceless minutes or hours with them. It's a no-brainer, and if you've ever been in that situation, then you'll know their charms are irresistible to what the heart wants.

"Alanna, you utterly captivated me with your endearing tale of Cornelius' and Blythe's tragic love," he whispered.

"Go on," I prompted.

Even though he had already won me over, I wanted to hear more.

"For some people, it's all about the sexual chemistry, that uncontrollable flutter that sends your body into a slippery meltdown. Well, that's not what does it for me, it's simply not enough. I crave a deeper connection, more mentally than physically, and you, Alanna…you get me, I know you do. I'm kind of enticed by you, and I want to know all there is to know about you," he gushed.

Wow! I was staggered with this sudden U-turn in curiosity for me. Where it had generated from was beyond me, but right now, I was experiencing a 'walking on clouds' type scenario.

"Plus, I have this! Come on, what do you say?"

Kalen extended his hidden arm from behind the wall to reveal a spangly state of the art camera that he proceeded to waggle in front of me. Yes, Kalen had his strange habits and yes, he had previously shrugged off any poorly attempted advances from me, but there was a noticeable change in his temperament. Was he falling for me like I had for him? Or was this all just an act to coax me out from the cosiness of my bed and into the brisk outdoors? There he could self-indulge in a spot of photography with me acting as his gullible tour guide.

Whatever the reason, I decided that if I didn't agree, then I would never know how he genuinely felt about me, and that was a much worse outcome than having my heart stamped all over.

"So…what do you say? The suspense is killing me. Say yes for me. Please?" asked a confident sounding Kalen.

"As you asked so nicely, then yes, I would love to," I lied.

It's not that I didn't want to. I really, really did, but I was hardly dressed for the occasion, was I!

"Erm, give me ten minutes and I'll be with you," I smiled, deceit etched across my face like a grotty 'ready to pop' pimple.

Kalen was overjoyed with my response, and without a peep dropped himself from off the branch and out of view. In all the years I had trudged up and down that tree, I had never once been as stealthlike as he had and at the atrocious time of 2:36am too.

∞∞∞

Panic set in! Under my gown, I was wearing a grubby old over-sized grey T-shirt with the word 'CUTE' emblazoned across the chest. A present from Nan, hardly my style but it was big and baggy and more for comfort than for statement.

'Cute' was definitely not the word I had in mind for my-self right now, but I had to work with what I had.

As previously mentioned, my hair was a tangled mess and my eyes appeared to have leased themselves out to a couple of green boogers. I was sending myself into a right tizz, but could you blame me? I wasn't prepared for this! Why oh why did it have to be so early. I was barely functioning to keep my eyes open as it was, let alone dress myself at this harrowing hour. This really was not how I wanted him to picture me in the morning, well not just yet anyway.

Ten measly minutes was all I had to look at least some-what decent. Well, actually it was now more like six after all that faffing around. I was never going to make him fall for me looking like this, but I would be damned if I was to leave the house resembling an extra from a zombie trailer. For now, it would have to be a prompt wash, a nimble brush of the teeth, a change of outfit — y'know, one of those quick out the door type jobbies!

Ta-dah! I was dressed and with a minute or two to spare! Inspecting my reflection, I adjusted my clothes accordingly, making sure to tuck the loose strands of scraggly thin hair be-hind my ears. Sighing, I hankered for more time to make the most of myself, but it was not to be, this really was the best I could do for now. With a quick spritz of floral body scent,

I lurked through the haze, tiptoeing down the stairs, past a sound asleep Jed and out the front door.

"Right then, let's visit my little piece of heaven!" I breathed.

Not wanting to waste another minute on my driveway, Kalen agilely scurried to unlock his car.

"Oh, where we're going, you won't need your wheels!" I mysteriously informed.

I offered him my hand, which he hesitantly accepted.

"Ooh!" I tittered unexpectedly.

"Everything ok?" asked Kalen concerned.

There was no ignoring it, I had felt it! A tingling sensation that rushed through my fingertips, flooding my whole body with a ripple of sensualness as he gently slipped his palm into mine. Expectantly, I looked at Kalen, hoping he too had experienced that bolt of electrifying chemistry.

"Did you feel it?" I bashfully questioned.

Returning my look, I was met with blankness and confusion. The expected buoyant acknowledgement to my audible spurt of rapture was non-existent. I'm sure Kalen had more than his fair share of girls falling head over heels for him, so why he was acting like I was out of sorts was a little ignorant. Could he not just be grateful that he had yet another girl swooning over his boyish good looks, rather than behaving impassive and restrained. A throwaway smile would have easily saved my blushes, but then again, if he wasn't into me, then he may not be able to behave in a way that he's not acclimatised too.

Maybe I was the fool for thinking otherwise, but regardless of all that, I couldn't shift that earth-moving feeling. Never had I felt pleasure sway through my body like it had done with him, and when he looked away — I let myself smile.

Six

TEA?

F riday the 7th September was finally here. It was a gloriously bright and fresh morning, and for the first time in years, I had woken up with an infectious smile slapped across my face. An uncontainable energy was charging through my veins and seeping through my open pores — I was bursting with delight! I could sense I was transitioning from that once glum and sombre girl to a much altogether happier young lady. Not only was I fulfilled with joy over this new sense of direction, but I was doubly bouncing from the impending eighteenth birthday festivities that I was about to encounter.

THUD!

A loud joyous party popper of explosion burst through my bedroom door, sending a whirlwind of merriment surging through my room.

"Mum!" I shouted, with a hint of giggle, "you could have at least knocked."

Mum began proceedings with the obligatory 'Happy Birthday' song, which she deliberately sang out of tune, no doubt piercing a few delicate eardrums if given the chance.

Mum, who was never one to shy away from an audience made the most of her moment by adding an operatic twist to finish.

"Outstanding!" I cheered, "that deserves a round of applause."

Clapping, I jumped from out of my bed and hugged her tightly. It was very rare that I would show Mum any sort of affection, but today I didn't want to let her go. It's hard to believe we were once inseparable, but it was true.

Growing up, I would often don her scarlet kitten heels and stomp across the hallway, which without fail would culminate in an exquisite vogue pose.

I remember Dad affectionately mocking us by referring to me as 'Mini Mum', but since he had left us, a void had surfaced and gradually us girls grew apart.

Mum had taken to spending most of her free evenings at 'The Old Crow', and I began to submerge myself into a lonely existence of daydreams and fantasies. Jed would often keep me company on those deserted nights when she was off out boozing, but he wasn't her, was he. I came to learn that there were certain times in your life when no matter how much you aged, you would always need your mum, but for me, she hadn't always been there.

Jed was still the same now as he was back then, he never changed and he also never timed any situation right. Balancing on his hind legs, with both paws raised, he barged into our overdue clinch, thrusting me onto my back and flattening me against the width of my bed. His ginormous paws rested on my winded chest, pinning me down as his slobbery wet tongue plastered my face — leaving traces of this morning's stinking tin of dog meat.

Mum didn't have to say a word, I could see by the restfulness in her eyes, that she too felt serenity. We were making much overdue progress in restoring our once faultless relationship.

Placing a steaming hot cup of tea on the bedside table, Mum chuckled at Jed who was now practically bathing me in beef and gravy chunks!

"Come on, boy," she commanded, tapping him on the

rump to remove him from off my sopping face.

As much as I loved that adorable lump of fur, I was gasping for a drink and preferred a dash of milk rather than a glug of drool in my tea. Jed did as he was told and allowed me to free my forearm and scrape his stringy saliva from off my gloopy lips.

Now anyone will tell you that they can make a cup of tea, but it takes a flawless individual to make the perfect cuppa. The art of tea cannot be rushed, and for me, perfection involved one cup, one tea bag, one teaspoon of sugar. Pour in the boiled water, stand for one minute — no more. Three gentle stirs of the bag, remove 'said' bag, add a splash of milk and a frantic whisk of the spoon — and there you have it, the perfect tea!

The secret lies in the splash and only a true perfectionist will have mastered that skill, and my mum had! A couple of delicate puffs later and the tea was ready to sip. Delicious!

In our household, the only time we received a cup of tea in bed was if there was something to celebrate or sadly to commiserate. Thankfully today was all about the celebrations as I was coming of age.

"Right then, young lady. Here's a little something from me."

Mum passed me a lightweight, medium-sized present, wrapped in silver foil and topped with a show-stopping baby blue bow that was bigger than the gift itself. Jubilantly, I carefully unravelled the ribbon and one by one, pulled back the folded foil corners.

Inside this impeccably wrapped parcel was a simple yet elegant mirrored photo frame with an image of two young people; a young man in his late twenties, affectionately ruffling the mousy brown hair of a young girl under three. These two strangers were genuinely happy, effortlessly laughing in the company of one another, and as heartwarming as it was, I was baffled as to what this photo had to do with me?

Mum rested her hand on top of mine and delivered a

comforting squeeze! That's when I knew there was more to this photo than I had originally thought. Agog as to what, I pulled the photo in closer and scrutinised the faces before me. I hadn't initially realised the connection...but actually, I did know those features! Those eyes. Those cheekbones. I knew who they were...it was me and my dad!

I couldn't stop my lips from quivering as years of built up pain rolled out into this one almighty tear, desperate to escape my sealed barriers.

I had never seen this photo before, in truth, I had never seen any photos of me and my dad, well not since I was a very small child. Mum had made sure of that! The moment he left us, she wilfully removed every single trace of Dad from the family home. You would never have known he had been a part of our lives, other than acting as the initial sperm donor!

Mum had been so enraged with Dad for leaving us as abruptly as he did, that she stormed out of the house. Ladened with his belongings, she torched every last memory. Cremating every little piece of him from out of our lives, or so I thought.

I turned to Mum whose eyes were swelling deep with tears. She still hurt, and I could see that it had taken a lot for her to revisit a time in her life that she had tried so hard to forget.

"I thought it was about time you had a photo of you and your dad. I've been incredibly selfish, Allie, and I'm sorry for that. Regardless of how I feel, he is your dad and always will be. How I felt at the time doesn't matter and should never have mattered," cracked an emotional Mum.

Turns out this was the one and only photo Mum couldn't destroy in the blaze. She didn't know why she kept it but she did, carefully hiding it from me for all these years.

"I know you were only a young girl in this photo, and the years have since been and gone. I can't give you back those precious days that you and your dad have missed out on. I wish I could — believe me! But what I can do is remind you of the happiness that you once shared and make sure you never lose it. Every time you look at this photo, you will see you and your dad — as you were, but also 'you' — as you are now," she wept.

I gazed at my reflection in the mirrored frame. She was right. There we were — the three of us. Mum had delivered the most uplifting of gifts — it was powerful, stirring emotions that I had buried long ago. I was deeply touched and couldn't have asked for a better present on my big day.

The hefty pent up tear that I had tried so hard to restrain, broke through the seal and plunged upon my cheek. Mum's face said it all. I guess she never expected to unearth my hidden sentiments. I had entombed my emotions a long time ago, having made it clear that I never wished to discuss them, so it was no surprise Mum was shocked by my reaction. She had not seen me weep since Dad left. I never expressed my true feelings to her or showed any type of emotion, other than the sometimes moody, sometimes disinterested exterior that I favoured to portray.

Mum had been vexed with Dad; she had been for years. She couldn't let go of the pain, and I refused to take either of their sides. I, on the other hand, blamed myself for Dad leaving us. I had my reasons. I also had this gap in my life, a gap that only a devoting father could fill. I loved them both, and as a consequence of the anguish caused, I spiralled into an emotional lockdown. I can tell you now that this little gesture of Mum's would have taken a great deal of inner strength on her part. It could not have been easy for her to revisit Dad's smiling face and to drag up all the memories that came along with it. I could feel the pain in her eyes as I affectionately ran my fingertips across the outline of his youthful face. I missed him. I missed him more than ever.

Today though was a remarkable day, we had made a breakthrough with a slight inkling of progress chipping through both mine and Mum's barricades. I was legitimately touched that Mum had finally fought off her ill feelings towards Dad. She allowed me to have a little happiness on the one day that this man should have been there for me. She would never forgive Dad, and I would never forgive myself. I would treasure this photo for as long as I had breath in my body and his image in my heart.

"Oh, come on, girls, I thought this was a party, it's like a flipping morgue in here," croaked an elderly female voice.

"Nanny Winnie!!!" I shrieked with joy.

"Happy Birthday, sweetheart," she hooted.

Nanny Winnie was seventy-three years old and sadly my only remaining living grandparent. Her frail frame stood within the archway of my bedroom door with a withered smile that stretched from ear to ear.

I had not seen my nan in months, which was not out of personal choice.

Unfortunately, Nan was suffering from symptoms that belonged to the early stages of Alzheimer's disease. She had isolated herself at home for the last two months and being the proud lady she was, she had refused to see any visitors, which included her own flesh and blood.

"I will see you when I'm good and ready and no minute before!" she would bellow down the phone.

This wasn't Nan being nasty, this was just a little setback, which she preferred to deal with in her own way — in private and with dignity. Nan was still the same woman that I remember from growing up. Although now she was a little slower, a little quieter and a little more forgetful than the one we remember.

Time and time again, Nan would frequently find herself forgetting what she had got up to that day, let alone that week. Regularly, we would have to remind Nan that we had heard that story before — many times before. Sometimes though it was kinder to let her be and pretend as if it was the very first time we had heard that one. It was easier than constantly informing her that she was repeating herself over and over again.

I prefer to remember the good old years when Nan was Nan. She was vivacious and full of life! Confidence she had in abundance, elegance came naturally to her and adventures were what spurred her on. I can't recall the number of times Nan would disappear for weeks on end with only a note to pinpoint her location. 'Met an old friend. Booked a cruise. See you when I see you. Love, Nan', was often the theme on her neon flower shaped post-it notes. I loved that about her though, she was unscripted, marching to the beat of her own drum and answering to no one but herself.

Oh, and let's not forget what a looker she was! She never left the house in any other state than immaculate. Her hair shone in a rich mahogany tone, tightly curled and pinned to her proud bonce, and on no occasion would she be seen without her trademark ruby red lips.

Over the years, time had aged her, and as expected her illness had taken its toll. She was never going to be as outstanding, but kudos to her as she still tried her utmost to be the woman she once was. To me though, she still looked as beautiful as she did in her heyday.

Her hair was a little less red and a little more copper — with her curls now loosely pinned with one or two locks escaping their wired grips.

Some days Nan would be boiling over with anger for her illness, cursing the way it was taking over her life and changing her from day to day. Nan knew that eventually everything she once held dear to her would be forgotten. Memories would be lost, faces unrecognisable, and for her, that was a bitter pill to swallow. It would be for anyone.

Then other days, Nan seemed...well, she seemed like the Nan we knew. You could be fooled into thinking that there was nothing wrong with her as she laughed and reminisced about the good old days over tea and crumpets. These days were becoming rarer and rarer, and so we cherished them, not once daring to mention her illness and ruining the few good times we had. Thankfully, today was one of those better days, and the Nan we knew was on form — if a little forgetful.

∞∞∞

"A little...erm...a little..." Nan struggled to remember that well-known saying, which was often the case, but we patiently bared with her.

"Ah yes...a little birdie tells me it's a special birthday... sixteen today! How the years have flown, my darling grand-daughter," she rejoiced.

"No Nan, eighteen today, you remember that, don't you?" I sympathetically replied.

"Don't be silly, I think I know how old you are, after all, I was there at the birth, young lady, and you're definitely not eighteen! You can't be, you're too young!" she snapped.

Both Mum and I could sense Nan was becoming agitated, and although she was adamant I was sixteen, she knew deep down she was most likely wrong. Mum decided the best course of action would be to step in and put Nan straight, rather than tiptoe around the mix-up.

"Winnie, she's eighteen...remember we went bowling with Allie on her sixteenth? You joined us and laid down three strikes! It was all you spoke about that night."

Nan scrunched her face, wracking her brain to locate the memory she had somehow misplaced.

Mum continued, "you know you sometimes get the numbers wrong. It's ok, it really is. You were with us then, and you're with us now. That's all that matters," she reassured.

Nan bowed her head in defeat, riddled with confusion and embarrassment, she knew she had forgotten.

"I'll fetch you a cup of tea!" announced Mum, ejecting herself from the awkwardness of the room.

Oh, I should have mentioned that tea was also a godsend when trying to comfort a person in upset, anger or distress. See, Mum knew that a cup of tea would instantly fix the atmosphere, and I had every little faith that it would too.

With Mum busily brewing, Nan plonked herself down on the bottom of my bed. Shuffling her way over to me, she patted down the bed sheets and nestled herself into a comfy position. Without a peep of a sound, she proceeded to pull a small velvet box from out of her cardigan pocket. The box was small, no bigger than the palm of my hand and decorated with a minimalistic holographic golden bow. She pulled my hand firmly over to hers and placed the box inside my clasp.

"Nan, what are you playing at, you know I hate for you to spend all your money on me," I disparagingly gasped.

"Allie, open the bleeding box!" she quipped. "Surely, I can spoil my only grandchild on her birthday — especially on one as special as this!"

Well, I couldn't exactly throw the present back in her face. It's just I hated the thought of her cashing in the little pension money she did have on me. Oh, what the heck, it was my birthday after all, and I did love a present!

Ripping the bow clean off, the ribbon was left to spiral gracefully like a feather until it came to rest upon my pillow. With the naked box in hand, I began to build up the anticipation by slowly removing the square lid from off its base. Although, I was enjoying the moment, I was equally as keen to unwrap its secrecy.

Inside, shrouded in gold tissue paper was the hidden gift, which I quickly unravelled, leaving the item underneath exposed. It all felt very mysterious and now more than ever I was fascinated as to what Nan had personally selected for me.

Inserting my hand into the snug box, I cautiously plucked the object from its refuge and secured it within my grasp. Smooth in texture, light in weight — it was cold to the touch.

One by one, I flexed my fingers back to lay bare the object snuggled inside my palm.

"Oh my! Nan, you shouldn't have, you really shouldn't!" I murmured.

In my hand, I held the most magnificent gem encased necklace. Set in solid Rose Gold and attached to a 16" chain — it was incredibly distinctive — like no other I had seen before. The focal point of this sleek piece was a glistening circular crystalline gem, containing a thin unknown limpid liquid; this precious stone twinkled specks of crushed amethyst within the delicate touch of light.

"Where on earth did you find such a beauty?" I gushed.

"Well, I didn't buy it, Allie. It was given to me by someone I cared very much for, and now I'm giving it to you. I hope I never forget how special this necklace was and still is to me, but the truth is, I most likely will. By passing it onto you, I know I never will," she sighed, with tears welling in her well worn-out eyes.

"How comes I've never known or seen this piece before? Did Grandpa surprise you with this when you were young?" I questioned whilst placing the pendant around the nape of my neck.

"Erm...well..." stuttered Nan as she fastened the clip of the chain in place. "The thing is —," but before she could assemble her words together, Mollie jostled through the bedroom door.

It wasn't unexpected, as every year without fail, she would pass by my house and wish me a 'Happy Birthday'.

Mollie was confident and loud; she wasn't shy about starting a conversation nor was she on ending one either. Similar to Jed, she could never read a situation, and this time was to be no exception.

Nan sternly nodded at me, and I immediately understood that we would pick up this conversation at a later date.

"I'll leave you two young girls to it," chipped in Nan as she sloped off out the room.

"Happy birthday, gorgeous," chimed Mollie.

"Same to you too!" I replied, albeit a little befuddled by Nan's behaviour and Mollie's particularly early arrival.

"You're up at the crack of dawn! Why on earth are you

here so early? You're up to something, aren't you?" I rambled.

It seemed very odd that Mollie should be at my house at *this* time of the morning and on her birthday too. It was simply way too early for visitors — family exempt of course.

"Can't a girl wish her friend a 'Happy Birthday' without there having to be some sort of hidden agenda!" she jokingly snapped.

"No...I just didn't expect to see you here until at least after lunch!" I sheepishly responded.

"Oh, you know me, I can never sleep when excited!" she replied, whilst shifting her weight from foot to foot.

"You absolute liar!" I blasted.

Mollie was known for being nocturnal, a night owl you could say. I couldn't count the number of times she missed college lessons due to her sleeping habits. You would be very lucky to see her crawl from out of her duvet during daylight hours, that's for sure!

"Oh ok, ok! I can't lie to you, I really can't. Your mum begged me to come over at this ghastly hour. You know I love you, but I'm seriously owed some brownie points for making the journey at this unpleasant time of day!" she hysterically ranted.

"I could have waited you know. What's the rush?" I probed.

"Your mum wanted to do something special for you. She said you deserved to be pampered like a princess. Oh, and before you start, I wasn't forced. I wanted to come over and do this for you. C'mon who else would I want to share my eighteenth birthday with!" she spoke full-heartedly.

I knew she wasn't lying either, as no matter what, we would always make the effort to see each other on our big day. It was an unspoken tradition. However, she knew darn well that pampering was not my thing and never had been.

"Now in return of this special gift that I bestow on you, I ask for one teeny-tiny favour in return," grinned a mischievous-looking Mollie.

This sounded interesting, yet slightly heinous, and I had a feeling it would not sit well with me.

"C'mon, spit it out will you!" I restlessly barked.

"Ok, here it is. I will just say it. Straight up. No beating around the bush," she ironically prattled.

"Moll, please just cough it up!" I interrupted.

"I want you to come to 'The Locust Lounge' with me! Tonight!" she blurted.

Oh, this was horrific! No, no, no, this I was not comfortable with. Why would I want to stand in a hot sweaty bar being drooled over by a group of horny lads stinking of booze and vomit? Let's be honest, they would go through the motions, lay on the charm, pretend you were the prettiest girl in the room. Then before you knew it, they were cracking on to your best mate. All they really wanted was one thing, and I think you know what I mean by that one thing! No thanks, I would rather stay in and colour coordinate my sock drawer.

"Oh…look…Mollie, thank you for thinking of me but you know me well enough to know that this really is not my thing. I would feel unbelievably uncomfortable, and besides, I have nothing new to wear. I mean, when have you ever seen me in a glam girly dress?" I grovelled, hoping she would pardon me from such a tall order.

Most people counted down the days until they hit eighteen. It gave them a rite of passage to do things legally. I mean let's face it, many of the underage kids in my village were already up to no good by the time they hit their fifteenth birthday; dabbling in areas that were clearly age restricted. For me, I couldn't care less about drinking and clubbing, you could keep it! Give me a cup of tea and a good book any day of the week!

"Oh Allie, you're way too old before your time. I'm doing this favour for you, so why can't you humour me this once and come along. You never know, you may actually like it, you old fuddy-duddy!" she insulted.

I know she was disappointed, she was after all, going to

a hell of a lot of trouble for me, and it wasn't just my special day, it was hers too. You know the galling thing about it all was that I wasn't even benefitting from this whole charade. I never asked to be spoilt with an oversized pink powder puff. I couldn't have dreamt of anything worse than having a shovel full of slap plastered across my face, but it was a gift and one that I was too polite to refuse.

Guilt had overtaken my body and left me with only one option....and so, I had to swallow my pride and go for it.

"Fine, have it your way. I will go, but I'm only doing this for you. Don't you forget it anytime soon!" I bit.

Surely an hour or two wouldn't hurt, and at least I could say I had honoured my promise. To be truthful, I was hoping Kalen would unexpectedly pop over and whisk me away for the evening, but who was I kidding, it was just wishful thinking. I mean we weren't even dating, let alone boyfriend and girlfriend. Perhaps an impromptu night out would take my mind off him.

"Eeeekkkk," Mollie screamed with ecstasy at my simple 'yes'.

"Tonight is going to be a — maze — ing! There will be a group of us girls from college — dancing, giggles and a few cheeky drinks will help us celebrate in style. You will love it!" she rejoiced.

A group of girls from college? Urgh, she forgot to mention that little golden nugget of information, didn't she! She knew I didn't mix with 'her' people. We weren't friends then and we certainly wouldn't be bosom buddies now. Oh well, I suppose it couldn't be any more distressing than the preening and quaffing that was about to befall in the one place I thought was a safe sanctum.

"Right, we have work to do. Let's make a start!" beamed a jubilant Mollie.

Combing her slender fingers through my hair, she grimly frowned as she examined the quality of my locks.

"Oh, don't you start, it's not that bad," I laughed.

"No of course not, Allie...it just lacks a lot to be desired, but we can work with it. I'm only going to be enhancing what you already have. Now how do you feel about injecting a little life into this...?"

Twisting my body around and grabbing a clump of lifeless hair, Mollie proceeded to eyeball me through my ivory hourglass mirror stand.

Vigorously I shook my head, "nope, not happening. My hair is fine — the colour that is. Cut it, yes but dye it, no," I bellowed.

"Oh, will you just trust me! It's irritatingly dull and lacking vivacity. Let me lighten those curls with a blend of silvery grey tones?" she blazed.

"Excuse me, it's not lacking life! I happen to like it just how it is. You're trying to clone me into one of you!" I snapped.

"Oi behave! Of course I'm not, but it would do you no harm to take a leaf out of my book and improve on what you already have!

Let me ask you this...has your relationship with Kalen even developed past the friendship stage? Are you dating? Kissed or touched his hand? I mean you've had your chances to snare him, but you're getting nowhere fast, are you!" she thundered.

"How on earth do you know what's been going on with me and Kal?" I glared.

"Alright, don't be mad but I bumped into your mum down Honeysuckle Drive. We chatted, and she happened to let slip that you've been meeting up with Kalen. She said you might need a little help..." came her wary response.

Wow! Turns out having a secret was impossible these days!

Her words wrapped their way around my numb tongue. I hadn't expected them or wanted to hear them, but she had spoken the truth and curbed any sort of response. I knew that Kalen and I were a working progress, but she was right, if we continued on the path we were heading, then I would most definitely be friend zoned!

"It's fine. If you don't want me to help — I won't! All I'll say, is if you don't snap him up soon, then no doubt Coral will!" she painfully added.

"What's that supposed to mean?" I meekly asked, with a feeling of dread surfacing in the pit of my stomach.

"Listen, I saw them late last night at the corner of Fig Street. They were discreetly talking to one another, and they were close — real close…if you know what I mean. He was caressing her hand with his and softly whispering into her ear. He might as well have been nibbling it! It may all be innocent, but you should know that you're not the only one that he has his eye on!" she revealed.

Her words soaked into my skin like acid. It's corrosive touch burning my tissue and dissolving my bones to dust. My heart felt like it was swimming in a pool of lukewarm jealousy — gradually drowning within the weight of turmoil.

Coral fancied Kalen, we all knew that, but did he reciprocate her feelings? I was sure it was purely one-sided as she was not the sort of girl you would want to take home to show mummy. The only thing that niggled me about all of this was that for some gut-wrenching reason, he had no qualms in holding her hand, yet with me, he had clearly been reluctant. He himself had said he desired a deeper connection, not a cheap thrill that was easy on the eye or anywhere else for that matter! So, what was he doing with her?

"Oh, look at me!" I raged.

I held nothing but detest for the reflection staring back at me from the mirror.

"Why would he want a drab, lacklustre, barren old me, when he could have a sexy siren instead!" I bawled.

Seeing the desperation in my eyes, Mollie rested her hands on my shoulders and addressed my reflection in the mirror. "If you trust me on this, I will make him yearn for you, like I know you yearn for him. Say yes?" she whispered.

"Yes — do it! Do what you need to do to make him mine."

I proclaimed with hunger in my eyes.

Mollie immediately set to work on my tresses, twisting and sectioning tufts of hair before lacquering with a considerable amount of thick gooey dye. She went back and forth to her pink and white striped PVC holdall, pulling out tools, appliances, creams, lotions and foams. She tweezed, plucked and waxed her way through every unsightly hair on my body.

Legs that once resembled the prickle of a cactus were now as smooth as the skin of a butternut squash. Caterpillar eyebrows were transformed into the curve of perfectly arched ballerina pumps. The wispy trail of hair nesting on my top lip — which I refuse to accept existed, was now no more, as was the odd chin bristle that I had somehow managed to acquire.

Mollie blow dried, tonged and va-va-voomed my mane before laminating in a glaze of extra strength hairspray. My face was lathered, smoothed, dusted and contoured with an array of liquids, gels and powders before Mollie finally announced we were done.

"Now to set off your new look, here's a little extra treat from me to you," she beamed as she threw me a skimpy pair of shiny black skin-tight faux leather jeans, a silky purple plunge cami and a set of killer heels. I was totally out of my comfort zone but was willing to try anything to make the boy mine.

Now I'm not joking when I say my pamper session had taken hours upon hours, but apparently, these things couldn't be rushed. Saying that, I couldn't have asked for a better day — giggling, chatting, drinking, and dare I say pampering, was exactly what I needed. Plus, it was only ever going to be over when Mollie said it was over, and with my new clothes, I was ready for the big reveal.

"My word...I'm good, Allie, I'm bloody good!" she purred as she stood back to admire her handy work.

I can't tell you how relieved I was to hear I no longer needed to be moulded into shape. I could not have waited any longer. I needed to witness the finished results for myself, and after an excruciating amount of intense preening, I was expecting to be dazzled by my overhaul.

Woah, woah, woah! She wasn't good, she was fantastic, and she had definitely exceeded my expectations! I couldn't take my eyes off myself. Was this really me? I had transitioned from this modest, low profile girl into an eye-catching, confident woman.

It was still me underneath the subtle slap, the hair dye and bronzer — but just a hotter version of my former self. I had never before felt the urge to doll myself up like this, but I liked what I was seeing. For once, I felt bold. Like I could go out and make an impact and people i.e. Kalen would pay attention.

"Thank you so much, Mollie. I love my hair, my makeup, my clothes. I love it all!" I gushed, spinning around to tightly hug her.

I wasn't the type of girl to hand out hugs willy-nilly, but I wanted to show her just how much I appreciated what she had done for me. I moved towards her, my arms stretched out in kindness, but Mollie wasn't ready to take the hug.

Something else had caught her eye...and now it had mine.

"Your nan invited me in, she insisted I pop up and see you," softly spoke the unforeseen visitor.

He was nervously lingering underneath my doorway, his eyes fixated on me as I strutted towards him. When I say strut, that's how I envisaged myself in my mind's eye, but in reality, I resembled a drunk exiting the pub at closing time. Heels were not my forte, especially ones as unrealistically high as these. They would take a while to get used to!

The visitor in question was Kalen, and for once I could

read his mind — he was speechless. His pupils had dilated, and one corner of his mouth had curled up. He heavily inhaled through his nose, releasing his breath slowly as he nodded his head in approval. He, like me was liking what he was seeing. The 'new' me had clearly caught his attention.

I flashed him a smile as I came to a standstill in front of him. I had made an impact for sure, but for some reason, he didn't say a word. It's like he didn't want to admit that a little part of his heart had been poked. I gave him a second or two to take it all in. It must have come as quite a shock to see me looking a little different, a little tastier perhaps.

I had to hand it to Mollie, she knew what she was talking about. A little tweak here and a little brush there makes all the difference. It certainly had the desired effect on Kalen. I was, however, hoping I would receive a compliment, but it seemed one wouldn't be making an appearance any time soon. I knew he had noticed my conversion from drab to fab but for reasons unexplainable to me, he chose to ignore it.

"Happy Birthday, Alanna," he sexily hummed.

"Huh, ah…erm, thank you. How did you know? I don't remember saying?"

I was puzzled as I had not revealed to him that my big day was fast approaching. I mean, I wouldn't have, it wasn't like me to draw unnecessary attention to myself.

"You mentioned it briefly in passing, don't you remember?" he assured.

"I did, did I? That's not like me at all," I informed, scratching my head in disbelief.

"Does it matter? You told me. I listened and now here I am," he barked.

He was obviously frustrated that I had doubted him, but I was mystified by his admission. Never did I tell people it was my birthday. I rarely celebrate and wasn't about to change that habit.

"Of course it doesn't, I'm sorry I doubted you," I whispered.

Right now, I would say anything to keep the peace and ensure I didn't enter into the ever-creeping friend zone.

Kalen gracefully accepted my apology, "it's no problem, now let me start again... 'Happy Birthday', Alanna."

He certainly didn't like to be corrected and was very much a man of conviction. If he was right, he was right and if he was wrong, he was still right! All I knew was that I hadn't told him...so who on earth did? I was beginning to make real movement with Kalen, and I would do anything not to rock the boat, so I put my unanswered question to rest.

Minus the quibble, I was delighted to see Kalen — that really was a birthday treat in itself! However, I was disappointed by his reaction or rather the 'lack of one' towards my new look. I could not figure him out. I mean he seemed to like what he saw, but he wouldn't acknowledge it. I had clocked the pleasing way he had glanced at me; so why the guise? Why couldn't he relax a little, push back the boundaries and make a girl feel desired? Or was it as simple as he didn't fancy me, and quite clearly didn't want anything more than a friendship? Perchance, I was still making the mistake of fighting too hard to make him want me. When actually, there was still no feelings to work with.

I was behaving the absolute fool. I was coming across desperate and daft, chasing after someone that didn't give a hoot about me. I had gone to all this effort to make myself delectable for a guy that didn't even want me. I was an embarrassment!

"As it's your birthday, will you let me take you out?" requested Kalen, cutting short my distressing thoughts.

Was I hearing this right? He wanted to take me out?

Pinch me will you! Or better still, slap me! I really hoped for my sanity I wasn't dreaming.

"You've been incredible to me since we first met, and I haven't had a proper opportunity to thank you for your kindness. Let me return the favour and show you somewhere that's special to me," he said.

Ahhh, oh dear, well this was awkward. Cancel the million pounds worth of fireworks, as I seemed to be rapidly entering that friend zone. Yet again, I had completely misread the signals. He wanted to thank me.

Thank me?

Seriously?

You had to be kidding me, right? How irrational of me to actually think I had a chance with the illustrious Kalen Snow!

If I wasn't humiliated enough, I could feel the burn of Mollie's eyes into the back of my impaled frame as she sympathised with the blow of words that I had been cruelly dealt.

"You've shown me a place that is truly dear to you, and I want to be able to repay the favour and show you mine. I know this sounds lame and maybe...oh maybe it's a bad idea..." he stalled.

For the first time, I felt indignation towards him, and you know what, I didn't want to go. I was fed up with being the 'mate'. I wanted to find my own Cornelius. I was itching for happiness. Didn't I deserve that too? Spending time with Kalen was most likely hindering any chance of me finding the one, as every minute spent with him, meant a potential 'Cornelius' would pass me by. It was Kalen I craved, but it was naive of me to wait around any longer for someone that wasn't in the slightest bit interested in me.

Mollie was right, there had to be more between Coral and Kalen than I had likened to guess. I was treated completely different from her. I was to be kept at arm's length, where with her, he had no reluctance in fawning all over her slutty persona. He was wasting my time and making me look like a gullible sap in front of my family and Mollie, who of course, had a front row seat to my mortification.

Sensing my rise in resentment, Kalen without warning withdrew his invite, all the while keeping rigid eye contact with me. "Yeah...best to forget it, you don't want to be traipsing around with me, not on your big day anyway," he suggested, in a long drawn out manner.

What was wrong with me? The words were eagerly awaiting to be spat out. 'No', just say 'no, no, no', but all I could think of was 'yes, yes, yes'. Kalen's eyes had me! They were pulling me in against my will. I wanted to refuse, to decline him point blankly, but I couldn't do it, it's like he had an invincible hold over me.

"Yes, I'll come with you, but I only have a few hours spare. I'm out with Mollie tonight for a joint birthday bash. Will that be enough time for you?" I caved.

"Plenty but only if you're sure…I wouldn't want to force you into doing something you weren't a hundred per cent comfortable with?" he grinned, seemingly satisfied with himself.

Kalen was immersed in me, his eyes searing into mine as he continued to hold my gaze. I couldn't refuse and tipped my head to confirm my acceptance.

Conscious of time, Kalen automatically grabbed my hand, leading me from my bedroom, down the stairs and out the front door.

"See you later tonight, Moll," I shouted as the door slammed behind me.

Within seconds of complying, he had torn me away from my home and into the unknown. With my nerves on over-drive, I had no idea of where we were going, and all I could think about, was how I could do with that perfect cup of 'nerve settling' tea right about now!

Seven

'HAGS ALLEY'

We had arrived at the entrance of Eldercrest Woods, the very woods I had spoken about upon on our first 'date'. These woods actually backed on to the rear garden of my home, but due to the density of the trees, the only way to access this glorious green heaven was via the pedestrian pathway known as 'Hags Alley'.

"Here we are, Alanna," shrilled Kalen.

You had to be joking me? I was utterly bemused by his choice of sanctuary. 'Hags Alley' was Kalen's special place. Really? A place I had avoided for most of my childhood and the majority of my teens. Of course I would walk through there when needed, but it was only ever out of necessity and necessity being the key word here! Nan was always the motive with her curious little bungalow concealed within shrubbery on the other side of the trees.

Normally I would avoid the alley like the plague, determined to hike the long route around the rim of the woods to Nan's. Although sometimes, there wasn't always time and well...a shortcut's a shortcut at the end of the day.

Nan did not take kindly to poor timekeepers. Dare to roll up one minute late and you would know about it. So, trust me when I say you would rather brave the fear of walking through the alley than to meet the wrath of my nan.

I can't stress to you enough how creepy I found that route, so I'll try and set the scene for you! Imagine a skinny, almost claustrophobic pathway, enclosed by a gathering of thick, 10ft plus trees on either side. These trees cowered over one another, creating an overlapping intense arch that blocked out the comfort and security of reassuring daylight. The further down the path you tiptoed, the darker, the colder, the damper the walkway became. At the very base, you would find yourself presented with a choice, thus being a decision on which route to take.

Split into two: right guided you straight into the welcoming open space of Eldercrest Woods and the passage towards Nan's abode. Left, well left was a dead end. It was defunct and of no use to anyone. This mangy old alley was the furthest thing you could find from being 'special', and I was astounded as to why Kalen would think otherwise.

For us local kids, 'Hags Alley' was a mythical legend which in fact had adopted its less than affectionate name from our generation. It was a huge talking point for scary tales, sightings and of course the unknown. Apparently, myth had it that an old hag otherwise referred to as the wicked witch of Eldercrest roamed within the alley's dark shadows. No doubt the tale had originated from the Cornelius and Blythe era!

The witch preyed on the innocence of children as they bounced through her path to frolic in the contrasting beauty of the innocuous woods. The story worsens still, as it had been said that this filthy sorceress would rip these children away from their families for the sweetness of their blood, the purity of their tears and the youthfulness of their grounded down bones. The crone would then go on to concoct sickening potions and spells from her atrocious acts.

Children were easy to hunt, as they were unaware of the extent of her evil. Swiftly she would abduct them by masking her interior and exterior with kindness and beauty, a spell she could easily cast.

It was alleged that many moons ago, a handful of children were declared missing on entering that very alley. No evidence to back these allegations had ever surfaced and not one individual was ever held accountable for their disappearances. With no leads or reasoning behind their absence, it was suggested by the jurisdiction that these lost children had simply run away. A tragic riddle — unsolved for decades. However, one key point always remained the same and that was of the hag's involvement. She was always firmly placed in the firing line.

Incensed by this less than convincing conclusion, the community found themselves in uproar and took it upon themselves to find the answers they so desperately sought. Loaded with tools, they hunted in packs, relentlessly combing the woods in search of the allusive witch and the lost children of Eldercrest. Sadly, they never did locate the old hag or the lost youth of their time. It was from then onwards that all children within the area were widely advised to avoid the alley at all costs. No one could confirm if evil was at play or not, but prevention was favoured over further heartache and loss.

Were these stories a work of fiction? Who knows but I for one preferred to keep my distance. The place gave me a serious case of the heebie-jeebies!

"KALEN!" I rudely shouted, "I'm not stepping another foot through that grim place, have you not heard the tales? I can't go in...I won't go in!" I wailed.

"You're not serious, are you?" he chuckled. "I've heard the tales, of course I have and that's exactly what they are — TALES! These are made up stories, created by over-cautious parents in order to scare their little darlings from wandering off into the big bad woods. Didn't you tell me the same about dear old Cornelius and Blythe...?" he laughed. "Everyone knows the stories are fake, and surely, you of all people wouldn't be taken in by a little hocus-pocus — would you, Alanna?" he mocked.

My cheeks felt like scorching embers, burning with embarrassment at my premature outburst. Had I been so gullible to fall for a nonsensical old fairy tale?

"You seemed certain there was no sorcery at play with Cornelius and Blythe, so why is this any different?" he added.

"Ah…Ah-ha-ha-ha, of course I know it's not real, I'm just playing with you!" I sheepishly lied, as I pathetically attempted to bury my nerves.

"Good, then stop stalling as I have so much to show you!" he retorted.

Biting my nerve, I tightly grabbed Kalen's bicep as he led me into the alley and on towards the ill-lit track ahead. My heart raced with the hot-blooded speed of a thoroughbred as the afternoon light faded behind us. Deep breaths Allie, I inwardly instructed, whilst simultaneously congratulating myself on every successful step placed. Each one, after all, had become an overwhelming accomplishment.

'Hags Alley' was only a two-minute stroll but when overcome with fear, it felt like a lifetime. Eventually, I caught sight of a beam of light signalling the opening of the woods, it was now within reaching distance. An immense sense of relief washed over me, but it wasn't to last. Instead of turning right towards the woods, Kalen alarmingly diverted off to the left — towards the dead end!

What was he doing? This didn't feel right. Why was he taking me down a closed path? What could possibly be that remarkable that it would be down there? Please don't tell me he was about to do something so unspeakable. Or perhaps the tales were true, and he was delivering me to the old hag!

As we trudged nearer towards the deadlock, a sudden gust of ice-cold wind blasted through the alley, gradually increasing into a gusty tide. Progressively, the severity of the wind ensured that each footstep became harder and harder to secure. Dirt and leaves vomited from their gravelly beds, swirling into the formation of mini tornadoes. These feisty columns of air released a distressed howling squeal that rang violently within my ears. There was nowhere left for me to turn, we had reached the inevitable standstill and worst of all, darkness had fully crept in. Any light we did have had intimidatingly ebbed away.

"Actually, I think I best go home now, Kalen...it's getting late and I do need to get ready for tonight. Mollie will be distraught if she was to find out where I was. She's only just done my hair..." I whimpered.

I couldn't care less about the state of my mop. I just wanted to get the hell out of there! Kalen however, wasn't buying into my implausible excuse and grasped my hand, squeezing it tightly. He made it clear I wasn't going anywhere.

"Don't be silly, you look fine" he bluntly replied whilst failing to actually inspect me. No sooner had those words left his lips than did the wind impetuously magnify, roaring as it thrashed through the alley.

"We are so near...close your eyes and do exactly as I say," he yelled, his voice competing to dominate over the racket made by the unexplainable ferocious wind.

I had no choice but to do as he asked. My eyes struggled to fight the force as it tested my strength and urged me to shut down against my will. Kalen had no such difficulties; he was wide-eyed and in control. He confidently stared at me through the breach in my eyelids, ordering me to 'hold on in there' and declaring that 'this would all be over soon'.

Without warning, he released my hand and immediately stood behind me. Gently, he placed his protective palms across my eyelids as if to shield me from whatever it was that was about to develop. Fortunately, he was careless, failing to securely seal my view and allowing me to peer through the small gap within the slit of his index finger and thumb.

I covertly watched with dread as he guided me towards a solid concrete wall. It was obvious he was going to hurt me, attack me, or .... well, what other good reason would there be for him to lure me into a pitch-black alley and trap me against a wall? Even if the hag did exist, then surely, I was far too old for the ingredients of her nefarious potions. No, no this was some sort of sordid trap conceived by Kalen to get me all alone. I was out of sight, with nowhere to run and with no one to hear my pleas.

Kalen would win hands down when it came to over-powering me. My strength would be no match for a man built to his specifications.

How stupid was I to have allowed myself to end up in this detrimental situation? I had been ludicrous for trusting him so early on. He told me himself, 'there were dark things', 'things I didn't know about'. Well, what the hell were they? I hardly knew him and had let my warm fuzzy feelings rule my foolish heart. He was clearly a psychopath with a sadis-tic hunger for befriending innocent young women for his per-verse pleasure. I had no idea if he was going to abuse, kill me, or both, but I knew that I had to act fast. There was no way I would surrender my body without a fight!

Kalen must have picked up on my sudden change of body language as he quickly shifted his fingers to close the gap, ob-structing the already insufficient view I had.

My dad was a firm believer in fighting back and had briefed me on the art of self-defence. He said if a boy does something to you that you believe is morally wrong — then you hit them, and you hit them hard! You want to wind them so bad that they hit the floor on all fours. They would then re-gret the day they ever messed with you. That advice couldn't have been any more apt than it was right now, and I knew exactly where to hit Kalen all right.

It was now or never I urged as I frenziedly twisted my body one hundred and eighty degrees to the left. The sudden power of my twist released the dominant grasp he had on my arms and made way for my raised boney knee as it lunged to-wards his groin.

The sound of unpredicted pain crashed through my ear-drums like the single strike of a Chau Gong.

'Well played', you say?

Hardly!

See, it wasn't the yelp from Kalen as expected. Instead, that yap was erupting from me! Kalen quick to respond, clocked the impending attack and stopped me at point-blank range. With a fist full of hair, he spun me around by my locks — shoving me headfirst into a spiteful tornado of grit.

Kalen didn't make a sound, no groaning, no shouting, no screaming, no nothing. I was at least hoping for a girly squeak or a prickly grunt, but it seems my kick did nothing but pathetically scrape his balls.

Turns out it was me that had actually come off a little worse for wear. I was lying in a muddled heap on the floor for god's sake! Safe to say, this was not how Dad would have wanted me to end up.

I felt a little woozy from my fall, but if anything, I was in shock from Kalen manhandling me so roughly, and in all the commotion, I had failed to notice the wind had actually ceased whirling. The stones and grit had immobilised and my surroundings had become placid...well, that was apart from Kalen's outburst.

"You want to tell me what that was all about!" he fumed. He was hardly impressed by my act of self-defence.

"Well, you're going to hurt me... aren't you? You take me to the dead end of an alley and inform me that 'it will all be over soon'! How do you expect me to react?" I fretted.

"Are you for real? I could never hurt you, Alanna. I can't believe you would ever think that of me," he groaned in despair.

"Well it's hardly a normal place to take a girl now is it!" I shouted as I hurriedly picked myself up from off the sodden floor. Oh, and I wasn't finished there... "your actions are bizarre, Kalen! You have treated me more like a tour guide than a friend. You take me to this pit of all places and on my birthday too, and you don't even notice that I've gone to all this trouble for you!" I wailed.

Irritated, I threw my hands down the length of my body to indicate my foxy new appearance. I was extremely annoyed and rightly so.

Kalen sauntered towards me, profoundly focusing on my eyes with every step he took. He placed his body up against mine, he was close, intimately so! I could feel the tickle of the hair on his arms sensitively stroking my skin as he heavily exhaled in and out. Then, with the back of his hand — he touched me. His fingertips slowly and gently caressing one side of my reddened face as I trembled in anticipation of what he was about to do to me next.

I closed my eyes, absorbing every second of his sensual touch as he hotly traced the outline of my puffed cheeks and aching lips. Reaching the bottom of my jaw, he raised my chin which ultimately resulted in my eyes meeting with his. Faintly, he brushed his lips against the nook of my neck, moving up and towards the tip of my ear. I struggled to keep calm as my senses were delivered into overdrive — controlled by the sensations he was inciting within me.

"Open your eyes, Alanna," he seductively whispered. My heart pulsated from the tingle of his touch and the warmth from his sweet enticing breath upon my skin. Quickly my anger softened. I began to forget how upset I was, as right now he had me, and once again I did exactly as I was told.

Slowly, I opened my eyes as Kalen veered my body away from his.

"Why did you bring me here? It's unpleasant, grotty and it's oh — it's oh so...woah...!"

I was lost for words, my tongue captured by the view that appeared before me.

"You were saying?" Kalen smugly asked. "Oh so...grubby, oh so basic...?" he sarcastically added.

"More like stunning," I spat.

This place was gorgeous, unbelievably breathtaking! How I had never come across this little piece of heaven before was a mystery to me.

"Welcome to 'Blossomvale', Alanna," he gushed.

∞∞∞

The alley was no more, where it was? I couldn't quite decipher, and how I had entered into this land of tranquillity was a question in itself. Well-hidden and secretive to access, it was hard to believe 'Hags Alley' was the hidden doorway to Kalen's special place.

Halted by its organic beauty, I struggled to digest this newly found nirvana. Girdled in a gazebo of skyscraper ferns — she was well masked from the outside world. Only an earth shaped hole dispensed itself from the gods above, allowing the glow of light to blister through.

Chickweed, Stinging Nettles, Wood Sorrel and Fungi braided the oversized glade, whilst the secrecy of monstrous white and pink plumes of Pampas Grass drew my undivided attention in. Only the serene plummet of a silky flowing waterfall warbled in the background, calling my name as my presence was closely noted.

Leaping silver bunnies with ice blue peepers recognised my arrival, twitching their button noses to my trespassing footsteps.

"Bunnies. Silver? Silver Bunnies? Silver bunnies with bluer than blue eyes?" I mumbled in surprise.

"I told you this place was 'special," he smiled.

And it was.

"But that's not all," he grinned as he ushered me in towards a world of peculiarity and attraction.

Slack-jawed, I watched in wonder as a swarm of stout-hearted chromatic bees buzzed acrobatically in true Red Arrow eliteness — distributing loose puffs of variegated pollen fumes on to me — their singular devotee.

The beauty of an almost skeletal-like dragonfly bounced animatedly to the pacifying notes of the orchid and pear feather-chested songbird.

The sweet smell of cherries scented the air, begging me to take a bite as I reminded myself to breathe.

"Sit with me...won't you?" Kalen coyly asked as he led me towards an enchanting rock cluster of clear quartz.

I didn't need to be asked twice and followed in awe.

Sweeping the loose blossom petals from off the face of the transparent rock — I perched myself next to him. This place was a dream, no wonder it was so hard to find. I wanted to know more, I did, but I was more concerned about what he was hiding.

"Kalen...tell me what these 'things' are?" I tactlessly blurted. I needed to know what was so dark and deep that he felt he couldn't tell me before now.

"I'm getting to it..." he promised, "and it's actually the reason behind me bringing you here."

"I'm listening," I encouraged, relieved at finally being a part of the big reveal!

"...in a second.... I actually have a little something for you, something I made especially and only for you."

"You made me something?" I repeated, chuffed at his unexpected sensitivity.

The thought of him taking the time and effort into creating me something unique was possibly the best present I could have ever asked for, second to my photo of Dad of course.

"Hold your hands out, and this time — trust me," he ordered.

Palms open, he gently placed a rich green, four-leaf clover within. Encased in a transparent, delicate thin glass and attached to a dainty woollen strap, it was a delight to behold.

"Keep this with you at all times, Alanna. Not only will this charm bring you luck, but you will always have a little piece of me with you," he whispered.

"It's absolutely stunning. Thank you, thank you so much, this means the world to me," I spurted in pleasure.

It wasn't so much the gift that made my heart swoon, but the meaning behind it. Kalen had first seen the clover at my 'special' place. He had made a point of remembering, revisiting and capturing it for me. Its origins meant more to me than the so-called luck it was supposed to hold.

"Do you like it?" he asked, concerned by the wet glint that was currently rehydrating my eyes.

"I love it," I whimpered. "The craftsmanship on this little trinket is outstanding. How the hell did you ever make it? It must have been incredibly fiddly to place something so fragile into something as flimsy as this glass case?" I probed.

"Alanna, you don't need to know the how, the what or the why. Accept it for what it is, strap it to your wrist and let it protect you," he smiled.

"Protection? I thought you said it would bring me luck?" I quizzed.

Luck I needed, but protection...? Protection from what exactly?

"Must you have a question for everything?" he snapped.

"No, but I do like to know the meaning behind certain things," I bit.

"You're doing it again, Alanna. Stop with the probing!" he griped.

"Now you're just being cantankerous, aren't you, and another thing —"

Before I could spit my words out, Kalen pushed his index finger into my lips, squishing them together like the soft fruit of a banana. A very clever attempt to shush me from uttering another word.

He leaned his body in towards mine with his fingertip still anchored tightly to my lips.

"Kal..." I mumbled, unable to squeeze a complete coherent word out.

"Uh, ah-ah! Be quiet for one god damn second will you," he hushed.

He was having no more backchat from me as he proceeded to trail his finger down my scorned lips before tenderly pulling my head towards his.

"God, you're infuriating, woman!" he spouted, with a hint of devilishness in his grin.

His glance saucily diverted back and forth from my optimistic eyes to my wishful mouth. All the signs were there. I knew he wanted to kiss me, but for some untold reason, he was holding back.

On that shabby chic seat, I had fantasised over this moment, time and time again. It was that well-rehearsed, I could easily describe to you the way he tasted on my lips. If it wasn't for his deliberation, my dreams would soon become reality. I could sense he wanted this as much as I did, so why the wait, it was excruciating.

"Hmmm, you are beautiful but that tongue of yours!" he groaned, biting his bottom lip and chucking in a backhanded compliment.

Ugh, this moment was dripping with unbearable heat, the sexual chemistry preparing for a divine climax. We had literally gone from zero to one hundred in a matter of seconds. An explosion was imminent, and the suspense was killing me.

Kalen was effortlessly sexy, his once frosty exterior had gradually thawed. He was laid back, yet intense — on the whole, a major turn on. I wanted to feel those supple lips of his against mine, and I had the strongest of feelings my wish was about to come true.

I know I had wrongly judged him in the alley, I had jumped to conclusions, and it was obvious I had made a mistake. I admit that was my fault, but my feelings for him hadn't changed. In fact, they had soared and right now, I couldn't care less about those 'things' of his.

Kalen's lips were now millimetres from mine, my body quaked as I felt his mouth brush against my bottom lip. His right hand stroked the back of my neck, tickling my sensitive skin as he cupped the base of my skull. This was it! My body shivered with excitement at the thought of my first kiss from what I truly believed to be my first love.

Lurching forward, his lips were about to fasten with mine — one-on-one contact approached.

Then, when out of the blue, 'it' turned up, swiftly bursting my perfect little bubble.

"Oops…sorry to break up this private soiree for two but seems you forgot to post my invite!" boomed the agitated voice.

Rudely, myself and Kalen had been halted in our overdue fondle by an unwanted visitor. Standing to our left, arms folded and with a face that could melt the sun, was my nemesis Coral. With her hands rigidly poised to her womanly hips and dressed top-to-toe in a raunchy capped sleeve jumpsuit — she meant business.

"Put the girl down. I need you — like now!" she raged.

Alarmed by her arrival, a combined mass of wings, fur, and feathers bolted. Escaping through and around the waterfall. It appears they detested Coral just as much as I did. Hardly surprising though, was it?

Coral wanted Kalen all for herself, and I had a horrid feeling she would not be leaving without him.

It was typical wasn't it, of all the moments she could have chosen to ruin, it had to be this one. I had patiently waited for Kalen to show me affection, to disclose how he really felt for me, but it was all dashed away by her in a second.

What really peeved me off though, was that not only was she present in the first place, but she was in a knockout crimson ensemble that could likely scarper any future chances that I had with Kalen.

As much as I despised her, you had to admire her for her 'no balls' attitude, but seriously, why was she here? Why did she need Kalen so badly, and how the hell did she know about this place, his 'special' place? Honestly, I was gutted. I thought Kalen had kept the identity hidden. I thought he had chosen me and only me to disclose his secret to. So why, oh why was she standing here, brazen and all.

I turned to Kalen for answers or at least a hint of re-assurance, but he was suspiciously useless. Coral was no better with a deadpan gaze smeared across her face. Kalen, on the other hand, had an expression etched with worry. Tension pulsed through his veins as he failed to muster up an excuse.

"Kalen!" Coral sternly pestered.

"Ok! Let me take Alanna home and then we can talk," he remorsefully suggested.

"Make it quick," Coral snapped, flicking her immaculate poker straight hair across the back of her callous shoulders.

She had some front bossing Kalen around like he was a submissive possession of hers. How did she have so much control over him, it was as if they were more than just...oh, oh wait! Mollie was right, wasn't she? She warned me that she had witnessed the two of them intimately whispering, and now all of a sudden Coral shows up here.

Coincidence it was not — alarm bells rang ragged. I had been cautioned to remain vigilant, to be wary of their relationship and then this goes and happens.

"Oh, I get it!" I ranted, pushing Kalen away from me in a fit of rage.

I could not believe he had the nerve to use me like this, when he was clearly fooling around with that bit of brass!

"You two are together, aren't you!" I bellowed in anger.

Kalen remained silent, instead, grabbing my hand and pulling me towards an assembly of Cherry Blossom trees. He proceeded to hoist back a canopy of pretty pink petals to reveal a hidden opening. Surely this was not the same bleak and murky alley that I had not so long ago arrived through? I had not recalled entering via this picture-perfect route, but then again, I had not actually been given an opportunity to glance at the entrance. It had all been such a frantic blur of fear and confusion, which Kalen was undoubtedly accountable for.

"No. I'm not leaving. Not until you give me an honest answer!" I demanded, yanking my hand free and refusing to budge.

"I'm promising you, hand on heart, that I will come back for you, but right now I need to talk with Coral, in fact, it's essential that I talk with her. In time, I will explain all. That I promise! Believe me when I tell you this." he pleaded.

"Can she not wait? Can you not just put me before her... this once?" I wailed.

"No, I can't do that," he responded bluntly, shaking his head firmly.

My heart was literally ripping at the seams. He had no idea how truly devastated I was to witness him choosing Coral as his priority. No amount of explaining could or would ease these wild thoughts racing through my mind. I took one bitter look back at her. My body filled with venom as she pathetically hurled a conceited smirk towards me.

"Little girl, go already will you!" she snarled; her triumphant hands bolted sternly to her curvaceous hips.

Was Kalen seriously going to allow her to speak to me like that? Well from the lack of sound or action from him, it was clear he was, and I certainly wasn't going to stand around any longer to be further humiliated.

It was pretty palpable that Kalen had no intentions of ever choosing me over her. He didn't even have to think about it. Crushed, I diverted my direction away from her and empowered Kalen to resume control. He tugged me strenuously by the hand and towards the path. In fact, his yank was so harsh that the necklace gifted to me by Nan, jumped out from underneath my cami, exposing its grand beauty in full view.

Like a greedy magpie to a scrap of tin foil — his eyes swelled as they locked on to my precious gem. Hidden away, he had not detected its presence until now, but his fixation was abundant as he drooled over the crystal dangling from its graceful chain. His concentration, however, was soon shattered by the high pitch shrill of Coral as she once again summoned her boy. Her patience hadn't exactly been negotiable in the first place, and now it had very much evaporated as she let out a final warning shot.

"Kallie, let her go! I will not ask you again!" she bleated.

Kallie...was it? Nice little pet name she had there for her lapdog, and like the faithful companion he was, he reared his docile head on cue. His response to her ear bleeding yap was to shove me through the overgrown path of Blossom trees. The congested branches caving in on me the moment I was man-handled through.

Facing the prospect of death by twig strangulation, I manically waved my hands around as I struggled to locate the exit. Feeling a prod in the small of my back, Kalen assisted by nudging me further in towards the direction I needed to go. I must have only shuffled ten steps max before I found myself wide open to the elements and back into the sombre hellhole that was 'Hags Alley'.

I swivelled around on my toes to face Kalen. This was my last ditched attempt to persuade him to stay, but before I could make any sort of plea — he had already gone — nowhere to be seen.

I clambered at the dried-out bush that stood in place of Kalen; it clung limply against the cold brick wall of the alleys dead end. The bush no longer held the brightness and beauty of the vibrant pink Blossom trees. Instead, the leaves were sparse and those that could be seen were the colour of ash brown and filled with gloom. Where had the tunnel of cheer-ful candy floss petals gone, and why couldn't I find a way back in? There was no clear opening, not even a gap that I could comfortably squeeze through. How I had found my way out was beyond me, and how I was to find my way back in was near on impossible.

"Kalen, don't you dare leave me here without saying goodbye! Come back here, you coward!" I screamed.

It was one thing to leave me for that spiteful hussy, but to not have the decency to walk me home as mentioned...or to at least lead me out of 'Hags Alley' when he knew how petrified I was...well it was inexcusable. To say I was upset was an under-statement. I was more than upset. I was extremely hurt and bubbling to the brim inside. He had been playing me for a fool. His 'special' place was not so special after all — it was not 'our' little thing. And if his hasty retreat was not a clear enough in-dication for me to leave, then the wind surely was.

With the force ramping up, it was just about manageable, and with a heavy heart, I now had the task of negotiating my way back home. That ghastly alley, however, was the least of my worries! No...I was more concerned over the unexpected urgency to get rid of me...and the real reason behind Coral's nauseating arrival!

Eight
THOSE EYES

I met Mollie and the girls outside the entrance of 'The Locust Lounge' on the cobbled stones of 'Thistle Lane' at 9:30pm. The lounge was pretty empty on arrival, but after an hour or so, the partygoers were out in full force and making all sorts of elaborate shapes on the dance floor. It was a sophisticated little establishment with two bars, one of which was solely dedicated to the fanciest of cocktails. Then, of course, you had your centrepiece, a green L.E.D light-up floor. A focal for every boozy, toe-tapping reveller that had succumbed to its luminous glow.

Swigging casually from a flute of fizz and throwing in a head bop every now and again — I had convinced myself I was acting like a seasoned pro. The tunes continued to blare loudly from the speakers, with the boom of the bass vibrating my body progressively across the sticky alcohol sloshed deck.

I refused to surrender my body to the designated dance area, choosing to instead observe the heavy flow of drinks guzzled by the revellers from the sidelines. As expected, the Lounge quickly turned into a clumsy, sweaty, sleaze-filled mess as the levels of in-toxicity increased at an alarming rate. This right here was the main reason for me normally avoiding these types of uncouth dives.

Bump! Bump! Bump!

Evidently, the surrounding drunks had difficulty standing on their own two feet and preferred to use me as a stabiliser rather than falling flat on their own faces. So here I was, uncomfortably shuffling from foot to foot, trying to master some sort of dance technique with the added bonus of dodging the odd incoming inebriated boozer. Mollie, however, was on fire — she was outright owning the dance floor with her girls. I couldn't help but think I was the only one letting the side down.

I'm no mover at the best of times, and I certainly wasn't going to be any better with the criticizing scrutiny of her on-looking pals, Sasha and Tasha. Yes, that really was their names! And no, they weren't twins, although they would have liked you to believe otherwise.

Sasha and Tasha were childhood chums. Joined at the hip from the moment they bonded over scented coconut lip balm and girly crimping tongs. They were bonafide 'Trends', and on any other occasion would not have thought twice about ignoring me, but any friend of Mollie was a friend of theirs and they reluctantly welcomed me into the fold.

They were often dressed in body-hugging outfits that complimented one another. Their makeup and hair identical. Carbon copies! It was easy to see why they were often mistaken for one another. Tonight was no exception, dolled up to the nines, they aimed to impress. Their bleach blonde hair had been effortlessly pinned into messy updo buns. Thick charcoal eyeshadow accentuated their smouldering eyes, and their pouty lips were drenched in bubblegum pink lipstick.

Tasha wore a fuchsia lace bralet with a white bodycon midi skirt, whilst Sasha, as expected, opted for the same outfit but in reverse colour. Mollie declined this trend, opting to rock a cute individual skater dress in peach — laser cut at the waist, with her natural halo of straightened curls floating over her warm, Sahara beige skin. Thankfully, my outfit was pretty much intact considering my earlier ordeal. My hair, however, hadn't been so lucky.

Now would probably be a good time for me to inform you of the complications surrounding my hair. Put it this way, it had a whole rebellious attitude of its own! It had taken a vast amount of taming and a world of patience for Mollie to soothe my out of control bouffant, transforming it into the masterpiece it was now.

You see, if you were to upset one tiny strand of hair on my sensitive head or risked baring it to the extreme elements, then consider it game over! Grizzly, clammy, humid or scorching temperatures would immediately ignite a frizz overload, and my once neatly straightened locks would double in size. Upset, angry or stressed — then poof, my tresses would triple in volume from the heat sizzling from out of my emotional scalp! Mollie would only have needed to take one look at my bedraggled mop to know something was up! So, before she even had a chance to lay her peepers on me, I made sure I was as good as new before leaving for the club.

Ugh, I felt ridiculous, sticking out like a sore thumb, trying but failing to let myself flow with the music. I decided it would be better for everyone if I quit before I gave myself an injury. Besides, I wasn't really in the mood. I was still seething from the shock of uncovering Kalen and Coral's dirty little secret. The last thing I wanted to do was parade myself on a dance floor, pretending life was a golden bowl of freshly picked ruby red strawberries with lashings of silvery cream. When in reality, it was a chipped mug of cold, day-old, magnolia chicken soup.

All I really wanted was a darkened corner. To curl up in a ball and desperately scream until I had no more squeal left to give. Maybe I could wail my lungs out here...right here in the club. The music was deafening and the revellers far too dazed to notice a distressed girl like me, crying her heart out for someone that didn't deserve another thought.

Unsettled by my overthinking, I hand gestured to Mollie that I was taking time out.

"Woah there! No you don't, young lady," she soberly instructed.

"Feet — are — killing!" I mouthed.

It was, of course, a lie. I'd hardly broken out into a sweat, but it was less mortifying than having to admit the truth to her.

"Bollocks!" Mollie yammered, her voice struggling to be heard over the thunderous music as she called me out.

There was no point in continuing to lie to her, she had already sussed me out and anyway, this type of heartache couldn't be disguised. I pulled Mollie to one side and bled my mournful heart out to her. I hoped she wouldn't judge me for being so futile.

"I knew it! I just knew there was something fishy going on with him and that narcissistic scab! Best out of it, Allie!" she empathised.

Mollie urged me to see things for what they were. She reckoned Kalen was 'a deceitful liar and a downright mongrel that was utterly unworthy of someone like me. As for Coral, she was an easy option that had been around the block more times than Bert the neighbourhood postman, and Bert had been on the job since 1989!'.

Mollie did have a certain way with words, and I couldn't have agreed more. She helped me to see sense and enabled my mood to switch from devastation to animosity in mere seconds. All I wanted to do was to forget I had ever laid eyes on that pathetic excuse of a man and enjoy what was left of our eighteenth. He had already spoilt my day, and I refused to allow him to steal my night too!

I did, however, crave that timeout and convinced Mollie that a five-minute breather would do me good. She offered to sit with me, but I insisted a little me time was what I needed right now. With her consensus, I found myself a secluded corner of the bar.

∞∞∞

Clutching onto my barely drunken flute of fizz, I watched in relief as the girls giggled and pranced around the club from afar. Every now and again they would beckon me onto the dance floor, attempting to coax me back down with their exaggerated moves.

To no avail, they would hysterically wave their arms around with the accelerated motion of a windmill. I continued to brush off their advances, pretending not to understand over the commotion of the music.

I was enjoying being alone, it gave me time to reflect. It also had to be said that I really had reached my limits in regard to the amount of hormone raging, clammy creatures that had tried to woo me with a 'buy one get one free' alcopop!

Overall, the timeout was doing wonders for me. I was starting to feel a little calmer, a little more at ease with the whole Kalen situation. Don't get me wrong, my insides were bleeding tears of hellish pain, but I was determined not to let him waste any more of my time.

I wanted to tell you that from here on out 'everything was going to be ok', but I couldn't commit to such a statement. Truth is, I had a problem, well it was more of a niggling issue. I hadn't mentioned it before as I thought I was being silly, overreacting maybe, but now all alone, I knew the feeling was all too real.

I had this overbearing sense I was being watched. This unwanted feeling of a stranger latching on to my skin, observing my every move. The vibe was intense, and for the life of me, I couldn't locate where it was coming from. This wasn't the first I had felt like this, oh no, it had happened before — twice actually. This was the same sensation that had approached me at 'The Angels of Eldercrest Church' and on my last day of college! I didn't know then what it was, neither did I know now but I knew it existed.

Intimated, I clutched tightly to Nan's necklace — the clover charm swaying underneath my wrist. Despite the hurt Kalen had caused, the clover still meant a great deal to me, and unlike him, I wasn't so quick to discard of it. Kalen had mentioned the charm would keep me safe, and although sceptical of his words, I needed a little reassurance.

Brave or stupid, I couldn't let the matter go. I needed to bottom it out! So, whilst I remained seated, I scoured the full length of the lounge in search of this feeling, and that's all I had to go on — a meagre feeling. I had no inkling of what or who it was, but wherever it was coming from, it was keeping tabs on me.

I scanned the room, skimming from person to person — corner to corner. It was as if all of a sudden everyone in the lounge was a potential suspect, and I was playing the part of Inspector Clouseau.

There was the barman with his neatly crafted handlebar moustache. He looked a tad shifty as he shuddered his silver cocktail shaker my way. Or perhaps it was the group of brash girls sipping their cheap dishwater tasting wine through a straw, all the while eyeballing me for no apparent reason. Then you had the two cocksure lads loitering around the entrance to the men's toilets. They had an air of mischief about them as they glanced to acknowledge my presence. Then last but not least was the lounge cleaner, an elderly hunched back gent with tightly permed grey hair. He was definitely worth a mention — crouched on all fours and peering up from his sick splattered rag with a face full of disdain.

Hmmmmm, as much as they all seemed a little crafty, I knew that this icky feeling was not transmitting from them. None of them, no matter how incriminating they looked, appeared to be the offending party. They weren't quite right! It had to be coming from another source, and that's when my eyes caught sight of it.

Behind the cleaner and towards the back of the bar, was a disused dimly lit cubby hole. You could fit no more than one person inside. It was a waste of space. There really was no reason for its existence. It was kind of irrelevant. However, it was quite apparent to me that this unwanted feeling had found a use for it. It was lurking from within.

Whatever it was, it wanted me to notice, allowing me to vaguely make out its frame as it stepped slightly into the light. It was definitely a man. A tall, toned, broad-shouldered man. His catlike eyes pierced brightly through the darkness — impossible to go unnoticed.

Then as quickly as they had emerged, they closed — disappearing, as too did his shadow. I needed to know more, I had to get closer, in fact, I wanted to get closer.

Ok, so approaching strangers in the dark was probably not the brightest of ideas but you try telling my feet that, they were having none of it and instead were leading the way.

"Er, what are you doing, Allie!" yelled Mollie, her voice finally achieving to boom above the music.

On spotting my wandering toes, she downed her drink, abandoning the dance floor to confront me. Believing I was sneaking out of the bar, she raced after me, barking for me to return, but of course, this was not the case at all.

"I'm not going anywhere. Go back and dance! I've seen someone I know, that's all," I appeased.

Yes, it was wrong of me to lie...yet again, but I needed her off my back, and if I told her the truth, she would only try and put a stop to it.

"A friend? You? That's questionable!" she teased.

Mollie didn't accept a word of it, she knew I hardly had any friends, and anyone I did know, would most certainly not be in a heaving lounge such as this one. She did, however, respect me enough to do as I asked and continued dubiously back to the dance floor. Like all good friends, she kept a nosy yet watchful eye on me from a distance.

I wasn't sure what was about to happen or why I felt it necessary to lie to her, but I knew I needed to do it. I had no control over my actions, overwhelmingly drawn towards this dark shadow of a man, hiding out in the darkest corner of the bar. It was insane!

∞∞∞

Shifting my body through the crowds of drinkers, dancers and pranksters, I was gradually edging in nearer and nearer to the mysterious figure. Closing in on the cubby hole, I could sense he was still there and that he too knew he was about to be exposed.

Rumbled, he stepped forwards and into the dimmed light, gradually lifting his head and slowly opening his eyes to reveal his identity. Due to the poorly lit lighting and much to my annoyance, he was still very much disguised...apart from those eyes of his. They were as clear as day — fresh and vivid, and the instant they met with mine was the moment my heart began to race.

The music that had fiercely raged in my ears, faded into the background. The hyperactive revellers surrounding my body began to distance themselves, moving only in slow motion, similar to the illusion of a white strobe light. Time appeared to crawl along for everyone else, except me and this mysterious man. Something was happening, something strange, something I couldn't comprehend.

I swivelled around to Mollie in the hope she too was witnessing what I was — but no, like everyone else she was operating at a snail's pace, mouthing my name in slow-mo. I blankly stared at her in a state of confusion, unable to fathom out what was happening. Was I experiencing a dizzy spell? Had I received a knock to the head. Or outrageously, had I been drugged? Some lowlife could have slipped me a pill, I was hallucinating, wasn't I! It would most definitely explain things!

I twisted back around to the cubby hole to check if my dark, secretive stranger was experiencing the same sensations as me, but as my luck would have it, he was nowhere to be seen. This proved it! I had unwittingly been poisoned and was now fabricating these outlandish scenarios and slightly dark Prince Charming fantasies. I had no idea what was happening to me, but I knew I had to get out, out of the lounge and fast!

Slamming my flute onto the nearest table, I clocked my exit but not before I let out an unexpected squeal. A hand had heavily slapped itself onto my right shoulder and was now contently resting there.

"Mollie!!" I snapped, but it wasn't her, and it was absolutely not the hand of a girl! I refused to turn around, not wanting to confront the owner of the masculine grip.

I had been acting incredibly odd, it was no surprise the lounge security had been alerted to my behaviour.

"Look, I'm sorry but I think some lowlife degenerate has tampered with my drink. I'm leaving, there will be no trouble here. If you could just remove your hand, sir, then I'll be on my way," I timorously informed.

"That's all very well, but I'll have to frisk you first, miss!" responded the security.

"Excuse me! You'll do nothing of the sort!" I gasped, furiously twirling around, ready to give this domineering jobsworth a piece of my mind!

"It...it's you!" I blurted.

Instinctively I knew it was him, don't ask me how I knew, I just did. Plus, those eyes of his were one of a kind. Like the Atlantic Ocean, I could easily drown within those deep icy blues. He was a little taller than me with thick, jet black hair and manly dark stubble. He was also the last person I expected to see standing in front of me. Well, I had thought I was tripping! Turns out my eyes had not deceived me after all.

"Erm, hi..." I giggled; my cheeks blushed with all the ripeness of a radish.

I was becoming incredibly girly in his presence. I

couldn't stop myself; he had the cheekiest of smiles and he was extremely easy on the eye.

He introduced himself as Zach Oakley and assured me that there would be no need for a strip-search just yet!

"You're Allie, Allie Pickering, aren't you?" he asked.

I was puzzled — he knew me, but how? No one really knew of me, well apart from Mollie and of course now Kalen.

"Don't look so worried," he chuckled. "I thought I recognised you. I know your dad...well I knew him."

"Did you?" I quizzed.

"Sure did. From time to time my old man would scaffold with your dad on the construction sites."

Zach didn't live local, in fact, I'm not sure where he lived, but in the past would often return to Eldercrest for short periods at a time. Both him and his dad would set up camp in the family campervan, it was a home from home.

"Good mates they were — your dad was always around ours," he added.

I was too young at the time to remember many of my dad's friends, but I thought that I would have remembered Zach of all people, especially as we were similar in age.

"I'm so sorry, I want to remember you...but I can't, and I find it even harder to believe that you remember me!" I laughed.

"Well, it was hard not to forget you, Allie. I had quite the crush on you when we were kids, but I was excruciatingly shy. I found it easier to remain invisible than to talk to you. I kept myself to myself, but hey, we were only young then, eh!" he grinned.

Oh my gosh, he had to be winding me up, there was no way on earth that someone like him could be interested in somebody like me — no way!

"Suppose you're not so bad now though are you...you and that mole of yours have aged well — it's adorable" he cheekily laughed.

Smothered in rose-tinted blushes, I threw a hand to

mouth, making sure to cop a feel of the prominent shade of onyx that straddled my upper lip. I'd always been fond of the little fella but never once considered it to be a turn-on for the opposite sex!

I could tell he was a naughty one and very sure of himself. He definitely wasn't shy anymore, especially as he was quite confident in telling me how things were. You know, he was completely different to Kalen, and it had to be said that it was actually refreshing to speak with someone that showed a deeper interest in me. I knew in five minutes where I stood with Zach, compared to where I did with Kalen, and I'd known him for months!

"C'mon then, what brings you back to Eldercrest — work or play?

"I'm actually on leave."

"Leave?"

"Yup, I'm currently serving with Her Majesty's Armed Forces, have been since I was sixteen. Keeps me grounded, gives me a purpose."

Yummy, it just gets better! There was something incredibly appealing about a man in green — the confidence, the strength — a safe pair of hands. He was reliable, committed, driven, and oh so sexy.

"So, Zach, where are you posted?"

"Down South," he vaguely replied.

"Where exactly?" I pushed.

"Don't take it personally, Allie, but I'd rather not say. Security and all that."

"Erm, hate to break up whatever 'this' is but we have to go, the cabs outside and the meters running!" whinged Sasha, or was it Tasha? I couldn't tell and y'know what, I didn't care! Was it really that time already though? It felt like we'd only been talking for a matter of minutes. Where had that hour disappeared to?

Come to think of it...what had I been drinking? I mean the lounge was completely back to normal. The music was on full pelt, and the revellers were gradually stumbling their way out the lounge at a normal speed — not slo-mo. And why in the world was Zach tucked away in a cubby hole? I was adamant I'd felt his eyes all over me this evening. If it's true what he said about the whole crush thing, then maybe he did still like me? Perhaps he couldn't bring himself to talk to me straight-away and quite literally backed himself into a corner. Seems he wasn't as bold as he made himself out to be.

Zach intrigued me. He was very sure of himself, illegally hot and he chose to call me Allie. I kind of liked that about him. Yes, his behaviour was a tad odd, but it only made me want to know more.

"Bye, Zach, see you around..." I wishfully whispered.

"You will!" he replied, making sure he was just out of earshot.

Nine

DAD

With a grin from ear to ear, he casually approached the grand wrought iron gates.

"Well, fancy meeting you here," smiled Zach.

He wore a slouchy grey beanie hat with a black leather jacket, skinny black trousers, a stone V neck vest and distressed black military style boots.

In his hand, he loosely held a beautiful bunch of cerise Germinis and pink Lisianthus.

"Hey?" I replied. "I've never seen you here before, and I'm here a lot! Who have you come to visit?" I pried.

It may have seemed slightly forward of me, but I didn't think he would be offended, he didn't seem the type.

"Well I hope you don't mind, Allie, but I'm here for your dad. After bumping into one another last week, it left me feeling a little nostalgic. It got me thinking, y'know, about the good old days and how much your dad meant to me."

"That's really thoughtful and so sweet of you, Zach. Dad doesn't receive many visitors these days, seems people have long forgotten him," I sighed.

It was true, not even Mum, his own wife would visit, she never had.

"Well, I'm here now, let's say hello to your old man. Come, you lead the way, Allie," Zach insisted.

He gently ushered me through the entrance and proceeded to follow.

∞∞∞

I made sure that without fail, I would visit Dad at least once a month — to let him know how I was, what I was up to and that I hadn't forgotten him.

Dad was a proud man, so I made sure he had a serene, spotless, graceful place to sleep. It's how he would have wanted it.

"Dad, it's Allie," I whispered, as I affectionately swept away the fallen leaves that had gently settled onto his blue pearl granite headstone. And as I always did, I kissed the top of the Angel's head that was kneeling by his polished stone. The thought of her — Dad's Angel, always gave me great comfort. I knew that with her by his side he was never alone, she was with him, loving him, protecting him — always.

"Hi, Harry, it's been a while," Zach softly spoke as he politely kneeled to pay his respects.

"I know flowers are probably not your thing, but there's not much you can do about it down there," he laughed.

I smiled at Zach as he tried his utmost to naturalize the situation, making sure not to make this moment any harder than it had to be. Zach took a few quiet moments to himself before tenderly laying the flowers upon Dad's earthy bed, and as he returned to his feet, he took a step back and lowered his head.

"My old man took it very bad the day your dad left us. He lost a great friend — he was irreplaceable! Harry was a wonderful man, I was extremely lucky to know him, even if it was only for a short time," he uttered.

"Thank you, Zach, your sentiments mean a lot, they really do," I choked.

It had been quite a few years since Dad was cruelly taken away from me. They say time heals and yes, in a hard, cold way it does, but never will it erase his memory, and never will I forget him.

"Tell me more about your dad, Allie?" he probed.

It was strange to be asked such a question as no one had ever enquired before, not even Kalen. Dad's friends had come and gone. Yes, they were rocks in the beginning, but life had moved on and eventually so do did they. Their priorities had changed. I don't blame them though, they had families and lives of their own to live. They weren't obliged to worry about me for the rest of their days.

My friends were too young at the time to understand the physical and emotional impact that losing a parent could have on a child. They couldn't relate, and I refused to engage and communicate. As a result, those that were around at the time were practically non-existent now.

Oh, and as for my family, well there was only me, Mum and Nan. We weren't fortunate to have a big brood or even a close supportive network of relatives nearby. Aunt Margo, Mum's sister, lived the other side of the country and was the nearest by far. She sent her condolences in the form of a cheap floral card, failing to even attend the funeral.

Mum crumbled to pieces after Dad's death, and Nan who had lost her only son, had no choice but to pick up the heart-breaking shards, stepping in when Mum hit the bottle hard.

In time, Mum successfully managed to control her alcohol consumption, but it didn't stop her from staying out all hours of the day and night. She missed key moments in my life: school plays, birthdays, achievements, heck, even puberty! These were irreplaceable memories that could never be recaptured. Where Mum dwindled, Nan flourished. She was there to guide me, to love me and without her, I doubt I would be the young woman I am today.

Nan, like me would regularly visit her son, but as her illness progressed, it was her visits that took an unfortunate decline. Some days Nan would forget that Dad had passed over and would arrive at our house open-armed, expecting to see him for a chat and a strong cuppa. Reminding Nan that Dad had died, never did get any easier, and what was worse was the look in her eyes as she learnt the news of losing him all over again.

I have to admit, I was shocked that after all this time someone was generally interested in hearing about my dad, and after waiting so long, I didn't hold back.

"Dad was far too young when he died. As you'll know he was in his early thirties, it was really no age at all. He had his life ahead of him. Time was on his side with big plans and un-fulfilled dreams to conquer.

I can remember vividly the way he smelt — sweet but earthy with a hint of spice. His hair was light brown and al-ways messy, but you know the kind of messy that looked to have been styled that way. He, like you, sported dark stubble and he had the fewest strands of grey that speckled the side of his head — very much the distinguished fox. Dad's eyes were warm and caramelized. They were kind and trustworthy. The type of eyes that wouldn't judge and would always keep you safe. He was a handsome man with an infectious smile. He was one of a kind..." I croaked.

"Carry on. Please?" Zach requested as I began to tail off.

"Ok, erm...he loved his sports, he really did, especially football. He would play five-a-side on a Sunday morning, no matter the weather. Nan told me that he played to keep him-self in shape. He wanted to keep up with me, a kid at the time, who was full of beans!

He used to walk through the door caked in mud. Grass stains on his crisp white shorts and sweat dripping from his brow. This one time, I recall he had taken a ball full pelt to the side of his head, and through no real fault of his own! He had caught sight of me at the side of the pitch, tripping over my shoelaces in the wet slimy mud. Worried for my safety, he took his eye off the ball — and that's when it hit. Even with claret trickling from the nasty gash to his battered head, he still bolted over towards me, scooping me up out of the sludge and into his strapping arms. His embrace kept me safe, as his kisses healed the near on invisible graze on my mucky knee.

Dad, on the other hand, had a black eye for months!

Oh, and then we had his hosting skills!" I blurted excitedly. "They were second to none with everyone wanting to be on the guest list, and everyone that was invited could not wait to take a sip of his famous 'Pickering' punch."

With every party, gathering and celebration, Dad would whip up a batch of his classified, mouth-quenching liquor. There would be uproar if he ever failed to produce the goods, and to this day, no one ever did find out what his secret recipe was!

"It was well-known in the community that it wasn't a party unless Harry, my dad, was there!" I chuckled.

"Don't I know it, and as for your dad's punch, you're totally right, that nectar was legendary!" Zach chipped in.

"Yeah, he certainly was the life and soul, bringing joy to all that had the pleasure of knowing him. So, when he died, a part of me did too. I guess I've never been able to fully recover from losing him," I sniffed.

It has to be said that I hadn't always been filled with such doom and gloom. I was once full of energy, love and light, but without him, the world didn't seem that bright anymore. I didn't feel that bright anymore.

Zach laid a consoling arm around my shoulder as we both stood in silence, reminiscing over the man we both once knew. This was the type of thoughtful gesture my dad would have made, and in that respect, Zach and my dad were very similar. Although like I said, I had no actual recollection of Zach, or in fact, his dad, but this whole bonding session we had going on, didn't feel wrong or even uncomfortable. It was comforting, familiar and it felt, y'know...right.

You're probably wondering by now how my father died, so I'll tell you. It was an unavoidable tragic hit-and-run. I've always blamed myself for his untimely death, and if it wasn't for my selfish greed, Dad would still be breathing in the same air as you and I.

∞∞∞

Let me rewind to the bitterly cold winter of 2006, the coldest winter to date. My dad who was already running late for work, had the added task of dealing with my demanding, but not so pressing need for a pair of 'must have' white Roller Skates with pink neon laces. I was only six, but I knew what I wanted, and I would behave like a right little brat in order to get whatever it was I fanatically desired. Mum had been working lates that week and had left it up to Dad to negotiate the school run. He was manic at work himself and was responsible for picking up a few last-minute Christmas gifts, which included these super-duper, top of the range skates.

As it was the 'silly' season, Dad was rushing back and forth — working, juggling chores and running errands. We also had dear old Nan booked in to celebrate with us.

Dad had yet to clean the house, pick up the food shop and collect the annual festive pine tree. It was fair to say he was quickly petering out of steam. It probably did him no good having me at the bottom of his feet either, nipping away and distracting him from his overloaded hectic schedule.

The weather was also toe-numbingly cold, icy and trounced with pure white snow. I loved this wintry time of year and to receive flutters of the white stuff throughout the day really added to the crisp magic of the season.

Wrapped in our snuggly duffel coats and winter warmers — Dad grabbed my hand and gave me a familiar wink. This was the affectionate wink of surrender, and he would often flash it my way. He only had to look into my innocent, cinnamon glazed eyes to give in to my demands. He was hopelessly devoted to me, and I knew from an early age that Dad would do anything for me.

"Come on, trouble, you know where they are, don't you?" he giggled.

"Yes, yes, yes!!!!" I ecstatically squealed.

"You're just like your mother, aren't you! You can never wait and you always get what you want!"

That I did get from her, but that was the only comparison I was willing to agree to.

Like me, I knew Mum still blamed me for Dad's death, although she would never again admit to it, but intuitively I could feel it. Her pain was hard to mask, and though she tried, it was clear for all to see that her heart had been destroyed.

Mum's tears flowed for days and nights on end. They were nonstop and for a child to view grief on a daily basis like that, well it was draining and life-shaping.

When the police arrived at my house with me in tow, I tightly clung to the lady officer's leg as she double tapped the front door. PC Piper was her name, she was professional yet sensitive and had promised to return me safely to my mum. She was accompanied by PC Sinclair, a hard-faced man with a gentle nature, who assured me all would be ok despite my ordeal.

Mum had been upstairs sleeping from her night shift when she had been stirred by the *rat-a-tat-tat* at the door. At first, I saw the netting from her window twitch, then I heard the loud pounding of her feet as she scurried across the floorboards. She had seen who was outside and erratically threw herself down the stairs to meet them. Mum though, did not want to open the door. She took her time as the realisation of what she was about to hear dawned upon her.

"Mrs. Elizabeth Pickering?" enquired PC Piper.

Mum looked terrified as she nodded, shielding herself behind the front door. But no amount of wood was going to protect her from what was about to come.

"Mrs. Pickering, may we come in? I'm afraid we have some bad news."

The words she dreaded to hear but were not yet spoken had sent Mum to her knees, and it was in those sickening seconds that she changed forever. Years passed, timed aged us but the silence always remained the same — barely speaking of Dad or the day the police came knocking. Then one morning when I was thirteen years old, that all changed.

It was a silly row with Mum over the cleanliness of my bedroom. It was like any other teenage girl's room, full of boy band posters, cuddly toys and glitter. Mix that in with empty fizz cans and dirty clothes strewn across the floor and you have a parent's nightmare. I apologised and assured her I would clean up the offending items as soon as I had returned from seeing Dad. It was the anniversary of his death, and I had handcrafted him a wreath from Spruce, Pine cones, Gypsophila and Moss — picked freshly from Eldercrest Woods.

Mum had clearly been drinking. Her blotchy raw eyes and the slur of speech tripping from out the side of her mouth were all tell-tale signs. The several wet and sticky red ring marks she had abandoned on the coffee table were also a dead giveaway.

"Actually, when you stop drinking, I'll start cleaning!" I snapped.

It was a brave outburst from, but I needed my mum, not the selfish boozer she had become. All she cared about was herself, and she had done so since the day she left me jilted on the doorstep with the police — frightened and confused, not knowing why Dad had left me.

Never did she soothe me or tell me it would be ok, and when I needed her the most, she deserted me.

Mum's eyes bulged with anger and without thinking she blurted his name in a garbled response, "If your dad wasss here, then yoooou would not daaaare to act like thiiiis, young ladyyyy!".

"Well he's not — is he!" I screamed in retaliation.

"Yerrrr, you made surrree of that — didn't yoooou!" she slurred.

Her eyes welled up from the hurtful words leaving her lips, and once she had said them, she couldn't take them back. The truth had been spoken, and her feelings towards me exposed. I had always felt that somehow, I was to blame for Dad's death, and now I had the confirmation that Mum strongly believed I was guilty too.

I know I wasn't the one driving the car, but I might as well have been, as it was me that placed him in that situation. The car in question was a black Honda Civic Hatchback, driven by a boy no older than eighteen years of age, he was still a kid himself. I was later informed his name was Scottie Rivers, a local boy that lived a few streets down from us. He was a good lad, training to become a sous chef with a young family of his own. He had only just passed his driving test the week before and had not yet become accustomed to driving in adverse weather conditions, and sadly, we were all about to pay a huge price for his inexperience.

He was seen by one eyewitness to grapple furiously with the steering wheel in a desperate bid to control the vehicle as it dangerously careered from lane to lane. The roads were severely icy, and Scottie had taken the corner of Primrose Hill too fast — ultimately resulting in a fatal sideways skid.

Dad unaware of the approaching out of control vehicle walked into the road, oblivious. The snow was thick, heavy and compressed, it had reduced his vision significantly. By the time he noticed the car — it was too late. Dad was dead. Killed instantly from the impact. PC Sinclair promised me he would've felt no pain.

Where was I? Well, I was still tucked away safely within our own car. Prior to the collision, Dad had ironically told me to stay put, it was too hazardous out there for me. Though now was not the time to obey Dad's rules, and on hearing the clash I rushed out of the car and towards the crash site.

A worried crowd of ash-soaked faces had already formed around the limp body on the slush-soaked pavement, which I quickly learned to be my dad. I had heard the commotion, seen the out-of-control car but luckily had not witnessed the horrific point of contact. As I pushed through the bystanders, my dad's face came into view. I froze, unable to move, only able to watch the events as they drastically unfolded.

Motionless, a kind lady no older than Mum had noticed me fixed to the spot. She took hold of my hand and pulled me away from view. Sorrow and pity filled her plump cheeks as she asked me my name, age and who I was here with today. I answered her questions and with a shaky finger pointed to Dad. I could feel myself entering a state of shock, and after answering the first few questions, I zoned out. Realising my distraught, the short rotund-faced lady knelt herself down to my level, placed her frosty cold hands onto my shoulders and introduced herself as Mrs. Genevieve Louise Snook. Her lips were moving constantly, but I couldn't hear a single word she was saying. The sound was muffled and distant.

I was an empty shell, unable to communicate, unable to function. Eventually, Mrs. Snook handed me into the authority of the police and disappeared with the rest of the crowd. This one stranger had shown me more affection in those first few minutes than Mum had shown me in the first few years of losing Dad.

Don't get me wrong, I knew Mum loved me. She always would. I was her only child, her baby girl but she would never fully forgive me for badgering Dad into getting me those blasted skates. In her eyes, if he hadn't had gone, he would still be here today and not waiting for her to join him in his lonesome casket for two at 'The Angels of Eldercrest Church'.

The fun-loving, caring Mum I once knew, died the same day as Dad. She never fully recovered from losing him, but now and again, if I was lucky, a glimmer of her former self would come shining through. I knew she would never be the woman she once was, but I was grateful now for the little moments we did have.

"Oh, Zach, I'm so sorry, I've waffled on!" I apologised.

I had truly lost myself within my thoughts. What must he think of me! Embarrassed, I turned my attention away from Dad's grave and on to Zach. I hoped my behaviour hadn't scared him off...but it appears it had.

Ten

GLORIOUS SPAM

He had some front that boy! It had been nearly a fortnight and still no sign of him. I couldn't believe he had the audacity to ignore me like this. Could he really be that busy with Coral to not even give me a second thought? I was disheartened and extremely angry inside. I wanted to scream in his face until I had no more breath inside my lungs to hurl. What kind of person, especially a man, leaves a young vulnerable female to walk home alone under the cover of darkness, and to top it off, not even check she had made it home safely?

Who exactly did Kalen think he was!

I anxiously grabbed the chain of my necklace, rolling the pendant between my index finger and thumb. My heart wasn't quite ready to admit it, but my head was insisting that I forget him and move on. If he didn't want me, then surely someone else out there did?

Mum had already been on my case this morning, grilling me on my state of mind. She was confused at how I could mope over someone that was clearly canoodling with someone else. As you may have determined, I had briefed her up on the basics of what had happened on the night of my eighteenth birthday — and she was now no longer a fan of Kalen.

"Why on earth are you making him your everything, when you are clearly his nothing, Allie?" Mum snapped.

Her words agonisingly harsh, sliced sharply through my

already opened wounds. I wasn't stupid. I knew how he was treating me, and if it was anyone else, I would have cut them loose a long time ago, but this was Kalen. He did something to me that I couldn't explain. I was weak for his mysterious ways and standoff attitude. He was a closed book, and I wanted to flick the pages, not just peruse the front cover.

'I will come back for you', were the words he said himself, and this was just another reason why I couldn't quite let go of him. He was a man of morals, living and breathing by three simple rules: promise, trust and belief. He had told me as much on our 'first date'. I knew one day he would come back for me as pledged, but I highly doubted it would be for the reasons I wanted it to be.

"Allie, I know you think the world of this boy, but you're not going to receive the closure you want or so desperately need. This boy has an unhealthy hold over you! It's eating you away. You need rid of him. Immediately!" she warned.

I knew Mum had a point, and although we were not as close as we once were, I still valued her opinion. We had certainly been able to move our relationship forward since those dark early days, and I guess I now saw Mum more as a friend than a parent.

"You hardly eat, you barely drink and when was the last time you had a good night's sleep? It's not healthy, and please don't get me started on how you hardly talk to me anymore. You're cutting yourself off. It's time to let him go and move on. You wait for him and I'll tell you know that 'the one' might just pass you by. Don't let him pass you, Allie!" she urged.

"I'm trying, Mum. I really am," I insisted.

It was the truth, I meant it, but if you've ever been ditched with no reasonable reason why. Then you'll appreciate, it's not so easy to 'just' forget and move on to the next.

You wonder what you did that was so wrong. Why didn't they call or text to let you know it was over? And nevertheless, you still wait for that beep, constantly gawking at the screen, not daring to touch the keys in case you accidentally delete an incoming call or message!

You start to blame yourself, questioning if it was something you said or did? It's an absolute horrid scenario to find yourself in, with lots of unanswered questions whirling around your head on repeat. I wouldn't wish it on anyone... well, perhaps Coral!

Mum had clearly had enough of my woeful 'little girl' moping routine, and this wasn't the first time she had told me so either. 'Go outside and get some colour into those cheeks of yours', was the constant theme of her rants. She hated to see me sulking and would often encourage me to leave my mood outside the front door. Though adding colour to my cheeks was the last thing on my mind.

"Tell you what, you can come out with me!" she stated

Not one to start a row, I did as I was told. If anything, I couldn't be doing with the aggro.

∞∞∞

Every other day, there Mum was at the entrance of my bedroom door, arms folded, right foot tapping, "Allie, clear off will you, autumn will have come and gone before you know it. Plus, your miserable face is giving me the right hump!"

In response, a grunt or a curt 'fine' was normally all I could muster up.

Grabbing Jed's lead, I would shuffle off out the house, and without fail, I would always end up in the one place that would warm my heart. This place was special to me, and I had chosen to share it with Kalen. It was the place where I had spoken fondly of my dad and it was where we had first spotted that four-leaf clover. It was also here that I had felt the unnerving feeling of being watched. It was my 'special place' — it was 'The Angels of Eldercrest Church'.

"Go on, have your freedom, but don't you dare bolt off!" I bellowed.

Jed was eager to explore his familiar stomping ground and couldn't wait for me to release him from the constraints of his leash. My words though, fell on deaf doggy ears, as only meagre seconds after uttering the command — he fled. Ignorantly catapulting himself off into the church field, leaving me alone with only myself for company.

The church grounds were stunning, and as odd as it may sound, I felt at home here.

I would breathe in the beauty of peace and quiet as I quietly strolled the impeccably maintained grave-lined paths. All that could be heard, apart from the pitter-patter of feet, was the delicate tinkle of assorted crystal hanging wind chimes as they moved within the grace of the wind.

Ethereally they floated from the flourishing trees of remembrance and twinkled within the catch of daylight.

Polished pebbles, pastel picket fences and lovingly hand-picked flowers of every colour, devotedly dressed the beds of loved ones passed.

The grounds were a beautiful haven of adoration and loyalty, oddly a welcoming escape from the harsh realities of life. Each and every one of these visits would always finish with Dad. An affectionate hello and a brief chat would ensue before dragging myself back home to repeat my cycle of misery.

Though on this particular occasion, Jed was acting somewhat out of character. He was lying within long stems of grass, his tail wagging berserk as he grumbled furiously away at me.

"Easy, boy," I soothed.

Taking a slow pace, I edged towards him, careful not to create a stare-off or to startle him with any sudden movements. It was not like Jed to display signs of aggression towards me. Something was bothering him, and it was coming from behind.

Tracing his captured gaze towards the peak of my right shoulder, it was clear that whatever had distracted him was stood behind me. With my skin prickled with uneasiness, I became fidgety, jumpy almost. Hidden eyes were on me. I could feel them! I was being watched, followed and listened to — and Jed knew it.

Creeping towards me, he didn't want to play, instead, he released an agitated growl.

"Calm down, boy," I hushed, whilst reaching out my palm in an attempt to stroke his heightened hackles.

Whatever it was, it was closing in and I needed to be ready for...*SWOOSH!*

"Woah!"

I had spoken too soon! Our prowler impudently came for me at full tilt, before momentarily stopping inches from my nose to invasively inspect me further. In an attempt to focus on its intruding presence, my eyes blurred as they crossed one another.

"What the!" I snorted, as the identity of our graveyard stalker came into view.

"A bug!" You're kidding me! The last thing I expected was to be alarmed by a beastie, especially one that saw no issue in infiltrating my personal space!

"Oh, for goodness sake, Jed, it's only a silly little butterfly."

Pure black, velvety and with a silver winged lining—this bug was a stunner, bigger than average with shedloads of confidence. With eyes the shade of espresso, they were rich and decadent, roasting into mine as they forwardly straddled my bridge.

With a flick of the wings, the unashamed character boosted itself from off of my skin and into the still of the air. Toying, it circled Jed's ruffled head one last time, before darting off into the mass floral display of graves.

'With the exception of the odd unwanted bug, 'The Angels of Eldercrest Church' was the perfect hideaway, a distraction from Kalen, a distraction from life. Not wanting to wallow further in all the 'ifs', 'buts' and 'whys', I turned my attention back to Mum, who was now dashing around in a distressed state.

∞∞∞

"Why is it that everything I want is never on these blooming shelves. Is it really that hard to purchase a can of spam these days!" spurted an inconvenienced Mum.

I grimaced at the thought of my tongue touching that muck. I hated spam with an almighty passion! Mum continued to tut and grunt her way through the aisle, scanning every nook and cranny for that hard to find, shiny can of spam.

We were at 'Crocker & Sons', our local family run supermarket. They had been stocking our kitchen cupboards for longer than I could remember. Mum had dragged me out to 'Crocker's' for a tad of fresh air and to treat me to a little lunch. Spam sandwiches were not what I had in mind for a little treat though! As much as I prayed that 'said' can didn't rear its porky little head, I couldn't help but agree that Mum had a valid point. The shelves always seemed to be bursting with the food you didn't want, and the food you did want was always out of stock. Thankfully, I wasn't too worried about the absent spam, in fact, I was grateful it was a slippery little shit to find.

"Ah ha!"

Mum let out a triumphant cheer down the canned food aisle. She had obviously found what she was looking for.

"Ah...you found it then?" I disappointingly grunted, as I walked through the parallel aisle dedicated to condiments.

Mum just as she did with her cups of tea, swore by her spam sarnies, they were the answer to any dire situation and in her eyes, good old-fashioned comfort food.

"Certainly have, Allie, but thanks must go to this lovely young man who jostled with me for the last can," she flirtatiously giggled.

Turns out some young gent had retreated from battle by surrendering the final can to my overjoyed mother. But what I found to be more ludicrous than Mum and some stranger battling over tinned meat, was that there was someone else out there that loved spam just as much as Mum did. Absurd!

"Oh well, isn't that just splendid! I must thank this magnanimous stranger for his most generous deed of the day," I sarcastically joked, as I entered the aisle and walked up towards him.

I couldn't quite make him out, but that's hardly surprising as he was hidden behind a piled high food cage of tinned tuna in brine.

"You shouldn't have. No, you really, really shouldn't have!" I chuckled as I pinged the playful comment his way.

"Here, dear, let me move this cage from out your way" grumbled Mr. Crocker. "Oh, and don't forget, it's 'two-for-one' on all canned fish today!" he hollered as he bumbled off, lugging the produce with him.

His son Petey was not cut out for this shop business malarkey and preferred to spend the working day seducing pretty girls over in the fruit and veg aisle. His father Barry or Mr. C as he was known, was fully aware of his son's shortcomings and spent most his day picking up after his boy, hence the jilted food cage!

As the cage, lethargically bimbled along, Mum's opponent came into full view. Keen to greet me, he spun his body around to meet with mine.

"For you, Allie — anything!" he cheekily beamed, whilst swiftly removing his maroon beret as a sign of respect.

"Zach...it's you!" I spluttered.

I felt myself clamming up. I was completely taken aback to see him again, especially after his hasty exit at the church!

"Spam?" I laughed, trying not to appear awkward about our prior meeting.

"Hah! I won't lie, I'm partial to the salty sandwich filler but it wasn't actually for me," he chortled.

I could blatantly see Mum's peepers lighting up from the corner of my eye as she pretended to pore over Mr. C's bargain canned fish.

Here I had a man stood before me that was good-looking, kind and funny. He loved spam but above all, he wasn't Kalen. I could sense already that Zach was a keeper in Mum's eyes.

"I'm back on duty tonight, but thought I'd do a quick shop for the old man."

Well, that would sure explain the dreamy camouflaged ensemble he was sporting! There was just something about a man in uniform that brought me to my knees. He was outrageously gorgeous and looked better than I ever imagined.

"He's not as agile as he once was, and unfortunately, getting out and about takes its toll on him these days," sighed Zach.

"Oh, I had no idea! What happened?" I sympathetically asked.

"Work! Put his back right out, didn't he! He's not been the same since. I often do his errands for him, y'know, anything that makes his life a little easier."

Wow, you think someone couldn't possibly be any more appealing than they already were! Then out of nowhere, they go and throw another tempting quality your way. I mean how thoughtful and equally handsome could one person be. He wasn't real, surely?

"Look, about the other day…I hope you didn't mind, but I could sense you were deep in thought. You seemed so peaceful. I didn't have the heart to disturb you, and I wanted to give you some alone time with your dad."

I felt so silly. There I was thinking the worse, when Zach had actually been a gentleman and left me to reminisce. With this new-found revelation leaving me to feel warm and satisfied inside, I knew it was time to introduce Mum to the reason behind my effortless smile.

"Erm, Mum, this is Zach," I shyly informed.

"Zach? Zach who?" Mum eagerly probed.

"Er, sorry, I never caught your dad's name?" I embarrassingly whispered.

"Oh right…" he replied.

He seemed rather upset I couldn't recall who his dad was, but the truth was, I didn't actually know.

"I'm Zach. Frank Oakley's boy. He was a mate of your late husbands."

Zach took charge, extending his hand out to Mum.

Mum, however, looked flummoxed, "Frank's boy? Who's Frank? Are you sure love as I don't remember your father?" she shrugged.

Mum wasn't shy with her opinions or thoughts, and she would often blab out how she was feeling or thinking without a care to who she may or may not offend. Zach was fully aware of the awkward situation evolving and swiftly interrupted Mum's indiscreet words.

"Allie, you never told me you had a sister, and might I add a younger one at that!" he teased.

Oh suave, very suave! Zach had switched a cynical Mum into a gibbering wreck within seconds of uttering that completely laughable and predictable line.

"Oh, stop it, I'm old enough to be your mother, and if you knew my Harry, then you know exactly who I am, you cheeky devil!" she giggled.

Mum was transforming into this super girly teenager in front of my very eyes, it was hilarious to watch — if a little stomach-turning! All that was missing was the twiddling of hair and the sweet flutter of eyelashes and we would be there!

"Allie, remember what I said, ok?" she conspicuously blurted, before winking and continuing on with her shop. She had a spring in her step as she glided her trolley through and out of the canned food aisle.

"Nice to meet you, Elizabeth!" Zach called as she exited.

"Call me Betty," Mum shouted, her voice full of delight.

It was clear Zach had made quite the impression on her.

"Your mum is just the sweetest!" gushed Zach.

Isn't she just! She was all sweetness and light when she wanted something or if she was on the receiving end of a good deal. But rub her up the wrong way and you had the mother of all bitches on your hands.

Zach had certainly charmed Mum, but it was going to take a little more effort than a tin of spam and a splash of flattery to fully win me over.

"Share then?" grilled Zach.

"Share what?" I asked with a puzzled tone.

I had a hunch this was about Mum's cryptic sentence, and guess what, I wasn't wrong! There was no way I wanted to let on to Zach that Mum was desperately trying to marry me off, nor did I want him to think I had feelings for him. I'm not saying I did, but then again, I'm not saying I didn't either.

"Your mum seemed keen for you to remember something. Sounded important. Can I help?" he prodded, knowing full well what he was doing.

"Oh, it's just a chat we were having. It's nothing serious and nothing to worry yourself about," I confessed.

Mum was, of course, referring to 'the one' walking on by and me foolishly missing out if I persisted in mooning over Kalen. I gathered by her comment that she liked the look of Zach and most likely thought he was a potential suitor for me. Mum might be right, but I hardly knew him, and I wasn't entirely over Kalen just yet.

I drew a line under the issue and was about to make my excuses to leave when Zach beat me to it.

"Allie, look, I must dash but catch you around sometime, yeah?" he chipped in.

"Oh, erm, sure thing," I was a little taken aback by his abruptness, but I guess this was his thing.

Our dialogue had been short and sweet and not as lengthy as I would have hoped for. I started to yet again over analysis every word I had spoken. Had I said too little? As I definitely hadn't said a lot. What if I came across stand-offish or even boring!

Urgh, maybe on this occasion Mum was right. Should I have done more to make him want to stay, or had I inadvertently gone and let the 'one' pass me by?

Eleven

CLOSURE

Y ou will be happy to know I had finally seen sense over the whole Kalen debacle. After two to three weeks of deliberation, I had decisively persuaded my heart to verbally agree with my head, and the outcome was that I was to wait no longer for him. What's more, I needed him to hear it.

It was vital he should know I wanted to be free of his hold. This sense of loyalty that draped over me needed to be scrapped. The aching urge that seeped through my veins, lacing my blood was to be drained and fast. I was more than done with feeling like a yo-yo, the little wooden yo-yo that he could release and recoil whenever he felt like it. I was after my closure and boy, was I out to get it!

I knew we weren't boyfriend and girlfriend, we weren't even dating, but we had something between us, something I couldn't quite explain. We were past the friendship stage but not quite lovers. We had no title and that was the overall underlying issue. It was like no other relationship I had heard of before, but that day in 'Hags Alley' confirmed to me he had roused certain feelings for me. Whatever we had between us was real, but I knew I wasn't strong enough to continue this twisted one-sided love affair anymore.

Unlike me, Mollie would have dates, countless amounts of them, and nine times out of ten, she would end up in a relationship with them, even if it was only for an hour or two. I struggled to secure the one date off of my own back, and even then, that one wasn't an actual legit date, was it!

Mollie was always the dumper and never the dumped, but she would at least have the courtesy to alert the affected party of their newly single status. Kalen, however, preferred to remain shady. Like I said, we were not just friends, there was more substance to us than that.

The way he melted into my eyes, brushed my skin, whispered my name or occasionally spoke in a suggestive manner were not the actions of a typical friend. I did, however, figure that his troubled childhood was probably to blame for his lack of sensitivity and non-existent dating technique.

He had confided in me that he had no prominent mother or father figure present to show him how to love or indeed be loved. I guess he had learnt from others, through TV or by self-teaching. These were all poor choices as he clearly didn't know how to communicate with a girl, let alone tell her how he felt.

I sensed from his touch, he felt more for me than what he was actually capable of letting on. If I had misread the signals, then I hold my hands up, but he needed to be upfront and let me know. I couldn't continue to live like this anymore.

I had rigorously planned in my head what I was going to say, how I was going to execute it and how he would respond. All I needed now was to find him, which wasn't going to be an easy mission. Mollie had heard via dopey and ditzy, aka Sasha and Tasha that Kalen and Coral had been spotted at various locations within Eldercrest. They were still close by, but where exactly would be potluck.

It was noticed that once again they were engaging in hush-hush conversations, their bodies closely locked together, practically inseparable. There was no mistaking it, he had feelings for her, no one could behave in such a manner without being emotionally entwined. I wished he could have been open and honest with me from the get-go. If I was aware they were together, I would have never pursued my feelings for him. I would have walked away at the first inkling of a union, and no way would I have made someone my all, when evidently, they saw nothing wrong in sharing their heart with more than just the one.

I didn't know why he was being such a gutless coward, but I very much doubted it was about to stop anytime soon. He couldn't treat me like this. I wasn't weak. I wasn't a moron. I deserved much better than what he had given me. Surely it would have been far better and all-round easier, if he had spoken the truth when Coral reared her ugly head in 'Hags Alley'. Scurrying around and avoiding me like I was the plague was a waste of time for the both of us. I had so much I wanted to say. Ok, ok shout and one day I would find him and make that happen — unluckily for him, today was that day!

Enough was enough and as much as I didn't want to, I knew I had to go there. I knew exactly where to find him. It was the one place he loved the most.

If he was stressed, he would go there.

If he was happy, he would be there.

This was the place where he made his feelings known for me, it's where we nearly kissed and where Coral thwarted my yearned for moment. It was also where I had realised Kalen had feelings for Coral, and it was the likeliest place where I would find them both together. It was of course 'Hags Alley'.

'Hags Alley' was always smothered in darkness. It didn't matter when or what time of day you visited; it would always be covered in a blanket of obscurity. If the sun was shining in full glory, the alley would be dark. If the sky was full to the brim with rain, the alley would be dark. I think you can see where I'm going with this one. Kalen had told me that the weather was never gloomy in 'Blossomvale', no matter what the climate was like for the rest of Eldercrest.

The sky was beautifully painted baby blue with the odd pillowy marshmallow cloud in view. The sun radiated, beaming brightly through the glistening waterfall of turquoise showers. Chirping birds were forever harmonizing as they gracefully glided above oodles of pastel florals swaying elegantly to the rhythm of the breeze. The ambience of 'Blossomvale' compared to 'Hags Alley' were worlds apart.

"I'm off out, Mum. I'm getting that closure we spoke of!" I whooped.

Mum was in the conservatory, comfortably slouched back on one of those traditionally British seaside deck chairs. Hers was a red and white striped canopy upon a white frame — just looking at it made me long for a lazy day by the beach.

I was lucky growing up as Eldercrest was only a forty-five-minute drive away from the coast, and as a young girl, no year would be complete unless we had spent a weekend away at Pebble Bay. Mum and Dad would hire out a four-berth caravan from Friday to Sunday at the 'Happy Holidays Beach Camp'. It had everything you could want and all in one place: an outdoor swimming pool, arcades, restaurant and nonstop entertainment. Though the massive draw for us was the beach, it was on our camp doorstep and only a five-minute walk away.

We would fritter the days away there, spending quality family time together whilst basking our bodies in the rays, regardless if it was overcast or not. Mum and Dad would set up base on the golden sands, stationing their complimenting deck chairs side by side — Mum in her red striped canopy and Dad in his blue one. I would be larking around by their feet, flicking sand into their faces and sprinkling their creamy ice creams with gritty grains. Mum would occasionally peer down from her gossip mag to acknowledge my need for attention but would always leave Dad to entertain me. I giggled in delight as he chased me around the deck chairs, using a bottle of squirty suntan lotion as his weapon of choice. Eventually, I would belly flop into the shallow waves of the sea to evade capture.

Those innocent days were magical and where I made most of my happiest memories, but sadly, they were now a distant thought. The last time we visited the bay was the year before Dad died. Mum never took me back.

Now here she was, cosied up in her woollen garbs on her faithful chair with a mug of steaming hot chocolate in hand. Dad's chair was sat side-by-side, next to hers, like it always had been. Though no one ever sat there, they daren't for fear of being scolded by Mum. It was like she was expecting him to eventually return home and take his rightful seat — like he always had. Of course, we knew this would never happen, but it seemed Mum still wasn't willing to admit it to herself yet. And just like those sunny beach days before, Mum recognised my need for attention — briefly peering down from the juicy romance novel she was captivated in and throwing a half-arsed sentence my way.

"Good girl, glad you found that two-timing little toe-rag. Make sure you give him what for!" she exclaimed, disinterested, as her nose-dived straight back into 'said' book.

Well...I hadn't exactly found him had I, but at least I was attempting to. Anyway, I had enough to do already, what with facing my fears and tackling that alley! I didn't have the energy to correct her as well, so I decided to remain silent and just get on with it!

Even though 'Blossomvale' was only around the corner, every step towards her seemed to take an age. My feet felt bulky, like bricks — they were heavy to move as if they were feebly attempting to stall the undertaking of the impending opening of 'Hags Alley'.

They were, however, no such match for my valour, and it wasn't long before I had come to a standstill outside the entrance.

Taking a deep breath, I stared blankly into the dank abyss. It seemed scarier than normal. My fear was palpable... maybe this wasn't such a good idea after all. Kalen might not even be in there, and I would be doing all this for nothing. To top it off, I would be left even more upset and distressed than I already was. Still, my anxiety was not enough to deter me, and I made the first step through.

Now, I know I was alone, but oddly, it didn't feel like it, as once again that feeling of being watched crept itself over my body, sending my hands and legs into a trembling cataclysm.

My imagination was winning over common sense, interpreting every dark shape, every eerie sound, every enigmatic movement as the vile hag. I clenched my fists and pushed my body into a sprint. It was the only way I was going to be able to commit to the mission ahead. I ran as fast as my sluggish feet could physically manage, maniacally pushing every branch, leaf and cobweb from out of my way.

The brutish gale did its utmost to savagely drag me away from the turning towards 'Blossomvale', but determination spurned me on and aggressively I battled against it.

The pull of the wind hadn't felt half this bold or strong when I was with Kalen, but I suppose there was two of us then — more weight to stop the drag.

I wrestled the tree branches, desperately seeking support to assist with hauling my wayward body along the path. As I struggled against the turbulence, I immediately became aware of a dark figure. Although sinister, it was similar to the one I had detected in 'The Locust Lounge'. I had assumed Zach was the owner, but evidently, I was wrong, as whoever it was, was back and it wasn't happy.

Dauntingly, I felt its presence lurking behind me, inches

from my body and no, this time I didn't want to come face to face with it!

The only way I can describe this wraithy outline to you is to refer to it as an unwanted visitor, a visitor intent on making its presence known but unwilling to reveal its identity. It's the feeling you get when you know you're being watched, you realise they are there, but you can't pinpoint where exactly. You can't fully see who or what it is. You can only sense them, and you rarely catch them. With panic beating in your heart, you daringly turn on your feet for a sighting, but all you glimpse is a swift dark movement, known commonly as the shadow.

"Urgh!!!!, I can't do this!!" I hysterically screamed.

The wind, the dust, the darkness was hindering my progress, and the whole situation was an energy sucking upward struggle. The added contribution of my unwanted guest was sending me into a frenzy and near on reducing me to tears. I had no choice but to concede defeat and bow out — that's if I wanted to keep my sanity and possibly my life. I was never one to give up, it wasn't my style, but these events were out of my control. I couldn't continue.

Angrily, I accepted my beating and with ease began to backtrack on myself, heading out of the alley and towards home. I wasn't engulfed in a rage of wailing wind nor was I struck by a fist full of dust.

'Hags Alley' was still.

I shook my head in disbelief. It was typically my luck that I was denied access by these freak elements. Yeah, I could have tried my chances and charged back towards 'Blossomvale', but something didn't feel right. I still felt like I was being watched, and I didn't particularly fancy being trapped in a windstorm with the unknown.

Wanting to get out as soon as possible, I reactively stepped up the pace, and I was almost there...when I heard it — stopping me dead in my tracks.

It was a humming noise. It roamed through the alley,

swept up by the mild breeze that was left in wake of the storm. It was human sounding, deep and sombre, looping the alley as it morbidly coiled its way through each and every branch.

The sound of the humming made me feel even more jittery than the unfortunate existence of the lurking shadow. There was an air of loneliness and sadness to its pitch — bordering on a slight haunting vibe. The anguish I could hear was unbearable, it clawed me in, leaving me determined to reach 'Blossomvale' and find the source of this unabating whine.

I felt a surge of strength within and without thinking stormed back through the ferocious gale, which of course was once again present. Utilising every last sap of energy I had, I pushed and pushed and pushed, spurred on by this troublesome wail.

God, did I groan and grumble as I fought to break through the barrier.

One last push was all I needed, and I would have made it through to the dead end of 'Hags Alley'. With a whole lot of grimacing and one supreme push — I was there! I had finally broken through, sweat dripping from my brow with my hair bedraggled from the invisible tussle I had endured. No doubt I looked a right mess, and maybe Kalen seeing me like this was not how I would have wanted it, but right now, I couldn't care less. I had only gone and made it, and I couldn't have been more elated!

Now jubilations aside, what I should tell you is that not only had the tornado of wind ceased but so had the distressed hum. As quickly as it had sounded, it had completely and utterly vanished. It was definitely of masculine tone, and I wondered if it had been a man silently weeping with the sound of sadness in his heart.

The only person I knew to venture this way was Kalen. Could this heartbreaking whine belong to him? I hoped not! As much as he had ripped out my heart, I still had feelings for him and would never dream to see or hear him in a vulnerable state like this.

The other thought I had, which bear in mind was a little far-fetched, was of the old hag. Could the myth be true? Was it so inconceivable for her to actually exist and do the most inexplicable thing as to capture a young lad for her own gain?

Only in the last two years had reports surfaced of a sombre murmur emanating from the alley, but as you've probably guessed, no one had ever been found or held accountable.

Many locals actually preferred to believe in a little-twisted fairy tale and without question put the cries down to those stolen by the hag.

My mind was once again leading me astray. It was getting darker by the minute and there was no way I wanted to be here any longer than necessary. Not one to rule her existence out, I quickly refocused myself on the matter at hand. Urgency in mind, I grappled with the brick wall, trying desperately to find the entrance. Where on earth was it? It wasn't at all obvious, and infuriatingly, I never had the chance to catch sight of it the first time around. It must be hidden, invisible to the naked eye!

Kalen loved the secrecy of 'Blossomvale', it was hard to get to, well hidden, unspoiled and perfect in every way. It was simply one of those rare, magical places that only the lucky stumble across. It's no wonder he created the diversion of knocking me down in order to distract me from knowing how to open the gateway to this little gem.

I slapped the brick wall, expecting there to be some sort of secret brick door that would magically crack open.

It didn't.

The only thing that did crack was the skin on my palms as I tried in vain to find a way in. The grisly trees that lined the walkway to the concrete dead end were compressed, and impossible to penetrate. There was no possibility of me entering through them. I couldn't fit an arm through, let alone my actual torso!

My only hope lied with the crumbly, rotted old tree that was strewn across one side of the flesh-snatching wall. The tree was clearly dead, barely clinging to the bricks — it looked like it would disintegrate with a single touch.

To look at, it shouldn't even have been considered as an option, but then again, what other choices did I have. There was no way I could scale the lofty wall with my bare hands. I needed an aid, and this battered old tree was my only option.

I placed my left foot in the nook of the trunk, and with my right foot, I heaved my body up the core, hectically trying to lodge my boot in any one of the many decaying old crevices.

This was ridiculous! I was close to doing myself an injury by scaling the tree in this manner, but what else was I supposed to do. How I'd slipped through the first time I will never know.

∞∞∞

"Who's there!" I yelled, demanding to know who or what had just rustled their fingers through my hair.

Naturally, I threw my free hand to my face, shielding myself from any further attempts to attack or interfere with me.

"Go away, hag! Don't you dare come near me! I'm not afraid of you, and I'll kill you before you even try to take me!" I threatened.

This was nothing more than bravado. It was me pretending to be a fearless independent woman, when inside I was a complete wreck! I'd never had a fight in my life...well actually that's not strictly the truth. There was that one time with Janice Carter, an ill-disciplined girl from junior school. She was a right cow, a proper nasty piece of work. She had short black hair with a poker straight fringe that hid half of her beady brown button eyes.

From the moment we met, she had it in for me and would go out of her way to make my school life a misery. She would yank at my long curly ponytail, fling elastic bands at my head and delve into my lunch box, crumpling my crisps into smithereens with her grim moist fingers. Once, she even incinerated the luscious golden blonde hair from off of my Malibu Barbie with a Bunsen burner. You name it, she did it!

One day without warning, I snapped. I'd taken all I could handle and offered to meet her outside the school once lessons had finished. We were to settle this once and for all.

Janice, as expected, couldn't resist my offering and met me at 3pm underneath the subway by the school gates.

My only hope was that our little tête-à-tête would go under the radar, but I was wrong, very wrong. A huge gaggle of girls and a pack of hungry boys had circled us, jeering as Janice squared up to me. I had falsely assumed we could solve this matter in a civilised manner, but Janice was never going to be the reasonable type.

She was in her element, engulfing herself in the chants of abuse that were catapulted at me from the feral herd that had slithered in. As with any brawl at our school, the coats would come off and once that happened you knew that the participants involved meant business. Janice ripped off her thick bright pink duffel coat and chucked it into the preying crowd behind. Matching her like for like, so did I, but please note I was most definitely not wearing a pink coat!

Janice stepped forward, her noxious face in mine, her fists clenched tightly. Never had I found myself in a situation like this before, so I was at a loss to know what the protocol was for a good school beating. I, therefore, did what any good amateur would do and mirrored my enemy — game face on.

"Ready?" she smirked; her garlicky scented breath curled my nose. She needn't use her fists as the stench alone was a weapon in itself.

Janice had been waiting for this moment for years, and no amount of stamping on my cheese and ham sandwiches would beat the thrill that she was about to frolic in. I nodded and squinting my eyes, I waited for the blows to rain down upon my body. My thinking was, that once she had got her kicks, done what she needed to do, she would leave me alone.

"Once I hit you, Pickering, I'm gonna hit you every day like this for the rest of your life. Make sure you get used to the feel of my knuckles!" she whispered, confirming my worst fears.

I braced myself, guarding my face against the impending cat attack.

"Oi, what the bloody hell is going on here? Miss Carter! Miss Pickering! Explain yourselves — now!!" ranted Mr. Bigglesworth.

As the Head of the P.E. department, Mr. Biggie (as we would address him) was built like a brick shithouse — big strong and sturdy and therefore not one to argue with.

However...

SMACK!

I hit her! Straight in the face. Blood gushed from her nose as she fell to the floor like a sack of spuds.

"Miss Pickering! Get to the Headmaster's office. Now!" yelled Mr. Biggie. His face was a picture! There was no doubt he was angry, he looked like a raging beetroot, but I could see from the glint in his expression that he was secretly rooting for me.

Everyone in the school, including the teachers, knew that Janice was the biggest bully going, and me — the underdog, had just brought her to her wobbly scuffed up knees.

The kids thirsty for blood went mental with a mix of laughter and shock as Janice pathetically pleaded for a rematch.

"That's not fair. I wasn't ready!" she screamed. "I demand you agree to a rematch. I was distracted, you sneaky freak!" whimpered the sour, blubbering loser.

Yes, I was sneaky in hitting her, but I had to. Mr. Biggie's sudden interference was the perfect distraction, and if it wasn't her than it would have been me. Let's not forget she would have made me suffer day after day if I hadn't got in there first. She had what was coming to her, and that one lightning punch had been my first and thankfully last battle of the fisticuffs!

∞∞∞

The wind continued to thrash. I couldn't hear a thing. All I could do was ride it out and wait for it to pass. It also didn't help that I was deeply bothered by the thought of the hag skulking nearby, and if need be, I would not hesitate in using that one deadly punch of mine!

SWOOSH!

"What the —!" I shrieked.

SWOOSH!

There it was again, this whirring noise, slicing through the wind, clipping my ears as it did so. I couldn't see anything, but whatever it was, it was only millimetres from me.

Fear had set in, and I was becoming a skittish wreck. Not knowing what it was and what it wanted was beginning to freak me out.

SWOOSH!

I couldn't hide my fear anymore and released a gut-curdling scream as I simultaneously released my footing from off the shaky tree. Someone or something was enjoying the effect that they were having on me. My heart jumped with every *swoosh*, which sounded like an out of place accelerated flapping motion. This thing was playing with my mind. My nerves were on edge. If whatever it was, was hell-bent on breaking me emotionally, then it was fair to say it was succeeding!

SWOOOOOOOSH!

This time the noise lingered long enough for me to catch the culprit in the act!

"It's you!" I shouted in confusion.

It almost seemed laughable that something so precious, so small could scare me half to death by simply flapping its angelic wings, but it was true. My little black-winged friend from 'The Angels of Eldercrest Church' was the reason behind my fear.

"What on earth are you doing here, little flutter bug? You freaked me out!!" I affectionately scolded.

My little friend couldn't care less about how I felt and playfully hovered in front of my nose, pretending to intently listen to my words. Then without warning, it vanished, darting off into a putrid cranny of the lifeless tree.

I waited a few seconds, expecting the flutter bug to emerge — unable to breathe in the vile odour of the moulding bark — but it didn't.

It was a hefty old size for what was meant to be a bitty winged creature. I wouldn't have been surprised if it had become stuck. It had definitely had one too many sips of nectar, that's for sure!

Now as much as it had initially scared me, I had become quite fond of the little fella.

Fella?

I had never actually identified its gender before, but it was most definitely a boy! He had that boisterous, daredevil attitude that you would associate with a male. Perhaps I should give him a name, didn't seem right to refer to the little one as 'it' anymore!

Let's think...

Dave?

Yeah, he could be a Dave. It was a strong, solid, sturdy

name, but then I guess it didn't quite match the air of mystery that surrounded his bewitching wings.

Erm...Mystique?

Now as beautiful as it sounded, I couldn't help think it was a tad girly for my tough, independent boy.

I've got it!

Baxley! I would call him Baxley.

It matched his dark, enchanting exterior. He was a leader, a free spirit and a protector — just as his name suggested.

"Baxley!!!" I called, hoping he would respond to my beckoning. I prayed he hadn't hurt himself or become injured within the rotten debris of that tree.

Y'know, it was pointless me calling him a name he wasn't born with, as the chances of him responding were slim to none. Oh, and let's remember he was a bug, so probably not that familiar with the English language either! He would have no idea what I was waffling on about, and for all I knew, he probably already had a name and it was most likely to be Dave!

I edged over to the tree and collected one of its cracked branches that had broken off and now laid rejected on the ground. I used it as a tool, slapping the remaining branches to steadily coax out Baxley. I was careful not to hit each branch with too much force for worry that the whole tree might disintegrate under pressure.

"Baxley...? Dave...?" I was willing to try anything to summon my little mate.

"Come on out, you...I've never been a fan of hide and seek" I pleaded.

Nope, nothing, Baxley was having none of it and refused to budge. I was now panicking that he had, in fact, become cemented in the same slimy sap that was oozing from out of the tree. There would be no way I could save him if his wings were smothered in that!

I would have to act fast if there was any chance of plucking him out alive.

∞∞∞

I pressed my palms up against the dying tree and breathed in deeply as I pushed a scrunched-up hand into the gaping hole that Baxley had flown into. The hole was more likened to a crack. It was skinny and long, and deceivingly, the space within the hole felt huge — not what I had expected at all. Baxley would have had no problem in manoeuvring his way around this little joint.

My hand roved around, blindly searching for Baxley but still no joy. I had a crazy idea that maybe, just maybe I could squeeze into the tree too. With a little more leeway, I would have a greater chance of finding him. Without too much thought, I bent down, allowing my legs to follow my hands...

It was working!

Aimlessly, I proceeded forward, sucking my stomach in and wiggling my body through the crack with unbelievable ease.

Not once did I feel claustrophobic or cornered. The innards of this tree were massive and clearly misleading from the outside. The majority of the core had decomposed, leaving an empty moist shell, coated with a gloopy film of mildew and habituated by hundreds of perky little glow worms.

Like burning chartreuse candles, they warmly lined the inside of the dampened walls, lighting my route and making it apparent that Baxley was nowhere to be seen.

I could sense their inquisitive googly eyes on my mammoth misplaced body, no doubt wondering what this towering giant happened to be doing in their glowy chamber of quietude.

With three small shuffles, I slinked through the opposite cavity and back into the outside, and whilst dusting off my hands, I stared back in amazement at the pink puffy tree I had just crept through. The realisation now dawning on me that I was, in fact, standing in front of a row of Blossom trees with a patiently perched Baxley resting on one of the picturesque twigs. And as delighted as I was to see the little flutter bug, I couldn't believe this ghastly decrepit old tree was a hidden entrance connecting 'Hags Alley' to the path of 'Blossomvale'.

It was obvious now that the corroded tree in the alley was formally a Blossom tree, but time and neglect had left it lifeless. The lack of daylight had destroyed its beauty, leaving it in tatters. As sad as that was, it made for a great decoy in persuading nosey intruders that there was nothing else to be seen here. You would never have known 'Blossomvale' existed. I mean who in their right mind takes it upon themselves to slither their body into an old tree!

For one, who would have thought you could physically fit, and two, there's the little issue of using your common sense to know you're not actually going to get anywhere once inside.

'What type of person', I hear you say, could believe that this nonsense would lead you straight into a hidden world...

...well me, that's who!

Twelve

'BLOSSOMVALE'

I was finally here in Kalen's secret hideaway and what's more, I knew exactly how I had gained entry. I was beginning to think there was a hint of the old hag about him, but now I knew it was simply a case of pushing me through a diseased old tree! I did have a tendency to let my imagination run riot, but I'm glad in this scenario I wasn't going crazy and Kalen wasn't a witch!

Willingly, I spun around, hopeful to lock eyes with the man himself but disappointingly he wasn't there. Don't get me wrong, I wanted to say my piece, let him know I was hurting but I was also excited to see his beautiful face again. But I guess it wasn't to be. It wasn't fate, and there was no closure to be had here.

It looked like it was just me, Baxley and the tranquillity of the garden, and she was just as wonderful, if not more so than I remembered. The stress I had suffered marching through 'Hags Alley' ebbed away as I breathed in my surroundings once more.

We were in early October, but you would never have guessed as the weather in 'Blossomvale' was like an idyllic summer's day. A sun trap — peculiar but most welcomed.

There was just something about 'Blossomvale', she felt like no other I had been to before. With an air of enchantment to her, it was no wonder Baxley knew about her too!

Talking of Baxley, I had made a little observation on his

small but instrumental role in getting me here.

'What?', I hear you ask.

Well…had the curious little fella purposely led me to the entrance knowing I would follow?

A butterfly…is well, a butterfly.

Surely, it's not normal for them to behave in this manner — interacting with humans of all things? Preposterous don't you think? But a little part of me couldn't help wonder if he was trying to communicate with me. Nan had always said I had an imagination inhabited by the spirit of a unicorn…so make of that what you will!

"You lured me in, Baxley, you little scamp!" I giggled.

Seemingly chuffed with himself, he eagerly flapped his wings, signalling his delight.

"Kaaalleeen!!!" I squawked. "It's me. Alanna. I just want to talk, that's all. Hear me out, and I won't bother you again. I promise," I meant it.

I had accepted that Kalen wasn't mine. He and Coral were obviously a thing, but I deserved my closure, he owed me that, and I would not leave without it!

The air was silent, no response was received, but through the corner of my eye, I captured a glimmer of movement shifting through the waterfall.

It was that rascal Baxley!

Once again — and without warning, he had darted off. But this time it was towards the fall, and stupidly, he had crashed antennae first into the billowing vertical waters.

"Baxley!!" I grimaced.

Why, oh why did he do that. There was no way his fragile wings could survive that amount of water impacting his tiny frame. Poor little mite didn't stand a chance! It was suicidal. Please be fortunate, I couldn't bear to think of him in pain or to see his dead body crumpled up like a soggy piece of toilet tissue.

I edged nearer to the rock pool, stretching my neck to catch a glimpse of my small winged friend, but instead of

Baxley, I shockingly caught sight of a blurred male figure. It was much, much larger than the flutter bug, not to mention human. It was also slightly smaller than Kalen!

It simmered behind the veil of water; his identity shielded by the lashings of liquid pounding onto the rockery. With my surroundings now compromised, I felt a little uneasy. I shouldn't be here. I needed to leave. Not wanting to hang around, I steadily began to back up, retreating towards the safety of the Blossom trees. If it wasn't Kalen, then who could it be and truth be known, I wasn't the type of person to wait around to find out.

My hands were now stretched out behind me, scrambling to identify a branch. This was my only way out, and eventually, I made contact.

I was still head-on facing the waterfall — my breathing was deep; I was petrified I would become unearthed.

I couldn't find the darn opening! Each tree was identical to the other, with little or no give to squeeze through. The deceased tree I had entered through was only visible from 'Hags Alley'. Smothered in an abundance of pink petals, it was completely unrecognisable from 'Blossomvale'.

Trapped, I froze to the spot, veiled by a sizeable amount of foliage which had slightly obscured my vision. I held my breath as the figure drifted through the fall.

I gasped.

Not in terror but in ecstasy as his body took one hell of a hard lashing. The translucent flow rained down upon his edible skin, cascading over his tight, toned and tanned torso.

I wallowed in pleasure as the muscles on his back tightened with the erotic touch of his fingers. They glided, gently massaging the spritz of cool aquamarine liquid through his silky wet, panther black locks. Tiny crystal droplets of fluid trickled off his chin, slipping over his supple neck and scattering across his steaming hot, hairless chest. Mmmmm, he was aesthetically pleasing to the eye.

I couldn't move...but not out of fear. In fact, I was fixated with that body, it was top-to-toe perfection.

Forgoing my branches, I inched further and further towards the male in the fall. I hankered for more, desperate to identify the owner of this scorching hot chassis, but before I could do any such thing — his body stiffened.

His hands rigidly gripped onto his scalp — aware he was being intrusively watched.

Slowly, he released his grip, allowing his arms to fall to his sides with ease. Calmly he swivelled his body in a clockwise motion, surveying the area before stopping dead in his tracks.

Positive eye contact had been made.

Those big blues of his were hard to come by. I knew them, how could I not.

"Zach!" I choked.

I was not mentally prepared to see his face staring back at me, nor did I think for one second he was the owner of that physique! I had always imagined that underneath his clothes he would have a pretty impressive bod, but I didn't expect it to be this mouthwatering.

I diverted my eyes, embarrassed he had caught me ogling him. I had no words either. I was utterly speechless, and the situation was only becoming increasingly more awkward with every silent second that passed. I hoped he would make the first move, and thankfully for me, he did.

"Allie? What are you doing here?" he questioned in a baffled tone.

What was I doing here? More like what was he doing here and at 'Blossomvale' of all places!

"I, I, I shouldn't be here...I better go," I blushed, not wanting to argue the point.

I twisted on the spot and quickly aimed for my getaway route, that's if I could ever find the opening of those blasted Blossom trees.

"Woah, Allie, wait a second…Allie wait!!" he demanded.

I couldn't. I had to leave. I was far too flustered to look at his bare skin any longer.

"Look, if you're intent on going, can you at least do me this one favour?" he cheekily requested.

Although I had my back to him, he very much had my attention. I just couldn't bring myself to look him in the eye or anywhere else for that matter. He was right though, I did owe him one, after all, he had caught me unmistakably perving over him. I had to make amends, to flip this shameful situation on its head and if a favour was what it would take, then a favour it was.

"Go on…what can I do for you?" I obliged, rotating towards him with eyes still half closed.

"Open those pretty browns and pass me a towel will you," he grinned.

I nodded and headed towards the neatly folded towel nestled on the shimmering rock meters from his feet. There was no question about it, he was definitely in reaching distance and more than capable of picking it up himself.

Still unable to look at him, I sheepishly covered my eyes and fumbled towards the target, using my left hand as a towel detector.

"Oh, Allie, open your eyes and grab it will you! I'm wearing shorts, but you already know that…don't you," he winked.

I couldn't help but smirk. He did have the shortest and tightest of black pants on. They left little to the imagination…but I wasn't complaining.

"Here!"

I thrust the towel at his torso, making sure my eyes didn't linger for far too long, but truth be told, I couldn't resist one more sneaky peak.

Zach was absolutely full of himself, and I could tell he was rollicking in my blushes as he sensually rubbed the towel firmly over his body, leaving no skin untouched. His eyes smouldered as he kept my gaze, not letting go — not even when he made his way off the rocks.

"Give me your hand, I won't bite…unless you let me," he purred.

I felt a shot of excitement burn through my stomach as I placed my hand in his.

The towel was now loosely rolled and resting over his shoulder, and despite wearing nothing but a pair of shorts, he was in control and owning this next to nothing look.

With Zach leading the way, he confidently pulled me towards a bed of vibrant swaying bluebells.

"Come," he prompted, perching himself down and insisting I sit with him.

I did what he asked, but this wasn't going to be one of our friendlier chit-chats, this was serious. I needed answers.

"What are you really doing here, Zach?" I asked directly.

I thought it best to be straightforward and not to sugarcoat the matter.

"Isn't it obvious? I'm having a wash," he sarcastically said.

"Be serious," I bit.

"Not that I need your permission, but a girl once brought me here. This place is dear to me, why wouldn't I want to come?" he curtly responded.

"Well, why were you suspiciously concealing yourself behind that waterfall?" I fired back.

"What's with the inquisition?" he uncomfortably laughed.

I had hit a nerve but why? It was a simple question that required a simple answer.

"If you must know, I was stripping down to the bare essentials and being the cautious chap I am, I chose to leave my clobber behind the fall. There are some unsavoury characters about these days, Allie, and they wouldn't think twice about nicking another man's threads. It's the only reason I keep my pants on. Plus, I didn't quite fancy walking back in the altogether now. So, where better to hide them than behind the fall, no one's going to get a soaking for a quick laugh now, are they," he explained.

"I didn't think anyone else knew about this place apart from me and...and..." I stalled.

"You and...who?" he probed.

"Oh, just someone I used to know, it doesn't matter, you wouldn't know them. I'm sorry for behaving a little weird. You being here just startled me, that's all," I comforted.

His actions made perfect sense, and he did have every right to be here too. Maybe this wasn't as hidden as I was led to believe, as after all, Coral knew about it, didn't she!

Wait...please, please tell me that Coral was not the 'girl', the girl that had introduced him to 'Blossomvale'! She, after all, was the only other female that I actually knew of that had been here. It would be just my luck that she had sunken her claws into Zach too.

"Fancy a dip? It's gorgeous inside and who knows, it might help you to loosen up a bit!" he teased, distracting me from my hideous thoughts.

"You've only just got out, Zach," I replied.

He had some front speaking to me like that. I knew he was only playing, but he didn't know me. I could be fun, spontaneous even but only if the occasion called for it.

"Well, I was only halfway through my soak when I caught you taking a cheeky peek at the goods. Anyway, you can never be too clean, perhaps you can scrub my back..." he dirtily grinned.

Zach whipped the towel off from around his neck.

Arms poised, he dived straight off the translucent rock and into the inviting cyan pool which lay beneath the crashing waves of the foam inducing fall.

Startled by his impulsive exit, I jumped to my feet, balancing myself as near to the rocks edge as possible. I just about caught sight of Zach's figure as his beautiful body wriggled through the flowing sea-green waters below, before disappearing out of sight.

"Zach?" I called, concerned.

The waves of turquoise liquid shimmered with every bounce of sunlight, but Zach who was submerged within was nowhere to be seen.

"Zach, you can stop showing off now, ok!" I barked.

One minute turned into two, two into three, then on the agonising fifth minute, he seamlessly broke through the watery surface. I couldn't hold my breath for longer than twenty seconds, let alone several minutes. He was either sub-human or a fish!

Now, if I hadn't of been living this moment for real, I could have sworn to you that what happened next was like a scene from a manufactured fizzy drink advert!

Zach's honed body pierced through the pool, olive abs rippling in true slo-mo fashion. He broodily rolled his head back, flicking his saturated strands to one side whilst inhaling a steamy gulp of cherry scented air. Who knew the effortless act of breathing could look so succulent!

For the finale, he ruggedly ran his manly hands through his model locks, casting the remaining drops of joy into my overheated direction.

"Might as well join me now?" he laughed.

His smile was breathtaking, he was fun and playful — I couldn't take my eyes off him.

I was beginning to like him more than what I had initially set out to, and what I hadn't realised at the time was that while I was with him, I wasn't thinking of anyone else. So yeah, why not, it was a harmless dip, and it would probably do me the world of good.

There was, however, one tiny snag...one that needed clarifying before I would allow myself to jump into the deep end with him!

"Coral? Does that name mean anything to you, Zach?" I quizzed.

"If you're referring to her as a love interest...then no. Didn't have you down as the jealous type, Allie?" he taunted.

"No, not jealous...just wondered," I smirked.

Phew! I can't tell you how relieved I was to hear the word 'no'! That grubby mare would most certainly have had her cheap hands all over him given the chance.

Satisfied, I coyly pulled on the sleeve of my jacket. I was nervous to undress in front of him, but I needn't have fretted as before my arm could be exposed — Zach cut short his offer!

Dripping wet, he sauntered his taut body from out the pool, much to the delight of my dribbling tongue. Then, grabbing his towel, he casually dabbed his face dry before swinging the cloth back over his shoulder and heading towards the exit of Blossom trees.

Was that it? He was just going to up and leave without saying a word? Had I done something wrong? Was he offended by my naked shoulder, or was I simply too late? Had I appeared too frigid? Had he become bored with my company and decided to call it a day?

Why me? Every time I grew close to somebody I liked, they instantaneously backed off. I must unknowingly let off a scent that repels men because I was at a loss to know what else it could be!

Zach halted.

With his back facing me, he raised his arm and loosely gripped the stray Blossom branch that lingered above his head. His bicep effortlessly tensed as he smoothly held on. I could tell he was deliberating over the words he was about to voice to me, but once composed, he let go, turned around and presented himself to me.

"Allie, you're coming to this party with me, it's in under three weeks' time, no 'ifs', no 'buts'. I've been invited to go...or should I say demanded to, and if I'm suffering than there's no one else I would rather suffer with!"

I wasn't sure if I should take that as a compliment or not but either way, he had me intrigued.

"Happens to be my cousin's birthday bash and it falls on Halloween. I can take a plus one, and that plus one is going to be you," he enforced.

Well, he hardly sounded over the moon about attending this party, but one thing was for sure, he was adamant I would be going with him! There didn't seem to be any other choice but for me to say yes, and frankly I wasn't too chuffed with those odds.

Zach was coming across rather weird. The cheeky chappy I had come to know was behaving very dominant and rather unfamiliar. Not at all his usual self.

"Oh, eh thanks for the invite, Zach, but erm, I'm not sure about going. Parties aren't really my thing," I announced.

Zach's face disappointedly stared back at me as I politely refused his offer. I say offer but offer it was not. It was more of an order, and he wasn't winning any brownie points by acting in this overpowering manner.

He said nothing in response to the blow I had batted, and I felt it my responsibility to fill this now uncomfortable silence.

"It's not that I don't want to go with you, I really am grateful you would think of me, but I'm simply too shy. I mean, I doubt I will know anyone that's going for a start. I don't know your cousin, and I would feel unbelievably awkward. I also have absolutely nothing nice to wear!" I whined.

"Well that's a shame as I too am incredibly shy and you should see my wardrobe, it's dire," he mocked.

Trust Zach to try and change my mind by messing around with my burdens. I knew very well that he was not shy. He was bold and fearless. A quality I desired, not only in myself but in a man.

"I'm certain you'll find something worthy to wear, besides I refuse to take no for an answer. I'm picking you up at 7pm, be ready, Miss Pickering," he maintained.

With his words issuing the final say so, he fired me a saucy wink, released his hold on the branch and strolled straight out of 'Blossomvale'.

"Zach, what about your...your clothes!" I hollered, my

voice trailing off as he disappeared through the curtain of pink petals.

He had left 'Blossomvale' in nothing but a pair of cheek skimming pants. Surely he would freeze out there!

I knew he was different. He was not like Kalen, Billy Rayner or any other boy I had come accustom too. He didn't care what people thought of him. He didn't live by the rules. He did what he wanted, and if he wanted something, he was the type of guy to go out and get it. It seemed I had no choice. I was going to the party if I liked it or not!

I plonked myself back down onto the face of the rock and frantically began to scour my thoughts for suitable attire.

Anxiety kicking in, I felt myself leaning towards a mini meltdown, when suddenly I was interrupted by a whirring buzz emanating from the fall.

"Baxley!" I rejoiced, "you're alive!"

What an awful person I was! Distracted, I had completely forgotten all about his kamikaze roll into the waterfall.

He was untouched, carefree and flitting in and out the fall like nothing had happened.

Daring, decisive and powerful — he was one hell of a flutter bug! I needed to be more like him and a little less like me, and y'know what, I wasn't going to allow Zach to call the shots here. I wasn't going to bow down to his commands, unless me, Allie Pickering, wanted to!

Thirteen

DOUBLE G

Can you believe nearly two months had flown by since I had last seen Kalen, and exactly nineteen days had dragged by since my interesting, to say the least, encounter with Zach, but hey, who was counting? It's also worth mentioning that the much-deliberated day of the Halloween party had arrived too. Now, I'm quite aware it was me who had said, 'I will determine my own decisions', but I still couldn't make up my own mind. I wasn't entirely sure if going to the party with Zach was the best idea, and I didn't have the guts to tell him otherwise.

Let's be honest, I didn't really know him and by going on this date, I could be jeopardising any possible future reconciliation with Kalen. I still hadn't had my closure with him, not heard his side of the story and jumping to conclusions was never going to help anyone. You could say I was in a right pickle with the much-needed answers not coming any time soon!

"Nan, come on, drink your tea, it's getting cold, and you know what you get like when that happens!" I warned.

If there was one thing I had learnt about Nan over the years, then it was to never serve her up a lukewarm cuppa. Jeez, the way she acted, you might as well have ripped the heads off of her prize-winning Petunias!

Joking aside, Nan was slowly worsening, it was heartbreaking to watch. She was deteriorating before me, and there was absolutely nothing I could do to stop it. But as hard as it was to see her like this, we both knew these days would come.

"Don't be daft, dear, I've drunk every last drop!" Nan snapped.

Not wanting to make a scene, I nodded in the direction of her cup — it was important not to ignore the unmistakable facts. Nan acknowledging my nod, focused in on her cup and identified that it was indeed full to the brim.

"Oh, I must have forgot," She shrugged, keen to shake off the misunderstanding.

These situations were more common than not these days. Nan found it hard to remember the simplest of things, and what hurt the most was that she was very much aware of this. Nan, as always, swiftly changed the subject when one of these episodes occurred. You could tell she didn't want to dwell on her illness.

"Now, come on, you're here for a reason, so what's worrying you, love?" she pressed.

Trust Nan to think about others over and beyond herself. She had always been the same, putting my trivial life's dramas before her own sizeable troubles.

"Nothing, Nan, nothing at all," I murmured.

"Alanna don't play dumb. I can tell something's bothering you. I'm your flesh and blood. I know when something's wrong. Stop postponing and tell me so I can help," she ordered.

She had her own problems. I didn't want to burden her with mine too!

"I know I'm not much use to you these days, but please let me do this one thing. I want to help," she pleaded.

Her eyes twinkled with tears of unsolvable sadness. All she wanted was to feel like she still had a purpose in life, that she was still capable of being needed by someone. I wanted to tell her, I really did but being absorbed in my own self-pity — I couldn't. If I'm honest, I didn't want to have to drag the sorry saga up again. I didn't want to have to explain how sick and confused inside I felt. How my emotions were boomeranging left, right and centre. When all I really wanted to do was bury them 6ft deep.

This quandary wasn't for Nan. This dilemma was for me to figure out and by myself. I was failing her, that I know, but I couldn't open up my heart to her. For if I did, I wasn't sure I would be able to close it again.

"Nan, I said I'm fine, can we not just enjoy our day together? We don't see much of each other these days, do we? And I don't want to have to keep justifying to you that I'm ok. I would rather us have a giggle like we used to, rather than making a plight out of nothing."

I had to be harsh, it was the only way to cease this conversation from escalating further.

"Ok, dear, if you're sure you're fine and you say you're fine then that's good enough for me," she conceded.

Guilt washed over me like a never-ending tide, but I knew in my heart it was for her own good as well as mine. She didn't need my worries, any more than I wanted to have to air them to her.

"Here, let me take our tea out into the garden. It's a beautiful fresh day, we may as well enjoy it while it lasts," I smiled.

The sun had broken through the last remaining dreary clouds, leaving the rays to beam brightly down upon us, and although we were in late October, it felt like a delightful spring morning.

Come rain or shine, Nan had always obtained the most glorious of gardens and now was no different. Autumn scattered flourishes bursting with warmth clambered through her wild and jungly haven. Mythical garden ornaments mischievously peeked through sharp blades of steep grass, adding intrigue and character to her peculiar little enclosure. But as pretty as this all was, Nan's garden was far removed from its flawless days. Needless to say, it wasn't only her health that had declined.

Back then, there would be no needle of grass out of place and absolutely no scraggly weed or shrivelled flower on show. She took immense pride in maintaining the garden to her high standards, which was also a huge reflection on herself.

Today though, the garden was looking a little unkept, a little overgrown and dare I say a little haggard. Many of her flowers were gradually fading away and as much as it pained me to say it, Nan was sadly heading in the same direction.

Snugly wrapped up in my woollies, I perched myself on to Nan's dark green, ornate iron bench. Unlike Nan and her garden, this seat was exactly the same now as it was back then. Cloaked in heavenly wisteria, it was the perfect hideaway. All I had to do was take a pew, close my eyes and I would be deep in thought, transported back to memories gone by, reflecting on the way things used to be.

I smiled with affection, reminiscing of the glamorous and fun-loving Nan I used to know as she swirled past my eyes in a merry-go-round of past recollections. I wished I could return to those days when I had no care in the world. When Dad was still with us. Mum was...well, Mum. The one she should have been before Dad had died, and Nan was free from this evil, self-eroding illness. I felt the lump rising in my throat, attempting to choke me with its constricting presence.

"You hungry, dear?" Nan chirped.

The interruption of her frail voice was well timed — suppressing my plugged throat, she snapped me back into reality.

In her hands, she was holding two piping hot bowls, piled high with sticky toffee pudding.

"You bet!" I coughed, clearing any excess blockage.

It felt just like the good old days — cake, tea and a well-needed natter.

Before Nan was diagnosed, I would regularly visit her, spending hours upon hours over the spring and summer months in her neatly trimmed garden. With a refreshing brew and a helping of scrumptious cake, we would waste the days away together.

Nan handed me a fork, her weary hand shaking as she parked herself next to me. In union, we took a mouthful of the squidgy sweet stuff. Our faces automatically filling with ecstasy as our taste buds revelled in the blissful punch of the caramelized gooeyness.

"Ummmmm," we both chorused, following up with a satisfying, "ahhh."

Nan didn't have to say another word for me to know how content she was right now. I could see that just by being here together, in the moment, meant more to her than she would ever let on.

"Nan?" I murmured.

"Yes, love?"

"Erm," I wavered.

"Come on, spit it out, tell me what's been troubling you?"

"Well, there's this lad I kind of know, and well, up until recently we've become quite friendly. We're nothing more than friends, but it just so happens he's asked me to a Halloween party tonight," I fessed.

"So, what's the problem?" Nan asked inquisitively.

"Well I want to go, I do but I also want to be the one in control of this situation. This boy is the type to always get what he wants, and I don't want to come across as easy or a pushover. Perhaps, I should play a little hard to get? Urgh, I really don't know what to do for the best. It would do me good if anything to get out and enjoy myself, let my hair down, but..."

"But what?" Nan questioned.

"But...but he's not Kalen, is he!" I groaned.

I know! I know what you're thinking! Here she goes again! You must reckon I'm mad, but I simply couldn't get that boy out of my head — trust me I've tried!

"Well, it's quite straightforward, isn't it?" Nan yapped.

"Is it?" I asked.

"Yes! Don't go," she calmly advised.

"Don't? Yeah, you're probably right, I wouldn't be much company anyway," I agreed.

Oddly, Nan wasn't trying to persuade me otherwise. She was very much on board with my decision, which if you knew my nan, was not like her at all.

"Yeah course, Allie don't go, he can take another girl, can't he! Pretty sure there's plenty more where you came from, no doubt lining up for him to choose from!" Nan quipped.

Ahh — there she was! There's the Nan I knew and loved! Here was little old me thinking Nan was in agreement with my way of thinking, but in reality, she was telling me how it would be if I decided not to go.

I really didn't want Zach to take another girl. The thought of him flirting with another made my stomach churn. But it was clear I wasn't fully over Kalen, even though it hadn't really started between us in the first place. It just felt too soon to be out with another man.

"Who is this Kalen anyway?" Nan muttered, she looked bemused.

"Nan, you know who Kalen is, it's that lad that visited me on my birthday. He gave me the four-leaf clover, you remember, right?" I reminded.

"Erm...I think so, oh...oh yes, yes I do remember him... nice boy," she replied.

Bless Nan's heart for trying, but we both knew she couldn't remember him.

Her eyes beamed as she watched their meaty yet sprightly bodies wiggle around untroubled in a blissful sea of hornwort and duckweed. She had eight vibrant goldfish in total and looked upon each and every one of them as her babies. They were her pride and joy, her reason for waking up in the morning — her escape from reality.

Nan was upset and irritated. Distressed that Kalen hadn't registered on her radar. But being as proud as she was, she would not allow herself to crumble, and as a distraction, focused intently on her carefree slippery offspring.

"Aren't they the sweetest, Allie. They swim around, day after day on a continuous loop with no cares given. Each day I visit them. I speak to them. I show them affection, and although I know them, they don't know me," she somberly said.

"With a memory lasting three pitiful seconds, I can never get too close to them. To them I'm just a stranger. I suppose you can say I'm a bit like them these days," she added.

A tear rolled down her soft cheek as she reviewed her own mental state. It was ironic that her memory should evade her in such a similar way.

"Allie, go to the party, will you! Sometimes things happen for a reason. Call it luck or call it fate, but this may be your very reason, don't you think?" she urged, briefly pausing before continuing. "Think what you will, but I strongly believe our paths have already been carved out for us. Maybe you were always meant to meet this Zach..." she convincingly added.

Hmmm, perhaps Nan had a point, but still, the uncertainty within me began to raise its ugly head again.

"Could it be possible that you and this Kalen were not meant to be? Did you not consider that this boy was removed from out of your path in order for Zach to enter it?" Nan confidently suggested.

"Oh, Nan, you do put forward a strong case, and I can see sense in what you have alluded to. I just wish I had your strength in knowing what to do for the best," I puffed.

"You'll know," she smiled.

Well, she obviously knew more than what I did, as I hadn't even concluded my own decision yet.

The thing about Nan was that she was a highly spiritual woman, with an ethos of what's meant to be will be. Her belief was that everyone was born with a map, the route already plotted, thus being the life we would lead. Us as individuals simply have to follow the path given, grasping or rejecting the opportunities that are presented to us on our personalised journey.

We could not change what we were gifted, but there would always be a small minority unhappy with their route. They would rebel, deviate from the plan, making the wrong decisions, time and time again. For the rest of us, well we were here to learn a lesson and that is why the route could sometimes be a rocky one. We would meet and lose people for reasons unknown, but there would always be an underlying cause for it, even if it wasn't clear in this lifetime. Some people would enter our lives for a short period, and then there were others that would stay until the end of our days.

Personally, I wasn't so sure about Nan's theory on life. I mean, I couldn't imagine she was overly chuffed with the thought of ending her days by forgetting how they had even started!

In the days, weeks, months and years after Dad had passed, Mum would regularly drop me off in the evenings at Nan's. As you are aware by now, Mum would be receiving her fix of intoxication and having me in tow was not the done thing. Although I hated how Mum behaved, I did at least respect her for having the decency to ensure I was cared for when she was incapable of doing so.

Usually and without warning, I would be dropped around Nan's with my sleepover kit and 'Rusty', my trusted teddy. 'Rusty' was given to me by Dad before he died. I first saw him at our local fete, where he was squashed into an old cardboard box with a couple of dusty books and a worn-out jigsaw puzzle.

The lady occupying the stall was in her early twenties. She was wearing a short-frayed denim skirt with an embellished bright pink tank top. Her face was caked in layers upon layers of thick orange makeup. Her hair was long, bleached and painfully scraped onto her crown. Her bright blue eyeshadow, brown lipstick and heavy lip liner combo still haunts me to this day!

She was excruciatingly chewing on a large stick of gum and bopping her head back and forth as she listened to the tunes blaring from her iPod.

"Oh, hiya," she spat.

The girl was so absorbed in her music, she had failed to see me fixated on her teddy for the last five minutes!

"Three quid and he's yours," she declared as she brutally yanked his fragile body from out the crumpled box he was stuffed into.

With outstretched arms, I took a hold of him. Adoringly squeezing him up close to my face as I absorbed in his cute button nose and well-worn ears.

"He needs a quick wash around the lugs but other than that he's in perfect condition," she mumbled as she continued to smack her lips together with every irritating chew of the gum.

Well he was hardly perfect. He was in desperate need of a new eye and the stitching from the seam on his back had unravelled. Filthy dirty from years of non-appreciation, I knew I had to have him! Unlike her, it didn't matter how old I was, I would never get rid of him.

"Where have you been, young lady!! I've been looking high and low for you. I thought I'd lost you! Don't you ever wander off again without me!" he raged.

That was Dad. He came from out of nowhere.

Flustered and agitated, he charged towards me with tiny balls of sweat dripping from his forehead.

Dad happened to be purchasing me a foot-long hot dog when he unexpectedly became distracted by an old school friend. Engrossed in conversation, he neglected to catch me tiptoeing off.

"Sorry, Dad," I whimpered.

I knew I had given him a shock, but I was an inquisitive child, and as angry as he was, it wouldn't last. It was just the thought of losing me that had ignited his temper.

"Erm...Daddy, have you three pounds I can borrow please?"

I clasped my hands together, tilted my head to one side and gave him the old pleading puppy dog eyes.

Hmmm, no joy, it hadn't worked, which was a first for me!

Dad was still a little ruffled by my disappearing act, and it was evident it would take more than my angelic little girl routine to win him over.

"I'll wash up for a week, if I can just have this teddy bear. Pleeaaase, Daddy!!!" I begged.

Dad who was now softening, carefully took the teddy from my palms for a closer inspection, "Oh no, darling, you're not having this piece of old tat!" he sniffed.

The girl unimpressed by Dad's rude remarks, tutted and immediately snatched the teddy from his judgmental grasp — giving us the cue to move along.

I was devastated to be leaving the squidgy unloved mess behind, but Dad didn't care. He dragged me away from the stall regardless, informing me I had no idea what muck that scuzzy old teddy would be harbouring.

I tried to muffle my cries by shoving the warm doughy bread into my mouth, but Dad had already noticed my tears and ushered me to one side.

"Now look here, you're not having that bear. It will be full of fleas and grime!"

Dad was stern, informing me that the bear was that grubby it resembled the colour of rust!

"You don't know where he's been, Allie, and I'm not prepared to let my special little girl get sick because I gave into her non-essential demands."

175

With those final words, he kissed me squarely on the forehead and took me straight home.

∞∞∞

Dad left for work that evening and I cried myself to sleep. Never had I wanted something as much as I wanted that bear, but then again, I was yet to meet Kalen!

Eventually, morning arrived, and my eyes were still bloodshot and puffy from the tears I had shed. It was only when I lifted my head that I noticed a lonely object resting on the base of my bed. Panting with excitement, I bolted upright — quick to realise what it was that was staring back at me.

Dad consumed with remorse had taken a detour before work, returning to the stall and collecting the second-hand teddy for me. Much to his joy, I shrilled with excitement at seeing the lengths he had gone to in order to make me happy.

I wasn't aware at the time, but Dad had been waiting all morning for me to stir, pacing up and down the landing for this very moment.

After the warmest of cuddles, it was clear that all was forgiven.

Dad suggested we call him 'Rusty', an affectionate nod to the state we had found him in. I couldn't agree more, it was a fitting name for the newest member of our family.

"No more guilt trips, Allie," chuckled Dad.

"Of course," I nodded, but it wasn't the first, and sadly it would definitely not to be the last time I badgered Dad's conscience.

∞∞∞

It had been a very long time since I had slept overnight at Nan's, but whenever I visited, I was always filled with a sense of nostalgia.

Nan was an only child, had lived in the same abode since she was a young girl of twelve. When her mum and dad passed away, she inherited the family home. She lived happily with my grandad Horace, building a life and raising her son there. Nan had always vowed to never part with the only home she ever knew.

The Pickering residence was an intimate and cosy pictur-esque thatched cottage that was endlessly scented with the burning sweet smell of Jasmine. Lit candles flickered through-out the quaint lilac interior, adding a touch of romance and warmth. Feathered dream captures tenderly dangled from window to window — wind chimes tinkling from room to room.

Legendary creatures, from glamorous mermaids to in-fatuating unicorns hung from thin pieces of rope on the vacant spaces of her extravagant violet papered walls. Dainty fairy figurines adorned her buffered shelves, and golden celestial cherubs silently prayed on her whitewashed mantelpiece.

Nan's home was a heaven-sent haven that single-hand-edly made my childhood come alive.

If you asked me what my favourite part of staying at Nan's was, then without fail, I would tell you it was her ability to conjure up a spellbinding bedtime story on demand.

I was lucky enough to sleep in Nan's spare room, which hosted a spectacular gold four poster bed. It was humongous compared to my wafer-thin body! And the best part? Well, it had to be its white lace canopy — draped from post to post. It was fit for a princess!

Nan would nestle me and Rusty in a rainbow of rich silky pillows and mink faux fur blankets. It was here that her stor-ies of enchantment and fantasy would evolve and capture my imagination for years to come. Her mind was a bottomless pit of magical dreams. With a vivid imagination, she would draw me in with all sorts of fairy tales, her speciality surrounding those pesky little magical folk.

However, no amount of daydreaming about those worry-free days was going to alter the impending decision that was creeping nearer and nearer my way.

Nan's matter of fact words clung within my mind, they were not going to fade away that easily, they never did.

'Don't go', she said, 'he can take another girl', she said.

Those words niggled at my skin, and she knew damn well they would! Deep down, it was the last thing I wanted to happen, but if I chanced it, then there was a high possibility it could occur. Nan had a knack of knowing how to strike at my nerves and usually, it was by pointing out the raw merciless facts.

There was no denying me and Zach had hit it off in such a short space of time, and it was clear I was feeling green-eyed from the waves of jealousy that were intermittently wafting over me. I tried to suppress the gargantuan monster from erupting, but the thought of him taking someone else other than me, did not bode well — and so it grew.

Being with Zach felt natural. He was incredibly easy to talk to, words flowed freely with us, making me feel at ease in an instant. With him, I felt he actually liked me more than just a friend. He knew me, he pursued me and he very much excited me.

Kalen, on the other hand, was a man of mystery. He was guarded about his feelings and rarely showed his emotions. I'm actually unsure if he was capable of possessing any of the key attributes Zach attained. It was time to face facts, Kalen's chance had come and gone, hadn't it?

"Yes! He had his chance, and he blew it — he blew it big time!" I loudly reassured myself.

I wasn't going to allow myself to mope around and wait for Kalen anymore. How stupid was I to think he would waste a second thinking or indeed waiting for me! Nan was equally unimpressed with me for longing for someone that didn't reciprocate the same feelings as me!

"There is no way that this *Calvin* is sulking around for

you, Allie, not like you are for him. If he was, then surely he would have come back for you by now!" she swiped.

"Kalen. It's Kalen, Nan, but you're right, of course you're right, he's not remotely bothered about me, is he! That party might not be such a bad thing after all!" I voiced loudly.

"That's my girl!" cheered Nan.

"I'll show him what he's missing alright!" I bellowed, puffing out my chest.

"That's if he's actually missing you, Allie.... How about you do this for yourself!" she warmly smiled.

There she went again with her wise words of encouragement, which she escorted with one of her contagious smiles. All she ever wanted was for me to be happy, and by offering me her simple words of wisdom, she knew she was halfway there. The rest was up to me.

Nan shakily lowered her head and proceeded to caress the bespoke antique wrap-around feather ring on her wedding finger.

"Allie, you know it's possible to love another, don't you?"

I knew that. I had plenty of time ahead of me to experience more than one love. I just didn't want to rush Kalen, especially if he happened to be the one, and as we know, I wanted my first to also be my last.

"I...erm, I..." Nan struggled to find the words to say before finally plucking up the courage to spit them out. "I once had another love. Before your Grandpa. Before I knew he even existed, but this was a long time ago now," she softly spoke.

Nan had never spoken to me about this love before, but it was obviously troubling her enough for her to feel the need to confide in me.

"You can love two men at the same time. I loved your Grandpa. I loved him dearly. I still do, but I also loved another," she added.

Nan strictly avoided any eye contact with me as she continued to lay her heart out.

"Both men loved me, and I too loved them, but they

offered such very different lives to one another."

Nan's eyes filled with heartfelt tears as she remembered with fondness the time she spent with Grandpa.

"He gave me twenty-three wonderful years. Years I will cherish for the rest of my days. I never wanted for anything with your grandpa. He truly treated me like I was his everything."

It was touching to hear my nan speak of my grandad with these strong enamoured memories, but sadly for me, my memories were scant.

I was no more than two years old when Grandad was taken. To Nan's horror, she found her husband in the back garden. Face down. Dead. Right next to her cherished pond. He died of a suspected heart attack. He was only fifty-five years young.

"He was a phenomenal husband, and I repaid him by behaving like the hideous wife I was! I treated that man badly, Allie. I was not worthy of such a devoted husband. My biggest regret though is that I never showed him how much I loved him, not once!" she whined as she refused to let another tear escape.

"Oh, Nan, don't say that! He knew, of course he knew you loved him," I reassured.

I had no idea why she was giving herself such a hard time over this, and why now of all days. I had to remind myself that Nan was sick, perhaps her illness was getting the better of her, interfering and distorting her beloved memories. I didn't believe for a second the words she was uttering were her own.

"You are and were always a wonderful wife, mother and nan. Don't you ever let me hear otherwise!" I angrily snapped.

I held Nan tightly in my arms, wishfully hoping our embrace would rupture these fictitious thoughts she was having.

"You know, I remember him today like he never went away. I don't have a photo of him, and my memories of him are profoundly vague, but when I close my eyes, I can picture him in my mind like it was only yesterday. I can't forget him, and in a way...I don't think I'm allowed too," she whimpered.

Poor Nan, she had so many photos of Grandad — shoe boxes full. She was clearly worse than I had initially thought.

"Why would you forget him? He took up a massive chunk of your life. I too miss him dearly, but hold on to the thought that one day, when the time is right, you will be reunited with him — we all will."

"No, Allie, not him, not your grandpa," she candidly revealed.

Wow! I was gobsmacked, there were no appropriate words I could splutter to respond to Nan's prodigious outburst.

"Well, say something," she pressed — the silence created an uncomfortable ambience that Nan was eager to squash.

"Who, Nan? Who are you talking about?" I questioned, still not convinced she was talking about anyone else other than my grandad.

"My first love, Allie. It was a long, long time ago, but he stole my heart, making it ever so hard to love your grandpa unconditionally — in the way that he deserved."

"Well, who was it?" I popped.

"It doesn't matter who it was, Allie. They existed. It didn't work. I married your grandpa, and there really is no more for me to say!" Nan bit, tightly slamming the back page on that story.

Realising she had already said too much, she halted the conversation, ensuring she still had the last word.

"Allie, all I'm saying is that you should go to the party, give this new boy a chance. You could be waiting a hell of a long time for *Kevin* to show."

"It's Kalen, Nan," I interrupted.

"Yes, yes Kalen...and the likelihood is he won't. Don't waste your life waiting, god knows I have. Times precious and what's more precious than your life?"

The tear that Nan tried so hard to quell, flowed fluently down her cheek, before splashing into the chilly pond below.

Fourteen

GOLD DUST

Y ou'll be chuffed to learn that me, yes little old me, your very own 'Miss hesitant pants' had at last made a flipping decisive decision. I was going to that party, and no amount of insecure thoughts or wishful thinking was going to stop me. Nan's words had struck me like a bolt out of the blue. I hadn't expected them, nor had I intended to react the way I did with them. It would be accurate to say that Nan had been conducive in the overall decision-making process here!

Now, with my mind finally made up, I had one more dilemma to face...what on earth was I going to wear? I needed to play this just right, and although I didn't know it at the moment, I would later learn that this was to be the party of the century. Invitations were like gold dust, and only the select few were blessed with one of these limited invites. This party was massively on the radar!

However, I had clearly missed the memo, as the first I had heard of this gathering was when Zach requested me as his guest.

I should be straight with you here, as I had in fact, not been invited to any party before, well, not one that didn't involve clowns or wibbly-wobbly jelly! To make matters worse, it was the fancy dress kind of party, so as you can expect, it would be adorned with a handful of scantily dressed tarts!

I needed guidance, and the only person I slightly trusted

to help me out with this little predicament, was Mollie. Her support was always valuable and as a 'Trend', she had been to her fair share of parties and would definitely be able to advise me on what *not* to wear. This type of social event was foreign to me. I had no clue of what I was letting myself in for, in fact, it was the first time I had heard of these types of tight-lipped parties ever existing!

Knock knock.

"Phew, I'm glad you're home, we need to talk!"

Rudely, I pushed my way past Mollie's flummoxed body and into her home.

"Well, in that case, you better come on in, Allie," she sarcastically chirped, whilst closing the door behind me.

Unamused, my face remained deadly serious. Mollie had always been a smart cookie and immediately realised I meant business. No words were spoken between us as she ushered me straight up to her bedroom.

∞∞∞

"Hi, Mrs White," I politely shouted.

"Good to see you, Alanna," responded Mollie's mother.

Her eyes shot up towards me, following me as I frantically sprinted up the stairs after her daughter.

Next to Mrs. White sat a small rounded boy with thick oval glasses and a face full of freckles. He peered up from behind a glorious white grand piano. His dumpy fingers swatting the keys as he eagerly strived to tinkle out a rendition of Greensleeves on the ivories.

Mollie's mother Rita or Mrs White as I preferred to call her, was a very well thought-of and respected woman of the community. She had a delightful demeanour, portraying herself as peaceful and laid back. Nothing seemed to phase her.

Since migrating from the Caribbean as a teenager, she had worked hard to carve herself out a career as a home-based music tutor and could be regularly heard teaching local children to play the piano, violin, trumpet and even the drums. I had always referred to her as Eldercrest's very own one-woman band as there wasn't an instrument she couldn't play.

Eventually, she met and fell in love with local boy Reggie White — smitten they were, and it wasn't long after that Mollie made an appearance. Ever since our births, our mothers had continued to remain the best of friends, even during Mum's inconsolable period of losing her way. Mrs. White never approved of Mum's drinking, but she never disowned her either, instead, vowing to stand by her and support her with the fight against her demons. Mum was lucky to have her; she was definitely one of those hard to come by friends.

Mrs. White was also a regular down 'The Old Crow', but she wasn't there to booze. Oh no, she was there on a work basis only, providing Mum with any instrumental back up she desired. Putting Mum's talent aside, I often thought Mrs. White bared the patience of a saint, as well as severe hearing loss to tolerate the noise pollution emitted from the majority of her pupils!

Take this young boy as a prime example of being musically thwarted. Poor Mrs. White would patiently teach, grin, suffer and critique one whole hour of musical torture, before being relieved of his presence when his parents arrived to whisk him away!

Though, she never complained or humiliated her pupils — she wasn't the type. She much preferred to display encouragement and praise.

"You coming, Allie?", called Mollie.

I must have been utterly riveted by this little man's out of tune jingling, as unbeknown to me, I had stalled mid-sprint.

Slamming the door behind me, Mollie herded me onto her diamanté encrusted chaise longue. Her boudoir was all about the glitz and glam. Big and bold, it was very different to my minimalistic, slightly beige habitat!

"Lay back, relax and divulge — let's see if I can't help!"

Mollie rammed herself onto her padded cream feathered vanity stool and began the inquisition. Though she didn't need to probe much. I willingly explained I had blagged an invite to tonight's VIP party with Zach, the lad from 'The Locust Lounge'. This, of course, was surprising news to Mollie, as for one, she was gobsmacked I was even on the guest list. And two, the last she had heard was that I was still whimpering over Kalen! She was of course over the moon to assist a novice and was euphoric to learn I was finally moving on.

"I'm a wreck, Moll! I have no physical invite, no inkling of where I'm going or who's hosting and most importantly, I have no clue of what to wear. Talk about hush-hush!"

Before I could finish my much-needed rant, Mollie rolled her head back and creased up into a burst of laughter. Why she found it so funny, I don't know. This wasn't a giggling matter; I was deadly serious.

Sitting upright in the chaise longue, I looked glumly at her, "I'm nervous! This is important. I need your advice, not your LOLs! So, are you going to help me or not?", I whined.

Mollie realising the severity of my sober plea — cleared her throat in an attempt to stifle her giggles.

She was now deadpan.

"No, you're quite right, I knew this was a matter of urgency, but it's worse than expected, it's an outright crisis!"

She was off again; she couldn't contain her snickering at the thought of my dilemma. Ok, ok, it wasn't life or death, and yes, perhaps I exaggerated the gravity of the issue, but a little bit of decorum wouldn't go amiss.

"Again, with the laughter, really?" I sighed.

"Oh, I'm sorry, I am, it's out of my system now. I promise," again she unloaded her throat, released a sly smile and proceeded to work through my problems.

"Now, these parties are extremely rare and as you know invites are hard to come by — they are exclusive! All and sundry aspire for one, but only the chosen few are selected. Put it this way, if you are a somebody then expect to find yourself there!"

"What do you have to do to be a somebody?" I quizzed.

Call me naive but it was essential for me to know the ins and outs of what I was about to walk into.

"Money plays a huge part. If you are the type to flash the cash, then you are bound to be mixing in the right types of circles. Popularity is then a given and is probably the most important factor to guarantee an invite," she proclaimed.

"Oh, I see..."

Well, I had neither riches nor adoration to my name. I wouldn't be surprised if I was turned away in repulse at the door.

"No one ever refuses an invite to one of these elite soirees. If you're fortuitous enough to receive one, then you'd be stupid not to go!"

Mollie informed me that the host, location and timing of these parties were kept a guarded secret in order to block unwanted gatecrashers from intercepting. If you were frivolous enough to divulge the party specifics with the wrong person, then you forfeited your right to attend. According to Mollie, no one ever did divulge!

"You know when one of these parties are on the horizon, as word spreads like a contagious disease. If you're on the list, then the message will get to you one way or another. The conventional methods are so last year, gone are the days of the paper-based and face to face invitations! No, at the very least, you should expect an anonymous text or email with the subject, date and venue.

Hosts will go to risible lengths to keep their shindig top secret and to ensure only the right people are invited. Think big! We're talking message in a bottle, pigeon carriers, sky writings and billboard notifications. I've even heard hidden messages have been advertised in local papers. Lipstick scrawls have been discovered on mirrors and my uttermost favourite were the invites drawn on steamy shower doors," Mollie excitedly spat.

She went on to tell me that even if you weren't invited, you knew it was forthcoming. You only had to walk through the streets of Eldercrest to stumble upon several smatterings of girls — whispering in huddled corners. They were most likely in receipt of their invite and discussing their selection of saucy outfits.

Then there were the lone wolves! These individual young men or women would locate their target, casually slipping a folded piece of paper into their unsuspecting palms. No eye contact made; no words spoken as both parties involved carried on about their business. The odd beep of a text or a knowing smile would alert you to another notified guest.

As you can see, verbal comms was pretty much a no-no. It all sounded absurdly cryptic, and if you ask me was way over the top. There really was no need for all this palaver.

"C'mon then, did a flying pink pig deliver your gold-plated invite?" I scoffed.

"No, Allie. It seems my invite got lost en route. Turns out I'm not as popular as you these days," she chortled, with a slight hint of envy spitting from her tone.

Well strictly speaking, neither was I!

Fifteen

BUTTONS, RAGS AND FAIRY TALES

Y ou may have guessed by now that I wasn't the sort of girl who owned a stupendous stash of fancy dress outfits and a myriad of novelty accessories. I didn't buy into the whole dress up game, never had, never would, but typically, now was the time I wished I at least owned a pair of bristly kitten ears.

Never had I needed to peruse the rails of extraordinary, outdated or outlandish costumes before. I didn't have the first hunch as to who I should go as, or what would be considered as acceptable attire. Besides, I begrudged having to splash out money on something I was only ever going to wear the once.

I mulled over the possibility of challenging myself to create a costume from the odd bits and bobs that were lying around the house. I was no designer and creativity wasn't my strongest point. If anything, my mind was lacking in the imagination department when it came to the needle and thread.

So, I sat there, spending what felt like an hour ruminating over what I could rip, sew and stick together, when eureka! It suddenly came to me! Not only was it genius but it was cost effective too.

I could utilize an old disused bed sheet, cut a couple of holes for eyes and voilà, your very own budget ghost! Yes, it wasn't the most attractive of outfits, but it was the best I could muster up in the few hours I had left.

All I had to do now was to source a bed sheet that would

go unnoticed. The last thing I wanted to do was to chop up one of Mum's finest Egyptian cotton sheets — she would hit the roof if I did!

With a cunning plan firmly implanted in mind; I heaved the rickety old wooden staircase down from the loft hatch and clambered on in. The loft wasn't the most pleasant of places to hang around in, and the only reason I had ever ventured up there in the past, was out of requirement more than anything.

In this particular case, I was on the hunt for the old wooden junk trunk. From what I remembered, it held a random assortment of bedding, buttons and ribbons. A collection accumulated from years of hoarding.

Mum downright refused to chuck any of these items away, as she always said that one day they would come in handy. It was comical really as Mum hated clutter. The chances of her ever needing any of this toot were questionable, but as they say, out of sight, out of mind.

This place was dusty, dark and damp with a strong intense waft of mildew. It was exactly how I remembered it! Corner-to-corner full of gruesome cobwebs and crawling with beastly boggled-eyed bugs. Sneaking through the loft gave me a serious case of the willies and the sooner I was out, the better!

Now, where was that light cord?

I fumbled around blindly, searching in the black....

'Bingo!'

Cord detected and engaged.

Chink!

The bulb pinged, flushing the enclosed space with a barely-there but much welcomed glow.

Relieved, I persevered on in pursuit of the trunk, which

luckily for me was not the smallest of items and was identified within seconds. With trunk located, I used the back of my sleeve to dust away the dirt — dirt that had been forgotten and left to collect over the years.

The trunk was a 19th-century antique, full of rustic charm, crafted from pine and enriched with a beautiful scenic carving. It was a delightful piece that was regrettably locked away in a depressing environment.

Conscious of time, I regained my focus on the job at hand — immediately diving into the oversized trunk and rummaging through the clumps of odds and sods.

To my surprise, there was nothing at all that would be suitable, not even a dingy old moth-bitten bed sheet. Instead, what I did find was not to be expected and quite the game changer....

I slammed the trunk lid shut, crumpling to the floor in a deflated and unsettled state. With my head resting in-between my knees, I pulled my body in tightly. How could she! She wasn't fit to call herself a mother. I can't believe she had been spinning me a sick lie for all these years!

There never was a chest full of tat. It was just an excuse for her dirty little cover-up.

That woman had looked me dead in the eyes and sworn she had burned Dad's belongings. She said she couldn't live with them under her roof, acting as a constant reminder of the man she had loved and lost.

I had trusted her profusely, I had sympathised and I had understood why she did what she did, but what twaddle that turned out to be! If my own mother could lie to me, then who the hell could I really trust?

All this time the trunk was hiding the most beautiful memories of Dad. Memories I could have called upon when times were hard. They were not a box full of buttons like I had been wrongly fed. With my tears in excess, I couldn't pretend I was ok with this — behaving like I hadn't just seen his 'stuff'. I had no choice but to revisit the trunk.

Kneeling myself in front of the wooden box of lies, I threw back the lid and peered in. I grabbed the first item within reaching distance, which happened to be Dad's prized turtleneck jumper. I squeezed it tightly, glued my eyes shut and imagined Dad was with me, wrapping his warm protective arms around me. I burrowed my nose into the moist fabric, hoping his scent would be as prominent as it was back when he was alive.

I spluttered.

It smelt utterly foul, like a bag of rotten old potatoes. I threw the fusty jumper to one side and sifted through the trunk some more. I picked up all sorts of objects — from his favourite dog chewed book — to his leather strapped watch — to the last valentines card he sent Mum.

"Oh, Dad," I wept.

I would surrender decades of my life if only to hold his hand one more time. Maybe Mum had unknowingly done me a favour by hiding his possessions, as now I had them, I wanted him back.

It was no good, I had to stop wishing for him. He was gone, and I had to come to terms with that. I had to take my mind off him and promptly. I couldn't venture down that cruel emotional road, not again and the only other person I could think of at this moment in time was Zach. As cold as that was, it was the only way I could stop myself from sinking. I could not allow myself to fall back within the miserable, empty existence that I had only of late escaped from.

Slamming the trunk lid shut, I coldly diverted my attention on tonight's party.

I wondered what Zach would be wearing? No doubt it was something of hideous taste, maybe a lurid gargoyle or a grotty gremlin outfit. He was a bit of a joker and appeared very confident – it was something I could imagine him doing.

Hang on, it probably wouldn't matter if I had a fancy dress outfit or not, as his friends were unlikely to notice me next to him anyway. Still, if I didn't join in, I would feel like I was letting him down by not adhering to the dress code.

Oh, you know what, the best thing for both of us would be is for me to pull out.

Crouching glumly up against the trunk, I desperately attempted to string a credible excuse together. One that I would be able to spout to Zach.

Knock Knock.

"Balls!" I cursed.

My thoughts had been interrupted by the loud sound of hammering against the front door. Mum was out walking Jed, which left me all alone, and I wasn't exactly in the quickest of situations to open the door. Though I did do my utmost to safely charge out the loft exit and race through two sets of stairs.

Almost out of breath, I grabbed the silver handle and swung open the front door, "sorry it took so long," I gasped, trying to catch my breath.

It was too late.

Whoever it was, had given up waiting and gone. Just as well really, as I was in no fit state to talk! I was panting like I had just run a marathon. I needed a timeout and leant myself up against the door frame for support.

Bowing my head in exhaustion, I caught sight of something from the corner of my eye.

Sitting pretty on the welcome mat was a glossy black gift box. It was tied together with a satin silver ribbon, so large it smothered the box underneath.

Gingerly, I leant down and snatched the parcel with both hands. No one had ever left a present on the doorstep for me before. In truth, the only meaningful gift I had ever received from a boy was of Kalen's four-leaf charm.

Must be for Mum, maybe it was from one of her repulsive admirers, she had many from 'The Old Crow' and not the type you wanted to call daddy!

Nevertheless, I twisted over the accompanying tag and softly read the words out loud.

"Allie, spread your wings, love Z."

Shut up! Was this gift really for me?

This was a first, and not wanting to share this moment with anyone else, I immediately whammed the front door shut.

∞∞∞∞

Laid out on my duvet, it was begging to be unwrapped.

I took my time, not wanting to ruin the suspense. I felt special, appreciated and I didn't want this feeling to ever end, but realistically, I couldn't hold it off any longer and so I ripped the bow clean off!

With the face of the black box now exposed, I slowly ran my palm across its glossy surface, before uncontrollably wrenching it away from its attention-consuming cardboard base.

"Oh my," I gushed in utter awe, as I nimbly lifted the contents.

In my hand, I held what could only be described as a magical fairy-tale in a dress — a fantastical OTT piece that had willingly unravelled its flowing full-length to me.

A two-piece — shaped with a detachable open-front, floaty and floor-skimming black tulle skirt. Which was dreamily swaddled over a ruffled thigh-length layer of super-soft black silk and lace. Gripped at the hips, it was affixed to an overlapping woodlandesque bustier, that was created from a plumy cover of overlapping autumnal Fern, Maple and Hawthorn leaves. Each leaf splayed towards the birds above, teasing them to nest within their roasted medley of aubergine, pumpkin and sprout-hued foliage.

Zach had even gone to the trouble of setting aside a

pair of matching rose-gold stilettos! These 'killer heels' were wrapped in a single stem of aureate ivy, with the smooth cap of the heel smothered in a handful of gilded Silver Birch leaves. And if that wasn't enough to leave you speechless—then wait, there's more!

Inside the box was one more piece: a circular wired meshed disc with a skinny silver loop on either side.

Fascinated, I tugged the inviting hoops together — the folded metal arrangement automatically twisting open to reveal a huge pair of spiky black, pearlescent glittered wings.

They were huge — and spectacularly realistic-looking!

I wasn't normally one for swishy girly dressy things, but this ensemble was out of this world. It was like no other fancy dress outfit I had ever seen before. It was far from average — it was breathtaking! And more than perfect for tonight's do.

Zach or should I say Z had gone out of his way to make tonight happen and had given me no plausible reason to pull out. I really was attending this party if I liked it or not, and secretly, I kind of did.

Sixteen

REVELATIONS

She popped her head into the bedroom, her eyes welling up like an overfilled dam, almost bursting at the brim. No words were spoken, just a quick nod of the head as a sign of approval.

Nan had been pottering around upstairs for the last half an hour when she clocked me busily preparing myself for to-night's party. She couldn't resist a proper gander and took the opportunity to have a little peep in.

"Perfect timing," I chimed.

Nan had tiptoed in at the precise moment to witness me clipping her beautiful aged necklace lovingly around my youthful neck.

"Time for a cup of tea I think..." she said, muttering to herself as she scarpered off. Quite clearly, refusing to hang around.

Although the necklace had been gifted to me, you could sense it held a serious amount of sentimental value to her. She held it dearly within her heart, and even being in the same room was enough to potentially breach the dam. So, she left.

Nan was over for a helping of dinner — bangers and mash were on the menu. This hearty warmer was one of her most favourable dishes. She couldn't resist the offer! Plus, Mum was working a night shift at the pub and had collared her into sleeping over. She wanted to make sure that somebody was at home and on hand if any problems derived from my first proper party. In my eyes, I was old enough at the age of eighteen not to need a babysitter, but if by being here made Nan feel needed, then where was the harm in that.

Alone in my room, I swirled around in circles, swishing the dress from side-to-side as I admired myself in the full-length mirror.

Borrowing Mum's crimpers, I had fastidiously crinkled random sections of hair before dusting with her stash of golden powdery glitter — for that extra fairy tale look. I felt very much the princess, if a little silly — well, I was dressed up as a huge twinkly fairy, it was hardly my normal turnout now! I couldn't grumble though; it could have been worse. I could have been dressed as a dusty old bed sheet!

"Pssst, psssst, pssssst!!" was the sound of three sharp signalling bursts.

He was here!

"This is it…" I whispered, glancing once more at my reflection in the mirror, whilst inhaling a deep breath.

I briefly closed my eyes and slowly exhaled in an attempt to calm my nerves.

Full of jitters, I rushed to my bedroom window to acknowledge Zach's arrival. It took longer than expected as the hefty dress decorating my frame was as awkward as hell to manoeuvre in. I could only describe this hindrance as trudging through a vat of dense mud!

Weighted down, I awkwardly blew a smile his way.

Had I met his expectations or not? I wasn't 100% sure, but from the look on his face, I needn't ask.

"Hey, princess," he cooed.

His flattering words dangled flirtatiously off his tongue, as he flicked his head back to remove his fallen inky locks from out of view.

I would say he was more than pleased to see me! This was exactly the reaction I could have only dreamt of.

"Mmmmm, mmmm, mmm, you look delectable, Allie. I could eat you just as you are. Come down! I want to get a proper look at you," he purred.

My heart throbbed with adrenaline, and my body ached with lust for every admiring glance he bestowed upon me. I couldn't believe these words were meant for me, and as a result, it sent me into a giggling frenzy. But this wasn't the only factor that was making me swoon. Oh no, he himself looked delicious, a proper swashbuckling dreamboat.

He was dressed from head to toe as a brooding Prince Charming, complete with an understated leather masquerade mask. His mouth and chin were the only pieces of flesh on show. Purposely teasing me, with the focus directed towards his kissable lips — they oozed sex.

The mask bore two medium slits for his hypnotic eyes to peer through, they alone could bring a girl to her knees.

He wore a dark shirt with a distressed laced jacket, matching waistcoat and belt. Long cuff gloves smothered his wrists and his knee-length buckled boots snuggled closely against his tight jodhpurs. To top of his thrilling outfit, he accessorized with a mighty polished sword that was strapped across his back and glistened with the bounce of light.

Coolly, I tottered away from the window, pretending to appear unfazed by the unforeseen interest that was noticeably beginning to manifest before me. Though, as soon as I was out of his sight, I galloped down the stairs, embodying all the elegance of a great African Elephant. If that wasn't uncouth enough, then tackling the stairs with these oversized wings were an obstacle in themselves. I looked like an entangled erratic mammal stampeding towards the nearest exit. How I was going to squeeze through these stairs let alone navigate myself around this party was a mystery waiting to be unravelled.

Now as beautiful as my new appendages were, they were a little on the large side, rigid in frame with scarcely any flexibility — they were hardly practical.

"Fancy a helping hand?" came the dreamy male tone.

Without hesitation, he grabbed my palm with his and pulled me through the last remaining steps.

"Er, how did you get in here?" my voice croaked.

Don't get me wrong, I was grateful for the assistance but quite surprised to see him standing in my lounge. Especially considering I'd only seconds ago left him standing on the gravel below my window!

Trying to muffle his laughter, Zach replied, "your delightful nan here caught me loitering by the front door and kindly invited me in. I'm pretty glad she did, as I would not have missed this for the world. I had no idea you were so keen!" he cheekily chirped.

I coyly glimpsed at Nan who was sat snugly in her favourite armchair in the corner of the room. She had a face full of mischief, chortling to herself as she pretended to have not seen or heard any of the commotion.

I have to say it was a treat to see Nan rejoicing in my amusing little blunder, even if it was myself that was paying the price for it.

There's no denying I was mortified, as not only had he seen me behave in such an unladylike manner, he also had to rescue me from the claws of 'said' stairs.

"Maybe these contraptions aren't such a good idea, how about we unclip you of your wings? Anyway, I like you just as you are, no need to change you is there," he romantically whispered.

Zach twisted me around, forcing my back closely up against his chest. With a barely-there touch, he swept my hair to one side. Purposely, he trailed his fingers across the exposed skin of my shoulders and over the base of my neck, gently freeing my arms from their shackles. His soft, sensual touch melted me. I could feel my heart thawing out for this guy.

"There we go beautiful," he smouldered, pulling me back around to face him. "Least this way, I might get the chance to actually dance with you. That's if you'd let me of course," he humbly asked.

"Hmmm…maybe," I teasingly grinned, knowing full well I was likely to do anything he asked of me right now. The way I saw it, I was his and only his for the night.

"There's no maybe about it, Miss Pickering. I know you will!" he smugly whipped back.

"You've a cocky one here, Allie," piped an amused Nan.

Zach was smirking from ear to ear as he charmed Nan around with his presumptuous attitude.

"No, there's nothing wrong with a little confidence, just make sure you behave yourself, young man," Nan added.

"I'm on my best behaviour, Mrs. Winifred. You can trust me with your granddaughter, she's in safe hands with me," Zach promised.

"Please call me 'Nan', no need for all these airs and graces around me, dear," she batted back.

Strangely, I didn't recall introducing Zach to Nan. Perhaps she had dropped her name into conversation when welcoming him in. Saying that, Nan would never use her full Christian name. She was never a fan of Winifred; it was always Winnie or Win. Seemed odd she would start now, but I wouldn't put anything past this awful disease of hers.

Thankfully, Zach had the good sense to realise I was losing myself in thought and broke my concentration before I went in too deep.

"In all seriousness, Allie, you look a vision, absolutely enchanting, you really do and that…that beautiful necklace compliments the dress perfectly!" he spouted.

Zach's eyes were mesmerized by the glimmering pendant dangling above my palpitating breasts.

"Do you mind?" he asked, his hand impatiently angling towards me.

"No, go ahead," I encouraged, perplexed at his sudden infatuation with my jewel.

I couldn't help but think this was his saucy little attempt

of trying to cop a feel.

Excited about this naughty little prospect, I had almost forgotten Nan was still in our presence and very aware of the situation. If she hadn't of alerted me with a deliberate cough then who knows where his hands would have wandered, but ever the gent, Zach ploughed on with his original request.

He heedfully raised the pendant towards the direction of the warm glow penetrating from the chandelier above and proceeded to slowly oscillate the gem from left to right.

The gemstone of untold liquid swirled within, drifting into a hazy turquoise and purple cyclone, growing in pace with every rotation. Never had I seen anything as spectacular as this before. It was like gazing into the Milky Way and being captivated by a thousand sparkling stars, twinkling and whirling for me and me alone.

Like a cold winter's morning, Zach's eyes frosted over as he enfolded himself within the enrapture of the liquid vortex. He was completely bewitched, not to mention undaunted by the deviant happenings within the stone, that he had almost forgotten he was in the company of Nan as well as me.

"What was that!" I exclaimed.

"What was what?" he asked.

"That!" I repeated.

"What?" he shrugged.

"That thing! The thing you just did with the jewel — the light, the twirl...you know, the swirly-whirly thing!" I screeched.

Why play dumb? He knew exactly what I was talking about! I had been the proprietor of that necklace for only a couple of months now, and not once had I known how to create such an optical illusion, nor would I think of doing so. It wasn't your everyday occurrence was it, and he unlike me was not stunned in the slightest by this little revelation. An explanation of some sort would be pretty fitting right now, and luckily for me, I didn't have to wait too long to be enlightened.

"Ohhhhh, the swirly-whirly thing...why you should have

said!" he joked. "Mum had one just like this when she was about my age — fascinating little piece of kit."

I had assumed the pendant was rare, a one-off, but evidently, I was wrong.

Nan never got around to explaining its origins to me and delving further never seemed appropriate. Resurfacing memories with Nan would often lead to pain and heartache, so for her sake, I shunned any further probing. I concluded that this unique little treasure was nothing more than a visual fallacy.

I couldn't help but feel a little saddened for Nan, after all, neither of us expected there to be more than one of these jewels knocking around. However, I wasn't at all surprised that someone else would want one or that Zach was entirely engrossed by it, after all, it was a thing of beauty.

Zach now sharply aware his fascination had been noted — swiftly dropped the gem from his grasp and moved on. Forgetting about it just as quickly as he had become enthralled by it.

"Allie, shall we —" Zach's words faltered.

"I'm going to have a lie-down, dear," interrupted Nan. "It was a pleasure to meet you...erm..."

Frustratingly for Nan, she couldn't remember his name.

"Sorry, my love...your name has slipped my mind," she bashfully mumbled.

"It's Zach, Nan," I nudged.

"Yes, yes, Allie! Just make sure you bring my granddaughter home safe, Zach or I shall be having words with your parents," she quipped.

Nan's tone had abruptly changed for no reason. She was coming across a little blunt and quite chilly. It was most unusual for her, but again, I put it down to the illness and the continuous humiliation it was causing her.

"Ok, that's enough! Sleep tight, and I'll see you in the morning," I said, kissing her soft wrinkly forehead and prompting her to make a move upstairs to bed.

Zach nodded his head in her direction, conforming to her

waspish command. I wondered had he accidentally said or done something to leave a sour taste in her mouth? Perhaps learning that Zach's mother also owned a necklace just like hers had hurt more than I realised.

It was likely she had come to believe that hers was the only one. It was special, it held a connection that tied her with my grandad…or was it with the mystery man she briefly spoke of? Well, whatever it was, it had ruffled Nan and led her into making a premature exit.

"Sorry, Zach, you were saying?" I pressed, eager for the atmosphere not to dampen the rest of our night.

"Oh, I was only checking to see if you were ready to leave?" he continued.

"Sure," I replied.

Zach regally lowered his sword, fell to one knee and bowed his head before me.

"I'm not worthy of you tonight, my fairy princess!" he mocked.

"Get up, silly," I giggled.

I could feel my cheeks burning with an outbreak of shyness.

"No, not until you do me the great honour of kissing me," he cockily requested.

"No!" I sharply shot back, which was followed by a sweet girly titter.

I playfully pushed his head to one side and instead offered my hand and only my hand to him.

"Nice bracelet you got there," he complimented, as he spied the clover charm swaying from my outreached arm.

"Oh…thanks…a friend gave it to me," I stumbled.

Just because Kalen and I were no more, it didn't mean I couldn't wear it. Zach needn't know the truth, and that's the way I aimed for it to stay.

"Come on then, you splendid creature, let's get you to the ball," he saucily winked.

Taking my hand, he pulled himself up onto his feet.

I more than anything wanted him to hold me tenderly within his arms. I wanted him to madly kiss me, but here was not the place, and I didn't want him to ask for permission either. I wanted him to grab me unexpectedly, nail me to the wall and roughly play fight me to the ground. I wanted him to ruin my lipstick, tousle my hair and dishevel my clothes. Where was the magic in being asked? It takes away the sheer intensity and the unmitigated spontaneity of the unknown.

Zach definitely had a risqué streak blistering to break free, and right now the prospect of that was more exciting than the facade he was planting on me.

"Where exactly are we going?" I queried, as we departed the house.

"The woods. I could have sworn I told you?" Zach replied.

"The woods! I blurted. "You never said the woods, Zach... I would have remembered the woods!" I trilled.

Oh no, I didn't fancy that, I didn't fancy that at all! No way did I want to spend an evening out in the open.

"Is there a problem?" Zach sympathetically asked...but all I had to offer in the form of a response was a pathetic childish shrug.

"Listen, she holds a party every year and each year the party has to be bigger and better than the last. This means the venues have to be too! I'm surprised you've never been to one before?" he remarked.

Zach clearly wasn't aware of my social prowess, and so I responded with another frivolous shrug.

"They're always really good fun, some say the highlight of the year. Ok, ok, maybe not quite the highlight of the year, but my cousin knows how to throw a party. You wouldn't want to miss it," he plugged.

Urgh, I hated that he had to reiterate whose party it was. It reminded me that I had no real get out clause, not if I wanted to be welcomed into the family bosom that was!

"Are you ok?" he questioned.

"I wasn't expecting an outdoorsy party, that's all. It's fine.

I'm totally fine with this," I lied.

By now you know how much I detested having to walk through 'Hags Alley' to get to Eldercrest Woods. Well, now combine that with a party outside in the cold, damp and murkiness of the night! Let's just say it's not how I wanted to spend my Saturday night. Plus, it was hardly the safest of places. Don't get me wrong, I'm no killjoy but who knows what could be lurking in those unlit corners, within the camouflage of the bushes and below the shadows of the streams. I hated lying, but I didn't want Zach to know how uncomfortable I was with all of this.

"Hey, if it's not your thing, then it's ok for you to say so. We don't have to like all the same things now, do we! After all, it would be boring if we did. I'll drop you back home, but I hope you can understand that I do need to go. There's always next year..." he said, with a hint of disappointment.

Nan's words rang through my ears like a bad case of tinnitus. If I didn't snap him up then someone else would, and I couldn't let that happen.

"I want to come, I do. I had in my head a heated hall or one of them rowdy house parties. This is a much better idea though!"

Oops, there was another one of those white lies again!

Resuming the pace, Zach explained that the woods were the ideal venue. They were large enough to hold the quantity of guests that would be attending, whilst providing the perfect eerie setting for a Halloween party.

He said there were no rules or formalities for hosting a party in the hidden outdoors, which meant it would run into the early hours of the morning. Besides, there wasn't a hall big enough in our sleepy village that was able to accommodate his cousin's needs.

I sincerely hoped Nan wasn't waiting up for me, as by the sounds of things, I wouldn't be back until the early hours!

Zach didn't stop there, oh no, he continued to sell me the party as he led me towards 'Hags Alley'.

"There's nothing better than spending quality time underneath the moonlit sky with old friends...and new acquaintances," he subtly hinted. "Those people you really care about and would do anything for, even if some of those people have only been in your life for a short while. I'm hoping I get the opportunity to do that with a special certain someone tonight."

He had a point, it did sound utterly magical, especially the part where he wanted to experience it with a 'special certain someone'!

There was something about Zach. He was a one-off. A keeper. And now I'd found him, there was no way I was letting him go.

Seventeen

THE UNKNOWN

I hated that putrid alley with a real passion, but with Zach by my side, I didn't feel scared. I actually felt secure in the knowledge that no harm would come of me.

Protectively, he took my hand, allowing the calmness to ease through my body like molten caramel — temporarily holding my gaze as he coaxed me in.

Ambling through, we had reached the belly of the monster, but before my anxiety had a chance to rear its ugly head... we had already passed safely through and out of its formidable-looking mouth.

Time hadn't stood still, fear hadn't frozen me, which I can confirm was an absolute first for me. Not once had I entered into that alley without an overwhelming feeling of dread, but tonight that had all changed. I was unusually placid. I couldn't even recall the journey!

Occasionally, I would pass through these woods in the day, but I had never been brave enough to venture through them alone at night. It was only natural that I was now beginning to feel slightly apprehensive as I took in my darkened surroundings.

I could hear the silent beat of the music pumping away in the distance. The deeper into the woods we walked, the louder the beat became.

The woods itself was a labyrinth of identical muddy paths, dressed in a mishmash of fallen soggy leaves.

Bushes and trees bordered the tracks, blocking the moon's glare from fully permeating through. Every little sound appeared heightened and any sudden move tracked. I could feel myself tensing. I was in unfamiliar territory, and I wasn't the least bit comfortable with it.

Zach squeezed my hand, assuring me there was nothing to be frightened off, and like a lusty fool, I believed him....

∞∞∞

Cupping my mouth from behind, he threw his vacant arm securely around my chest, and with my arms tightly pinned to my side, he dragged me into a wholly blackened alcove.

Branches slapped, stroked and tickled every inch of my body as I was lugged through what looked like a derelict cave.

Access was hidden by foliage sagging across the entry point, which was scrawny and the width of only two persons standing side-by-side.

The cave itself was in the shape of a lager bottle, and with only one way in and one way out, we inevitably came to a standstill at the base.

Zach removed his hold from across my body but left his hand to remain firmly upon my shivering lips. He softly murmured into my ear to remain quiet and to by no means move.

Seriously, now should have been the time for me to worry about what that 'thing' was outside the cove, but all I could concentrate on was his hot and spicy breath against my skin, sending titillating goosebumps throughout my flesh.

I felt giddy! I was gasping for him to replace his hand with his squishy tongue, but realistically, I knew now was not the time, not here, and most definitely not with that 'thing' outside.

It had shot past me ridiculously fast. A white blur of commotion. I couldn't even tell you if it was human or not. What if it was a knife-wielding maniac? Or a dangerous bloodthirsty animal? For all I knew, it could well be the hag!

Panic was well and truly setting in. I could feel myself hyperventilating. My breathing had become erratic. I was freaking out by the unknown, and the tragedy of it all was that I could be bludgeoned or mauled to death before I'd even had the chance to taste Zach on my lips.

"Keep calm, Allie, nothing will hurt you, not while I'm here protecting you, and I will protect you!" he boomed.

A beam of light from the silvery moon bled in from a small crack from the roof of the cave. It was all we had, but it was enough to make out one another.

SWISH, there it was!

SWIISH, and again!!

SWIIISH, *SWIIIISH*, again and again!!!

The shadow of this 'thing' was faintly detected by the outside night light as it pelted back and forth past the cave at speed. It hadn't stopped. It hadn't seen us!

Zach slowly released his hand from my mouth, twisting me around to face him and pulling me closely into his chest.

Eyes wide with fear, I looked to him for reassurance. I wanted him to convince me that whatever it was, had gone and that any deranged thoughts I had, were all just a silly figment of my imagination.

"Z…Zz…Zach, what was that?" I trembled.

"Ssssshhhhhh, keep shtum, Allie, it's still out there. I don't know what it is, and I sure don't want to find out any time soon," he bleated.

Full of fret, I burrowed my cowardly head into Zach's gallant chest and squeezed him tightly. If I couldn't see it, it didn't exist. Right?

What felt like minutes upon minutes of excruciating loitering, was in reality, only a seconds worth of edgy waiting, when *CRUNCH*... our hiding place was no more! We had been sniffed out.

"Uh!! What was that?" I squealed.

I hoped it was my imagination playing torturous tricks, but by the way Zach had reactively pulled me in tighter, it proved to me that he too had heard it.

CRACK!

"Zach!" I squeaked, flapping my arms around in dismay.

It was amongst us!

"Keep still, will you!" Zach exclaimed.

His halcyon exterior was slipping. He was worried, and he more than displayed it through the abrupt timbre of his voice.

"Close your eyes!" he ordered.

I didn't need to be told twice.

Zach was stern and clear with his instruction, and as demanded, it was now deadly silent within the cave — apart from the heavy sensual panting that was exchanged between the two of us. However, as already established, this was not the time to feel hot and sweaty under the collar, but I simply couldn't help fantasise as his breath forced its way into my open mouth, flooding my throat, windpipe and eventually dominating my lungs.

I gasped.

The injection of CO_2 had overpowered my respiratory system, leaving me a tad woozy but breathing steadily with an overall sense of coolness and composure.

I had been on the fringe of breaking point, but Zach had accomplished something phenomenal — he had subdued me without the use of spoken words or restraints. He had an effect on me like no other. I felt like I was under his control — spellbound by his presence.

"Allie, it's time. Open your eyes...it's here," he bravely uttered.

These were the words I hoped I'd not receive, but unwillingly, I raised my eyelids to see not one, but two grim figures lurking around the orifice of the cave.

The moonlight projected their abhorrent shadows onto the grainy grey cave walls.

They appeared hunched back and of neither human nor of animal form. Their grim outlines growing in size with every step closer and closer taken.

My heart raced — beating erratically, whilst my breathing continued to remain regular and under control. I was determined not to make this an easy kill for them.

Stillness.

They had halted.

They knew we were here and were listening to every breath drawn.

I turned to Zach. He reciprocated my gaze of trepidation and tightly squeezed my hand, as if to say, 'this is it, brace yourself, they're coming'.

With that one knowing look from my brave soldier — they came, and they came at an impeccable speed.

Surging from a static position, they increased in pace at a frightening rate. Within seconds they would be nose-to-nose with us.

Catching sight of them in the flesh, my heart constricted. I doubled over with aversion. My faithful organ could take the anguish no more, stabbing me one final blow of pain which seared through my blood vessels like a red-hot poker.

They were stood there brazenly in full view of us, one behind the other, rocking on their heels from side-to-side.

The taller of the two was at the rear, with his shuddersome head resting menacingly on the shoulder of his fellow reprobate.

Both were draped in black oversized longline T-shirts with tight fitted leggings. They topped off their look with matching white featureless face masks.

They had a vent for their mouths and two small pin-pricks in place of their eyes and nose. They were identifiable as human but not the type you would want in your company.

Full of faith, I turned to Zach, expecting a meticulous set of orders or at least a hasty plan that would extract us swiftly from the cave and out of this mess.

Undoubtedly, he had to have a plan. This was Zach after all — he had an answer for everything.

He was a forward thinker, a problem solver. The type of man to have a handle on a situation like this, but I couldn't have been further from the truth...because rather than the shrewd and peaceful retreat I longed for, I was instead met by a pumped-up Zach, engaging in a standoff with these two beasts.

He began to pugnaciously mirror image the smaller crea-ture of the two — the one that appeared to be the leader, and the one that he needed to beat into submission. Yet neither Zach nor the beast moved, spoke or attacked. It was raw face to face eyeballing with a ten-metre separation gap between them.

Zach didn't appear worried or upset, in fact, he was game, militant even. I, on the other hand, was beside myself with an-guish, not knowing if I should intervene or not. If I did, then what would I possibly achieve? I could end up causing more trouble than it was worth.

This was excruciating, not knowing what was about to happen. Who was going to make the first move, and what the outcome would be? I really hoped that Zach knew what he was doing, as right now, I didn't have much hope for the both of us. But by the looks of things, I wasn't about to wait too long to find out — it was time!

The deathly wall of silence had been shattered by this stubby thing as it extended its hand towards us, summoning for Zach to move in closer. I gripped Zach's bicep, knowing full well he would not accept my intervention.

"Allie don't do this," he pressed, as he peeled my tightly glued fingernails from off his sore flesh. "Stay here, don't move and let me sort this!" he soothed.

"Don't go! Stay with me!! I hysterically whimpered, desperately praying he wouldn't leave my side.

As pathetic as it was, my plea hadn't gone unheard. Zach spun around and rested the back of his hand against my quivering cheek. He softly stroked my flustered skin with his manly fingers, assuring me that nothing would come of him.

"You have nothing to worry about. I can handle myself. Trust me to sort this, ok?" he stressed, as he reached across his shoulders to draw his sword from out of its sheath.

I relented. It was the least I could do, what with him being so brave and me acting like a wimp and all.

"Allie, if you get really scared, close your eyes and think of me. I'll be right here with you," he soothed.

Thwack!

Zach hit the floor with a gut-wrenching *thud*, his sword swiftly followed, clattering beside him.

The beast had ruthlessly taken the opportunity to immobilize Zach whilst his back was turned. It was sly — a disgusting malicious act, carried out by only the callous of cowards.

If only I had seen this thing approaching, I would without hesitation have pulled Zach from out of harm's way, but I didn't see it, why didn't I see it?

Zach didn't stand a chance. Well, how could he when he was blinded by having to pander to my incessant whinging. If it hadn't had been for me, his legs would never have been kicked out from underneath him. It was all my fault, and all I could do was watch as the venomous beast leered over Zach's collapsed body — motionless and vulnerable, sprawled out on the stone-cold floor.

I wanted to cradle him in my arms, protect him from this invidious creature, but I couldn't. I was incapable of moving. Frozen where I stood, my legs and arms were rigid. My lips powerless, ineffective in calling his name — unable to stir him from this unfolding nightmare. I could only look on in horror as the situation amplified from bad, to worse, to catastrophic!

The spindly one of the two had now scurried over, brutally snatching Zach's inert ankles and dragging his lifeless body from where he fell. He proceeded to aim for the cave exit at a breakneck pace.

I painfully gulped back my tears of despair at seeing Zach in this appalling situation. I could only speculate as to what was about to happen to him.

As for my fate, I didn't care. I was fully aware I was now all alone with this short savage and likely to receive a less underhand beating. It too was aware of me as it slowly tilted its head towards me in a torturous fashion, perversely scanning my body from head to toe.

It breathed heavily through its nose, sporadically snorting up clumps of tacky phlegm. The sound so vulgar it made my toes curl in repulse.

Its breathing increased in volume, which could only mean one thing — it was closing in on me! I rammed my eyes tight shut, wishing to see Zach, just like he had told me to, but he wasn't there, of course he wasn't. The chances of seeing him in my thoughts were just as likely as him recovering from the slaying he had been sentenced to. It was a sweet thought, but that's exactly what it was, a thought, a little piece of hope in what was a dreadfully dark place.

I only had one other option and that was to face this thing head-on. There was no way Zach would want me to die, not like this, not without a fight. Then it dawned on me, I had his sword! Little had I known, his weapon was actually real. I had naively assumed it was a prop!

Determination raged through my blood like a rebellious

teen as I flicked my eyelids open and prepared myself for the worst.

"Come on then!" I roared as I scanned the barely lit ground for his sizeable blade and the compact fiend. "Show yourself, will you!" I incited.

On the spot, I twisted and turned and twisted again, exploring every inch of the cave. But nothing.

I flipped and swivelled and swivelled some more, but still nothing.

The weapon was missing, and the brute had scarpered, but why? Why Zach? Why take him and leave me?

I know he had told me to stay put, but something didn't feel right. Moreover, what type of person would I be, if I was to leave him out there all alone with just those flesh beating ghouls for company!

"Come on!" I sternly urged, but this time my order was aimed not at the beasts but at myself. "Snap out of it!" I snarled.

Frustrated, I painfully yanked at my hair, grabbing ample clumps, all in an attempt to build up the courage within to move my dormant limbs.

"He needs you! Move!" I bawled.

Lunging at my cheeks, I animatedly slapped them a handful of times, alternating from cheek-to-cheek.

Ah ha, it was working! My feet began to shuffle. One in front of the other. Granted, they were wobbly and in need of some work, but there was no question about it — I was moving! From frail baby steps to a drunken stroll, I was gaining memento and took the courage to plunge into a confident jog. Before I knew it, I was deep into a run, running for Zach, and there was no way I was going to let these beasts take him away from me, not now, not ever.

"Zaaaaaach!!!!" I squawked, as I burst through the mouth of the cave, fists poised, ready to brawl.

Only Zach, the vulnerable, half dead Zach I expected, was far from needing the assistance of my new-found grit.

I can confirm that with a beat in his heart and blood running through his veins — he was in the living. What's more, he was standing firmly in between the two beasts, and he was holding his own. This was actually better than I had anticipated, and although he was breathing and unhurt, he was still in a rather tricky and unpredictable scenario.

All three of them turned their gaze towards me as I prematurely halted in my tracks. I had no idea what was about to happen, but the feeling of helplessness was now stronger than ever before.

They had Zach cornered, and although standing strong, I didn't fancy his chances with two against one. The only thing I could think to do was to run, to run into Zach's arms and hold him dearly. If he was going to die tonight, then I would die too. It was that simple.

My feelings for Zach had inadvertently spilt out into a puddle of overcharged emotions. I hadn't expected them to be this strong and so soon, but rather than suffocate them, I chose to encourage them — to let them breathe. I had all of a sudden become this hopeless romantic, ready to die for a man I hardly knew. It was crazy!

If the 'old' me, could see the 'new' me right now, she would be pulling me over to one side and dishing out some strong words! Still, it didn't stop me, and I dived straight into his arms, ignoring the rather perilous audience that glowered upon us.

Zach swathed his arms around me, squeezed me tightly and stroked my frayed hair with his teasing touch. Now was my chance. I was likely never to get it again, so I stepped up on the tips of my toes and pulled him in. Every cell of passion I owned in that inexperienced body of mine, flowed through into his welcoming mouth and into this one dramatic kiss.

His lips were soft, plump and incredibly edible. They were everything I had fantasised they would be and more. He kissed me back, exploring every inch of my mouth with his accomplished wet tongue — attentive and generous, I didn't want this moment to end.

As formerly mentioned, I had always dreamt my first kiss to also be my last with that one person. I just never expected the two to coincide with one another.

"Waheyyyy! Eat your heart out, Casanova!" ribbed the stocky, smaller, cockier of the two beasts.

"Yeah, don't mind us, will you!" snickered the skinny, taller one.

Taken aback by these two over-friendly voices, I apprehensively pulled my satisfied lips from off of Zach's. I stood rigidly, blankly staring at him in utter confusion as to what was actually happening. Zach, on the other hand, was buzzing, with a huge grin on his face that could stretch from one end of 'Hags Alley' to the other.

These voices were not menacing, dark or nasty as expected. They were completely the opposite — warm, friendly and full of devilry.

"Oi, come here you!" Zach shouted, as he leant into snatch the back of the neck of the shorter beast.

This thing was in the process of making a sharp getaway, but Zach had other plans for him.

Heavy-handedly, he threw him down in front of me, roughly ripping off his terrorising blank mask to reveal the beast inside.

"Allie, with regret, please allow me to introduce you to the Mapleby brothers," sighed Zach.

"Like the tree!" the lanky one jokingly pointed out.

"Yes, like a poxy Maple tree," Zach huffed. "Do you have to point that out every time I introduce you to someone new, it's not at all annoying!" snapped Zach.

"It's our thing, it's what we do," they chirped in unison.

Clocking my reaction to their timely response, they informed me that they also had a habit of speaking the exact same words, at exactly the same time.

"This stumpy little cretin here is Forrest, and the gangly gormless one over there to your left is young Heath."

Zach marched his way over to Heath and yanked his mask, allowing it to ping back onto his face with a stinging *smack*.

"Jeez, Zach!" he wailed.

"How d'ya do?" piped Forrest, holding out his hand to greet me whilst intentionally ignoring his brother's gripe.

"Erm, a little shaken and confused if I'm honest," I retorted as I grudgingly shook his hand.

"It may be hard to believe but these two jokers are my very annoying but most lovable and genuine of friends. We go way, way back. You could say we are more like brothers than mates," spoke Zach with affection.

"Oh right…" I responded, not knowing what to actually say after what had just happened.

"Here, don't be blaming our boy, he wasn't to know it was us — well not at first anyway," babbled Heath.

"Yeah credit where credit's due. You played along well, lad," added Forrest.

"Sorry, what? You knew exactly who they were, and you still played me?" I snapped, angling my rage towards Zach.

I was flabbergasted and downright hurt by his odd behaviour. It's a side I hadn't encountered or expected before.

Zach's eyes widened with guilt, glaring at Forrest in horror as he realised, he had been dropped headfirst into my brewing temper.

For me, the revelation was one step too far, and without further probing, I turned my back on all three of them. I was off! No way would I stay after being made such a fool of.

"Allie, wait! It's not how it seems. It really isn't. Just hear me out?" Zach shouted, while aggressively seizing my arm and pulling me back towards him.

He was not asking me to listen. He was telling me to!

"You're hurting me, Zach" I whimpered.

I knew he hadn't intended on being this forceful towards me, he was clearly set on making me listen, but he was going about it the wrong way.

Infuriated as I was, I couldn't help but feel a little attracted to the debut of his overpowering demeanour, although domineering, he was incredibly sexy.

"I don't mean to hurt you; never would I want to! I just need you to listen," he whispered.

"Well this better be good, or I'm walking — no more games!"

I stood firm to my word, arms folded, tongue stuffed into the pocket of my plump cheek. I didn't care who was watching. I was unimpressed, and I was making sure that Zach damn well knew about it.

Forrest and Heath were aware they needed to make a hasty exit. So, in support, they joined together to stiffly pat Zach on the shoulders before recoiling. Anyone would've thought he was about to be fed to a hungry pride of blood-thirsty lions.

Looking remorseful, he shovelled his hands into his trouser pockets, lowered his head and raised his eyebrows upwards and towards me in a most forgivable fashion.

"Beautiful, I'm sorry, I really am, but truth is, I couldn't resist an opportunity to get your irresistible little body into my arms," he teased, hoping to soften the mood, which I can tell you was not working.

"Ok, it was stupid of me, but if I'm brutally honest, I thought you were the type of girl that could take a joke!" he openly confessed. "There's no denying this whole debacle had spiralled out of hand, and of course I was going to put an end to it before it finished the way that it did...but they simply beat me to it! Before I could do a single thing, the rotters swiped my legs out from underneath me."

"Costume or no costume, you're telling me that you knew who they were from the moment you laid eyes on them?" I replied, bewildered.

"Erm...yes", he sheepishly answered.

"How? How could you possibly tell that it was Tweedle-dee and Tweedledum over there?" I asked, pointing towards the boys who had ridiculously moved no more than a few metres away.

"There's no way you could have identified those two in that getup! It could have been anyone?" I questioned.

"I sensed it was them, Allie. We all have senses, don't we? Some of us are just more in tune with our bodies than others," he hit back.

You had to be kidding me, there was no way he could have known it was them from the start. For one, it was too dark, two, they were masked, and three, they weren't exactly meeting and greeting were they.

"I've known these lads for more years than I can count. They're practically flesh and blood, why wouldn't I know it was them? They're also the biggest pranksters I know. It was always going to be them. Forgive me?" he finished.

I have to say, I was quite floored by his odd excuse. It was one thing to have an inkling but to have absolute faith in something that could potentially be fatal was madness!

Zach's conviction in the Mapleby brothers was a risky one but one that had paid off. Maybe there was some truth in what he was saying.

"It should never have gone this far, but like I said, I never got the chance to stop it, did I..."

His half snarly, half playful comment was fired at Forrest, who was now sincerely nodding in agreement.

Forrest proceeded to clasp his palms together, pitifully shaking them at me in the hopes of a pardon. His public display of grovelling had amused me to the point that it had actually weakened my austere exterior and extracted a cheerful smirk.

Zach now spying his opening from Forrest, took the opportunity to try and win me back over, in which case, I have to say he unashamedly did.

Forcefully, he took my hand, which was rigid with anger and pulled me in closer to his body. I responded with disinterest, sloping my head to one side and away from him, not wanting to be lured in by his charm.

Did that stop him?

No.

With complete control, he pulled my face directly in front of his. I didn't fight his hold. I didn't attempt to.

He looked deeply into my eyes — he was heavy in thought.

Drawing a deep breath, he directed his eyes upon my rigorous lips before returning to hold my gaze.

"I'm glad this happened, Allie," he purred — his ripe lips millimetres from mine.

Again, I could feel his hot breath penetrating my heavy panting. I tried not to react, I didn't want him noting the swift change in temperature, the dilation of pupils or the uncontrollable racing of my heartbeat. Aloof I was, exhaling deeply and pursing my lips back together in the unimpressed expression that they had become accustomed to.

"You can be as moody...and as frosty...as you like...but at least now I know...you want me!" he continued, ensuring his lips grew closer to mine with every drawn-out word he heavily mouthed.

"I guess that if this is all it takes for me to get a kiss from you. I should have done it sooner," he smirked.

My lips gradually cracked from their wrinkled appearance, and the creased expression on my taut face instantly disintegrated. As much as it pained me, I really couldn't stay angry at him, especially when his flirtatious lips were practically touching mine — they were begging to be nibbled.

I closed my eyes, expecting him to make the final push — to kiss me tenderly with a hint of filthiness, but rather disappointingly — he didn't.

There was no more hot and heavy breathing, no more

touching, no nothing.

I flicked my eyelids open to see what the holdup was, but rather than puckering up, Zach had backed up and instead was stood there just gazing at me. The brooding smile he had slapped across his face was enough to tell me that this was all just another silly game to him. It was obvious he was delighted to have softened the flames from my stewing rage, transforming them into a sweltering appetite, but it was clear he wasn't prepared to back up his actions.

From the corner of my eye, I caught Forrest and Heath congratulating one another with a high five. This was in typical boyish appreciation of Zach's alternative flirtation techniques. I, however, was less than impressed, as once again, the joke was on me.

With all my emotions floating around in disarray, I had momentarily forgotten that the Mapleby brothers were watching. Perhaps if they hadn't of been lurking nearby, Zach might have been more willing to kiss me, instead, it felt like he was showing off, acting the player in front of the lads.

"You know you're cute when you're grouchy, kind of makes me like you even more," smouldered Zach.

He was at it again, reeling me in with his playful words. Although this time, Forrest and Heath decided that they too would try and butter me up....

"He's right you know; you have that whole huffy but smoking hot vibe going on. I kind of wouldn't mind trying you out for myself," they gushed, with a hint of unexpected sleaze.

Zach chuckled with the brothers as they boldly attempted to win me over. His laugh was gorgeous and annoyingly infectious. I couldn't help but let out a faint giggle.

"No, this little treasure is a bit of me, boys," Zach cockily claimed, before throwing a possessive arm around my shoulders and dragging me off into deepest depths of the wood.

Eighteen
UNWANTED

Forrest and Heath were twins, though not identical, in fact, they looked nothing like one another. The only attribute you could say was twin-ish about them was their corresponding, closely shaved, icy blonde hair. There was no denying that these two stood out from the crowd, and it wasn't just down to their barnet —their height raised a few eyebrows too!

Forrest was scraping in at 5 ft nothing with Heath punching in at a whopping 6 ft 9 — hardly similar.

Both boys were easy on the eye, not my type but they would certainly melt the hearts of many a female. That they did have in common! You could instantly fall for their pale green cucumber eyes, let alone their averagely good looks.

"Sorry about scaring you, Allie. We were after our boy here, and we had no idea that the sly dog was bringing a date with him," apologised Forrest.

"He kept that quiet, but then again, this one's always been a dark creature when it comes to the ladies!" blurted Heath.

Great! Sounded like there was a whole different side to Zach I was yet to discover. Probably had a harem of girls lined up in waiting. Take your pick, eh Zach! In my eyes, he was the full package, it would be hard for any girl to resist him. I just hoped I was a one-off and this wasn't a regular occurrence for him. To learn he would bring a new girl to every party he attended would hurt me gravely, and I certainly didn't want to be just another number.

"If we had known he was bringing you, Allie, we would never have been so extreme. I hope we haven't upset you," explained Forrest. "Seems nothing can fool our man here, not even this, and we went to a hell of a lot of trouble to get him this time around!"

Heath remained silent, dispiritedly tugging against his robes in sheer disappointment at the failure of their prank. Turns out this was an ongoing tradition between Zach and the Mapleby brothers. For years, they had each attempted to outdo the other with lavish horseplay, only this time it had gone a step too far.

"Friends...?" the twins appealed.

"Oh, go on then," I replied, much to the boys' delight.

"I take it you two are coming to the party then?" asked Forrest.

"Course!" interrupted Zach. "There's no way I could miss my cousin's big day."

"Good, for a minute there, I thought you were actually escorting your date out to dinner dressed like that! But hey, with you Zach, it wouldn't surprise me!" scoffed Forrest.

That reminded me, "your sword, Zach...I couldn't find it," I exclaimed.

"Not to worry, Allie, where we're going, we won't need it," he smirked.

Out of the two, Forrest was definitely the more boisterous one. He was in charge, not shy, said it how it was and was a major fan of his own voice. Heath was the complete opposite. He was laid back, allowed his brother to do the talking, oozed calmness but also came across as the scattier, goofier one of the twins.

"I got to say, it's wonderful to finally see our Zach with a girlfriend but do me a favour and don't take him away from us, will you!" snorted Forrest.

I could sense a little seriousness in his tone.

"Oh no. No, we're not dating," I bashfully smiled.

I didn't want to presume too much, too early on. I didn't know for sure what would happen with me and Zach and if in fact there was actually an 'us'. All I knew, is that in spite of our little tiff, I was still basking in awe of him and no way did I want to scare him off by saying or doing the wrong thing. I had evidently already done that with Kalen and refused to do the same with Zach.

"Y'know...you're certainly not his usual type," divulged Forrest.

"Oh really?" I quizzed, keen to hear more.

"Oh yeah, the girls he normally goes for are quite...well, quite unique. They have their own identity; they know who they are and aren't afraid to express it either."

"Oh right," I replied, feeling rather dull in comparison.

"There's something about you though, you're different, very different. Not in a million years would I have placed the two of you together," he jabbered.

"Ok, ok that's enough, we don't need to dig up past girl-friends now, do we!" snapped Zach.

"Just saying...she's different, that's all. Can't put my finger on it...but she is," babbled Forrest.

He seemed adamant on finding the answer to his vague question by impertinently scanning my body from head to toe. His invasive ogling may have gone unnoticed by Zach but not by me, and he was met with the raise of one rather unimpressed eyebrow.

Zach was too busy rolling his eyes in embarrassment of their brazen behaviour to register the exchange of unceremonious glances. I had to wonder if Forrest was always this 'friendly' to Zach's female acquaintances!

"Where you from anyway, Allie? Can't say I've actually seen you around here before, and I know everyone from the ground upwards," he boastfully announced.

"Forrest!" Zach sharply interrupted, "what's with the third degree, you're a little full on mate, can't you see you're making her nervous!"

"Hey, it's no trouble. I'm local," I replied.

"You're local, you say? Really? I know everyone from all corners around these parts, and I don't know you!" he curtly stated.

"Yeah, we know everyone, and we don't know you!" repeated the parrot that was Heath.

"Surely you don't know everyone!" I laughed.

Forrest was glaringly taken aback by my comment. Perhaps I should have left him to believe he was this amazing, popular, individual that he clearly thought he was.

I could sense he was about to probe me further when Zach squeezed my waist tightly, intentionally diverting my attention away.

"Allie, the party is just through here..."

"Here?" I spluttered.

"Trust me," he grinned.

Vertically in front of me lay an old discarded tree trunk, excavated and enveloped in a carpet of squashy green moss. Did he actually expect me to crawl on all fours through that musty old log and in this dress too! The thing looked absolutely grungy and not fit for human entry!

The trunk had to be at least 18ft long, around 3ft wide and encapsulated into a tremendous grassy mound. I stretched my neck with the purpose of locating the exit, but it was impossible to view as the log itself was hidden underneath raised ground.

Zach was surely having me on? I glanced back at Forrest for confirmation, hoping to be greeted with juvenile sniggers, but instead, was met with a mistrustful stare. Locked within tense whispers, it was clear the brothers were trying to suss me out.

Unwanted, I tried to shake off the overwhelming feeling of rejection, but with Forrest staring directly through me, it was easier said than done.

His eyes analysing me, intimidatingly pierced into mine. His face was blank, no emotion, no expression, oddly similar to that of his featureless mask! I felt like I was being judged. They didn't know me and vice versa. I was 'a nobody' to them, and nobodies didn't often receive invites, did they, regardless if they were a plus one or not!

∞∞∞

They scrambled through the wooden tube like two rats up a drainpipe, scurrying as quickly as their scraggly legs could take them.

"Your turn! Head down and crawl," directed Zach.

Seemed legit...so I did as I was told, squirming and writhing through the dark festering chute. I could just about make out the outline of the twins as they raced ahead towards the impending light.

Once again, I didn't feel nervous or scared, not with Zach close behind. His looming presence made me feel safe, even though I knew I was venturing into the unknown.

The trunk itself was coarse to the touch, and after several shuffles, the grime and grubbiness I had initially experienced had disappeared. Spotlessly clean, there was no filth, creepy crawlies or mildew to contend with. It was almost as if the initial scum was acting as a deliberate deterrent. After a couple of wobbly and cautious shuffles, I was drawn into complete darkness.

Was I about to faint?

It wouldn't surprise me!

The tunnel was uncomfortably stuffy, confined and unbearably oppressive. I had never collapsed before, so your guess was as good as mine, but it would definitely explain the psychedelic affair I was about to endure.

Firing through the tube of black and fusing as one was an unexplainable vivid haze of colour. Wired, I laboriously crept on, trudging through the never-ending slender tunnel of paint-suffused smog. The joyous colours of the rainbow, competently skimming the outline of my dubious body before blasting ahead of my being and climaxing into a radiant golden-white light.

A vexatious white noise filled the empty gaps of the trunk, temporarily bunging its core. The further I crawled, the louder the sound hissed, until ceasing as I tumbled through the exit and into a drained-out heap on the floor.

"Took your time there didn't you, girl!" chirped Forrest as he plucked my worn-out torso from off the soil.

"What the hell?" I blurted.

I needed a moment to digest THAT! Because whatever THAT was, it wasn't normal, nor had I ever experienced anything like it before.

I suspected my body had suffered a slight malfunction from the earlier shock instigated by the Mapleby brothers. A light-headed episode was what it was! There was no other explanation for it.

Illness aside, time did not appear to be a pal of mine. As not one second was given for me to gather my thoughts before Heath, with no concern for my health, took it upon himself to manhandle me off towards a majestic chandelier of warmly lit lights.

∞∞∞∞

A leafy path of Weeping Willows lay ahead, they must have been 40ft plus. Purposefully lining the route to a further settling which was positioned into the formation of a substantially enclosed circle. The path of yellow-tinged parasol greenery was adorned with a scattering of clear glass open top mason jars, each filled with a single flickering tea light.

Loosely tied with rope to their assigned branches, they swayed romantically in the breeze, perfectly lighting the destination ahead.

"In case you hadn't of guessed by now, the party is just

through here," Zach announced, as he swept back the draping branch behind the final glimmering candle.

The Willow was a glorious tree with its elegant branches dramatically sweeping towards the dirt. Its dense circumference of foliage providing the ideal place to host a top-secret party within. Hidden away from prying eyes, there really was no way to peek in, and I very much doubt you would be able to peer out without tweaking a lance-shaped leaf or two.

The music leaked through the rift, blasting over my strained body and glueing me to the spot. Catching sight of the legions of bodies inside, I tightly squeezed Zach's hand. I was unable to speak.

Sensing my jitters, he slowly reared his head towards the twins and fired a short stern glare in their direction.

Without saying a word, they nodded and scarpered through the breach.

It was all becoming very real, and if my nerves weren't kicking in beforehand, they certainly were now. I felt sick. My gut spitting up the feeling that something here wasn't right. But it didn't matter — Zach wouldn't let it matter!

"See, Allie, you have nothing whatsoever to worry about," he reassured, with the addition of a not so helpful boot.

Nineteen

BAD SMELLS ALWAYS LINGER

Here we go...time to meet the family! I was by no means ready, but it really was now or never.

"Hey, hey, hey, there she is, there's our girl!" chorused the twins as they welcomed over the star of the party.

I strenuously stretched my neck to catch sight of their much-adored host, but it was becoming impossible with the hordes of guests bustling to and fro. Zach noticing my handicap and without so much as a warning, intervened, throwing me in front of the inane faced birthday girl.

"Let me introduce you to Coral, my sweetheart of a cousin," he enthused.

What!!! Was this some kind of sick and twisted joke! He had to be kidding me, right? No way would I accept that Stone was Zach's very own flesh and blood. She was a vulgar abomination to his peachy perfectness! They were polar opposites! How could they possibly be related?

"Oh yes, it's Annie, isn't it?" she pathetically replied.

"Allie, my name's Allie! We spent just shy of four months together at Eldercrest College!" I reminded.

Like she couldn't remember! She had spent enough time humiliating me. Oh, and let's not forget the twisted she-devil had halted the beginnings of a potential and most likely beautiful relationship with Kalen! She knew exactly who I was and responded with a smug-ridden smile. No doubt her warped little mind would cease any future relations with Zach too!

"Cousin Zachary...it's wonderful to see you...thank you so much for coming. You too, boys! It's been ever such a long time coming though, hasn't it!" she self-righteously piped.

With a stilted air to her speech and presence, Coral sounded somewhat different to how I remembered. She also spoke like she hadn't seen the boys in years and that included Zach.

Dressed from top to bottom in a skin-tight, frozen white, PVC jumpsuit — the Ice Maiden was her daringly bold choice of outfit. She fitted the glacial and stolid part to a tee, well that was apart from hurling the odd bitchy smirk now and again in my direction.

To everyone else, she was an expressionless goddess with no raise of the eyebrow or wrinkle of the nose. Her irises were a powdered, cloudy grey shade. They were most peculiar and her skin, paler than normal. There was no denying she had gone to town on the makeup for her self-centred party.

Coral really wasn't the type of cousin I expected or had hoped to meet. She was opinionated, outspoken, cruel and blunt. She was everything I wasn't.

"This is it then? This is the 'thing' you seem to be pitifully infatuated with?" she groaned loudly, seemingly unimpressed by his choice of company.

Zach aghast by his cousin's unceremonious comments, rolled his eyes and replied with a simple 'yes', keeping it short, sweet and to the point.

Don't hold back, eh Coral, why don't you say what you really think! I mean was she for real? I was standing right next to the pompous turd. Need she be so rude!

Yes, I was slightly bruised by her harsh words, but that was all irrelevant to the one key point here...Zach was with me!

Snootily, she surveyed me up and down, breathing heavily through her dragon flared nostrils as she took in every piece of me.

"You're not what or who I expected to see stood before

me, but I suppose now you're here, you might as well stay. Keep yourself to yourself!" she snipped.

Wow, what kind of greeting was this. It was hardly the warm and chirpy welcome I had envisaged. You know what? She could stick her rule and her bitchy attitude as I was only ever here for Zach. Like I wanted to mingle with her sort anyway!

Coral turned her attention back to Zach, commending him on his choice of outfit for the evening.

"Mmmm, don't you wear it well," she hissed excitedly, whilst simultaneously turning her haughty nose up at mine.

An obvious dig in order to rile me, but I wouldn't bite. The negative vibes directed at me from Coral had not gone unnoticed by Zach either, and he did his very best to divert the conversation away from me.

"You never cease to amaze me, you look incredible, and it's got to be said that once again you've outdone yourself. The party's heaving!" he raved.

"Yes, you really do look the part, very...erm...delightful," I politely chimed in, keen not to retaliate to her low and infantile depths.

However, inside and hiding behind my cool exterior, I was a raging mess. I was vividly imagining all the vile names under the sun that I really wanted to call that pretentious wench.

Coral was by now intensely glaring. She either had the power to mind-read my thoughts or she was trying to scare me off with one of her heinous stares. Once more, I decided to be the bigger person. I ignored her actions, instead, thanking her for my invite, after all, it was the courteous thing to do.

"Thank...thank you for the...for the," I stuttered.

Bizarrely, I was struggling to divulge the words that would not normally be so difficult to say. It didn't help with Coral vexatiously searing her eyes into mine. It was like she was burrowing into my mind, faltering me to speak — she was trying to break me!

Spit it out, Allie! My thoughts blasted, as I toiled to articulate what I really wanted to say.

"INVITE! Thank you for the invite, Coral," I blurted.

Yes, they were erratically vomited out, but none the less they were dislodged. I had no idea what had come over me, but I bet it was linked to Coral's unwelcoming behaviour and the apprehensive effect it was having over me!

"Polite, aren't we, Ollie!" she solemnly baited.

"No. No, you must have misheard me, it's quite easy, my name is Allie — Aaaa...llie!" I hurled.

"Does it matter? Ollie, Allie, both predominantly male names, wouldn't you say? Hardly feminine," she scoffed. "Anyway, there really is no point in little old you affirming your name to the likes of me. I'll have forgotten all about you after this conversation!" she guffawed.

It was just my luck that Coral had to be connected to the only two boys I had ever had feelings for. What a nasty lizard she was! I wasn't even going to grace her answer with a response.

"Boys, there's nibbles and my delicious succulent goblin punch for you to feast your ravenous mouths on," she teased, her words slipping sexually off her tongue like an erotic negligee.

She was eminently seductive which brought her great power over the twins. In the palm of her hand, they hung on to her every word like two soppy pubescent boys. To them, Coral was a phenomenal sultry divinity, and to her, they were just another plaything, a puppet if you will.

Queerly, Zach's cheeks were freshly blushed, as he too seemed to be enticed by her arousing behaviour, and if he knew it or not, I was fully aware.

It was no secret that during our college days, Coral would present herself as risqué and provocative, but tonight she was ramping up the heat more than ever before. The twins were doe-eyed and literally foaming at the mouth, unable to function as they were overcome with icky boy feelings.

"Go on, go enjoy the party and, Zach, do me a favour — take your charity with you!" she barked, ushering us deeper into the party.

∞∞∞∞

Sinister clowns, ghastly ghosts, haggard witches and fantasy fairy tale characters bayoneted the woodland flooring. They heaved as one to the music, their identities masked with the persona of others.

Coral scrupulously watched on as I affectionally clasped hands with her cousin and headed towards the gaggle of guests.

Why was she so bothered that I was with Zach? He was her cousin after all! Was it not enough that she had already stolen Kalen from me! Did she really need to intervene with Zach too? She had absolutely no say in who he chose to spend his time with, and quite frankly, her possessive interest in him was becoming a little unhealthy.

Zach was not immune to her prickly behaviour either. I had watched on as he snatched her hand mid passing, sharply mouthing her the word 'behave'.

"Like I wouldn't!" was her concise reply — her lips curling as she relished in the notion that she had hit a nerve with him.

"Take no notice of her, Allie. Once you get to know her, you'll love her — honest!" he optimistically chimed.

I sarcastically smiled in response. There was no way we would be friends, not in this lifetime anyway.

"Ok, maybe love was a tad of an exaggeration, but she's not such a bad apple, not really. She's just a little misunderstood, that's all."

There was no doubt Zach was a trier, but girls like Coral were rotten to the core and no amount of skin scrubbing would change that. Besides, I thought he had previously denied knowing the obnoxious flame-haired troll that was Coral Stone.

"You said the name Coral didn't mean anything to you?" I probed.

At 'Blossomvale' he had openly admitted he didn't know her, but it was clear he more than knew her.

"I never said I didn't know her. I said if you were referring to her as a love interest, then you were wrong, very wrong!" he hurled back.

"Oh, Zachy, before you go, there's just one more thing," Coral cooed, unsurprisingly summoning the attention back onto her.

"What now, Coral?" Zach groaned.

"You know very well WHAT!" she whispered in his ear.

Zach paused, his body language was growing increasingly uncomfortable and shifty within her company.

"My birthday present...? You have brought me my birthday present...haven't you?" she pressed; her face was steely as she glared intently at Zach.

Her eyes briefly diverted to me as she prompted a response, "Zachy?"

"Start behaving and I'll make sure you do," he urged.

He too flicked his eyes my way before responding to her ill-mannered demand.

Pursing her lips together, she absorbed his words of warning, but she wasn't happy about it. Refusing to respond, she instead opted to stare at him with a scrunched up vindictive expression. Never had I known anyone to be this piggish. I sincerely hoped this present of his was outstanding, as by the sound of things, she would kick off if not!

Click Click!

Raising her right hand and snapping her fingers twice, Coral made it distinctly clear her tiff with Zach was finished. Her concentration was now diverted, immediately fixating on to an area over and beyond our shoulders.

She was distant, appearing to be in a trancelike state, sluggishly rocking her head back and forth. I instantly turned behind to catch a glimpse of whatever it was that had mesmerised her...but nothing! There was not a single thing out of the ordinary to be seen, apart from her horde of excitable partygoers.

"Is she ok, Zach?" I questioned, worriedly.

Although I didn't care much for her attitude, I was concerned for her wellbeing. I was only human after all.

"She's fine, she just has these...what do you call them... erm, dizzy type spells. She's had them for as long as I've known her. She will be away with the fairies for a minute or two but will snap out of it shortly," maundered Zach.

Unconvinced that this was just a 'dizzy spell', I took a second glance over my shoulder.

Well, well, well, no wonder she was magnetised!

There they were, three of the most striking of men you could ever wish to see together at one time. Oddly though, they appeared to have materialised from out of nowhere, and I only say this as they were not exactly the type of trio to have gone unnoticed.

They smoothly swaggered through a chance grey mist that sheathed to no one but them. A fleeting breeze crashed against their sculpted torsos, drawing their crisp white T-shirts tightly across their chests to reveal their brawny physiques.

As they made a beeline for Coral, their fellow guests automatically took a step back, resulting in a clear partition for them to float through. The three men moved quintessentially slow as the pace around them continued at a regular rate, similar to those events that had happened at 'The Locust Lounge'.

Making their presence known, they scoured the party, gravely clocking as many individuals as possible. Their arrival was reciprocated with an assortment of frowns, snubs, winks, flirtatious waves and lip biting. It appeared that they, just like Coral, were well-known and going by some of the looks they received, they were quite the force to be reckoned with.

They were tall, toned and tasty with skin slicing cheekbones and biceps that were bursting through their black skintight T-shirts. They had turned the heads of each and every one of Coral's guests — for good and for bad. Dressed in matching ripped black skinny jeans and faux black leather jackets, they could easily pass for a well-coordinated, bad boyband of pop.

The first wore a collared rock jacket. He was the tallest of the three men. He had outgrown his wavy dirty blonde, shoulder-length highlights and sported light facial hair. The second was smaller than the third. He wore a sleeveless studded stressed jacket with cropped black hair and rough dark stubble. The last of the three wore a leather hooded biker jacket with his dark brown hair shaved to the sides and quaffed on top. All three wore fingerless leather gloves and ankle steel-toe cap boots.

It dawned on me that I too was inordinately enraptured with their arrival, which was not the best of ideas, especially with Zach standing right next to me. I would have hated for him to have jumped to conclusions, so composedly, I tugged on his arm and nodded towards the attention of my focus.

"Allie, what's the issue here? I can't see anything?" he sighed.

Huh?

Within seconds of me averting my attention, they had gone, vanishing into thin air!

"Men...there were men. Three of them. Zach. I saw them — I swear! Ask Coral! She was the one freakishly gawking at them!" I bleeped.

I couldn't blame Coral for behaving enamoured with them, but I wasn't about to admit that to Zach, was I!

"Ask her! Ask that cousin of yours!" I sternly pushed.

If anyone would know, Coral would, after all, she was the

one transfixed on them from the outset and so on.

"Ok, ok, ok, whatever makes you happy!" he relieved.

He had no interest in what I had claimed to have witnessed, but to keep the peace, he was prepared to do as I had asked, even if he was a little sarcastic in his tone.

"Right, Coral, fess up, what's all this—"

His words abruptly broke away as his eyes locked on to a transitory mist that had unanticipatedly taken shape from behind Coral.

They were back!

Speechless, I couldn't fathom out how they had made their way to Coral without passing Zach or myself. Could the fleeting thick layer of smog actually have acted as a barrier and hidden their return from view? Well, whatever it was, it was outright weird, but none of that mattered as much as their unattractive interest in Coral. They had visibly taken a shine to her, as she had with them, and funnily enough, she quickly snapped out of her so-called dizzy spell!

They snaked around her body, silent and inexpressive. It didn't take long to figure out they were her entourage. They fitted her Ice Maiden theme well. An impressive upgrade from her 'phonies', who were yet to be seen.

Synchronically, the men menacingly eyeballed Zach, alternating the same intimidating glare to myself before repeating once over. Zach stood his ground, refusing to be subdued by their childish antics.

The air was rife with the gritty scent of testosterone, speculation and trepidation as the tension between Zach and the men ascended. The party continued to play within the background, but it was clear that all eyes were alert and expectant on what was about to come and from whom.

However, the wait for them was in no way prolonged and the move was made...

...and it came from Zach.

Taking the higher ground, he squeezed my hand and took a step backwards. I presumed he would stand firm and not crumble by their bullish conduct, but instead, he had backed off. There's no denying I was proud of his response, but with respect, I was wholly confounded as to what the heck was actually going on here!

I was left to surmise, and as we now know that's never a good idea. Therefore, I could only conclude that once again we were in a school type scenario.

These men were at the top of their game. They were the elite and alongside Coral, they assisted with running the roost. No one dared to stand up to them, fight back or dictate to them, not even Zach. I was relieved he had chosen not to scrap, but at the same time I saw a conceded side to him, it was a side I didn't much like.

Relishing in their win, the men tightly squinted their cold dark eyes and wickedly flashed a half smile.

Click!

Coral who had remained impartial throughout, clicked her fingers again. Two of the cortege responded by stepping either side of her and taking an arm each. They twisted her around — her back was now directly facing us. The remaining lackey placed himself behind her, as if to protect her from any unwanted harassment.

Click!

Once more she sliced her dictatorial fingers together which resulted in their slow embarkation, but Coral wasn't quite finished there. Halting in her tracks, she shouted over her shoulder as she made one final comment.

"Don't forget, I'll see you later, Zachy...for that present you owe me," she instructed, before strutting off.

"Care to enlighten me on what that was all about?" I burst. "I know she's your cousin and all, but you have to admit that was pretty strange!" I churned.

I had to say it. I had to! Her behaviour was hardly normal. I mean she was prancing around like the queen of flaming Eldercrest and as for those men? What had they come as? Her three ripped musketeers? She needed to take a good hard look at herself as I would be a long-time dead before ever bowing down to that narcissistic mare.

Zach screwed his face as he absorbed my statement, "Seems normal to me, Allie. Granted she's a little theatrical, but I'm afraid that's just her way. As for the company she keeps, that's her business, isn't it? Try not to look too much into all of this," he mitigated, shrugging off my remarks.

"Well, can you at least tell me what the issue is with you and those men?" I probed.

"Those men which you keep referring to, are in no way shape or form men, they're nothing but puerile boys, and you would be a fool to think otherwise," he snapped.

He went on to advise me that Axel was the owner of the long glossy blondish mane. He was big, burly, rugged and wild — and particularly close to Coral.

Mace with his cropped hair and warm russet skin was the most volatile of the three, hence the nasty gash framing the side of his face.

And then there was Ike. With his neatly quaffed hair, pearly white teeth, perfectly plucked eyebrows and golden spray on tan — he was very much your modern-day man.

"If you really must know, I'm not a fan and never will be, and I most certainly do not appreciate them leading my cousin astray. That's all there is to it!" he huffed.

Fair enough, I could see his point, but I couldn't help wondering if Zach was a little jealous of all the extortionate attention that these sexy young chaps were absorbing.

"Let's eat," mumbled Zach, signalling his abrupt withdrawal from the conversation.

Full to the brim with delicious nibbles was a large collapsed tree — it was the perfect makeshift table. I mean, c'mon, you had to hand it to her, the girl was resourceful!

Now, this was also a good time if any to grill Zach about his crucial gift.

"You have brought Coral a gift...haven't you?" I probed.

The only reason I asked is that at no time had I clocked a present on his persons. Unless it was made from thin air, I highly doubted he could fit an item in those body-hugging garments of his.

"You bet. I couldn't have come empty-handed now, could I!" he replied.

"Well that's a relief, I would've hated to have seen her when she was angry," I joked. "Where is it then?" I added.

"It's on me, Allie. Don't you worry that pretty little head of yours. I have it all under control," he assured, opening the right side of his jacket to reveal a small pocket inserted into the silk lining.

"It's here, safe and sound. She can have it later, let's make her wait," he grinned, patting the pocket in an impish manner.

Zach released his hold on the jacket, allowing it to rest neatly back onto his body. I hadn't noticed it earlier, but a slight bulge appeared to poke through the fabric, underneath his chest pocket. It was clearly visible; I'm surprised I hadn't seen it before.

"Well?" I delved.

"Well, what?" he said.

"Well, what is it?" I asked.

You could tell a lot about a person by the type of gift they had hand-picked for you, and, I undeniably wanted to learn more about Zach.

"Aren't we inquisitive? It's a surprise, and let's not forget that this is for the birthday girl, and you're NOT the birthday girl, are you, Allie!" he teased.

"I appreciate that, but —,"

"But — nothing, Allie! Be patient. You'll find out soon

enough, don't you worry about that…"

He said surprises were created for a reason, and it wouldn't be a surprise if everyone knew about it. He was spot on with his reasoning, but it didn't stop the anticipation from being a sheer killer. I liked that he had a certain way of doing things, and if he didn't want to do something — he wouldn't. In a way, he was very much like Coral, straight to the point but with less of the attitude. He had rules and beliefs, as did I, and if Zach wanted me to wait, then wait I would. Although, I'd be lying if I said I wasn't just a little bit concerned as to why he was making me wait so long….

Twenty

CLOSER THAN CLOSE

Forrest wafted a large bowl of unsalted chocolate nuts underneath my nose.

"Peanut?"

"Nah, she looks like your sticky toffee pudding kind of girl. Try some cake — get it down your neck!" Heath boomed, whilst trying to force feed me the sweetest smelling raspberry-buttercream cupcakes you could imagine.

"Guys, I'm fine. Honest," I mumbled with a mouth full of heavenly goodness.

"Jelly beans then!" they crooned together, ramming their hands into a ginormous trough of assorted chewy sweets.

Their cupped palms overflowing with bright colourful gummy beans were thrust towards my tight-lipped face. I shook my head vigorously at the boys. They were plainly averse to taking no for an answer.

My tummy was full of knotted nervous energy, and no matter how tempting it was, I couldn't eat another crumb. The mere thought of what could happen this evening between me and Zach, was enough to loop another knot in my already surging entanglement. However, I reckoned it couldn't hurt to peruse the incredible spread of sweets, treats and naughty nibbles on offer.

There were stacks of crunchy cookies, masses of fluffy marshmallows, heaps of cream-filled pastries and trays of banana and chocolate pies. Glazed apple candies dangled teasingly from the come-hither limbs of the trees above — begging to be hand-plucked.

Mouthwatering trifles, flavoursome treacle tarts and glorious bowls full to the brim of chocolatey soup, garnished the sliced faces of discarded tree stumps. The amount of fudge, honeycomb bites, jelly sweets and syrup smothered fruit available for consumption was out of this world. Not to mention the lateral lying excavated tree trunks that were filled with crushed ice and playing host to an assortment of thirst-quenching drinks. There wasn't a fresh carrot stick, flaky egg vol-au-vent or chilled prawn ring in sight. This was pure sugar rush central!

"Allie, at least try a doughnut! As once those vultures come, you'll not get a look in, and they will come, trust!" piped Heath.

No sooner had he voiced his warning, then did the rabble descend on us. The earthy floor trembled with the sudden surge of voracious revellers lunging themselves into any sweet-filled gap available. With every man and woman fending for themselves, it was quite apparent that etiquette was not compulsory here.

Face upon face grappled with the goodies, overfilling their jaws until they could no longer contain the goop. Cream, syrup and saliva dribbled revoltingly through the cracks of each and every engorged mouth.

Not one to turn down an invite, 'Stonie's phonies', aka the three tacky little mermaids had arrived. Unsurprisingly, they were amongst the mob of greedy gut-busting piglets, and they wasted no time in taking centre stage at the feeding zoo.

Here they were, shovelling Victoria sponge slices, mini pecan pies and a family-sized almond tart into their mouths... and all in one go! Had the legendary Triton never told them the rules of binge eating before a swim?

Judging by the conduct of her guests, Coral had made a grave error in catering for a dessert only buffet. These partygoers were literally bouncing off the branches with the amount of sugar they were inhaling. It was as if they were eating as much as possible in one sitting for fear, they would miss out on a second helping.

Minutes was all it took for the spectacular display of gooey delights to be pulverised into a mass mess of syrupy slush. Open mouthed, I turned to Zach for his reaction, assuming he would share my sentiments, but it was evident, he did not. He sluggishly shook his head and unperturbedly shrugged his shoulders in disapproval of their greed, but the remains of a cream-filled éclair in the crook of his mouth told me otherwise. I raised a finger to the corner of my mouth and forged a cough, "you missed a bit," I tittered.

Sheepishly, Zach simpered, and with the back of his hand, he promptly removed the remains of his tell-tale scoff. Feeling slightly embarrassed, he timely excused himself, leaving me in the care of the twins.

"Goblin punch!" Forrest yelled.

"Get that down ya!" encouraged Heath.

There really was no need to deafen me, but it was becoming increasingly hard to hear anything over this blaring music.

"Come on, Allie, you must be thirsty? It will help you loosen up a bit and maybe put those nerves at bay, eh!" Forrest persisted.

He had a point; my throat was starting to feel a tad dry. Anyway, a small glass wouldn't kill me. Plus, I could do with a helping of Dutch courage before I had to come face to face with that poison filled cousin of his again!

Calm, clear and inviting — the lake was the ideal chiller. It was also in perfect reaching distance from the pulped buffet display.

Curiously floating upon 'said' liquid freezer was a hefty sized frosted bowl, and with utensil in hand, Forrest proceeded to fill the glass ladle to the rim.

The dreadful smelling liquor squelched into my delicate glass, nestling tightly together as it filled the vessel full. It was no wonder Coral had segregated this foul refreshment away from all other beverages. It smelt vulgar and positively off-putting!

Its appearance came in the colour of an unappetizing blood red, with swirls of deathly black and streaks of toxic green. It was thick in consistency, and worst of all, it contained lumps.

Forrest pushed the glass base up towards my lips, "bottoms up, Allie!" he wickedly grinned.

With the glass hovering against my skin, I was instantly hit by a whiff of its pungent odour.

"Yuk, I can't, I can't touch that! It smells like rotting flesh, and as for those lumps, no way!!" I wailed.

"Lumps?" Forrest giggled, "that would be the blackberries, they're harmless!" he assured.

"Forrest, the smell…!"

I couldn't bring myself to drink past the stench.

"It's not the best, is it," he laughed. "After a few of those bad boys, the smell will be the last thing on your mind!"

Hmmm, wasn't sure I liked the sound of that, but with the peer pressure ramping up, it was looking highly unlikely that I could pull out.

"C'mon, what exactly is this revolting concoction made of?" I quizzed.

"A little dash of rum, a glug of vodka, a swig of Tabasco, a few sprigs of mint, a handful of blackberries and one very top-secret ingredient. It's undoubtedly the best punch around, and it will give you that much-needed kick you're after!" he bragged.

"How do you know I'm lacking courage!" I snapped.

"It's written all over your face, now less moping and more drinking!" he urged.

Heath insisted on helping and took it upon himself to

pinch my nose, blocking the foul twang of drainage from hitting the back of my throat.

"Now open that cute little mouth of yours and drink!" ordered Forrest.

"Aaa...lie, Aaa...lie, Aaa...lie," the twins chanted, their faces full of expectancy, willing me to join in and let myself go.

The rim of the glass rubbed against my bottom lip as the nauseating liquid lathered my tongue and swilled through my throat. I prepared myself for a wave of intolerable retching but instead was pleasantly surprised — the taste was barely offensive. The fiery burn of tabasco blended perfectly with the cool hit of mint, providing the ideal icy-fresh aftertaste. It had a slight zing to it, which I guessed was courtesy of the secret ingredient.

"Line up another!" I joyfully declared. Granted it was good, but it was nowhere near as tasty as my dad's! Trust me, I once tried!

"Woah! What are you doing!!" boomed Zach, his outrage bringing the boys chanting to an abrupt halt.

Much to his disapproval, he happened to have rejoined us just as the evening's proceedings were beginning to hot up.

"Lads, seriously what are you playing at? That punch is lethal, she will be smashed in no time!" he bellowed, displeased.

Lethal!!!! If I had known how potent the juice was, I would never have entertained the idea.

Zach snatched the glass from out of my clasp and furiously smashed it onto the gravel below. He was anxious and fidgety, shuffling from foot to foot, refusing to make eye contact with me.

"What's the problem, Zach? I can do as I please you know," I snapped.

"Hey, I'm sorry, but I'm doing this for your own good," he said, seizing two more filled glasses from Heath.

"Moronic game you tried to play there, boys! You know damn well what would have happened if she had taken another sip of that grog!" he growled; his anger directed solely at the twins.

They declined to respond, instead concentrating on their toes, pretending not to hear a word he had to say.

"Allie, one more swig and you would have been off your face, your night would have been over before it had even started. I promised your nan I would get you home safe, and that's exactly what I intend to do," he barked.

Talk about a wrist slap and although I didn't expect a telling off, I did appreciate that he had my best interests at heart. To add further to the blow, he told me the twins were only egging me on to get a cheap laugh. The effects of the virulent punch slapping against my organs would have kept them entertained for days. They basically wanted to watch me crash and burn, but thankfully, they weren't getting that from me — not tonight.

"Sorry, Zach, the peer pressure must have got to me. This really is unlike me. It was silly and irresponsible. I don't know what I was thinking!" I bashfully whimpered.

Zach noting my indignity — cupped my head in his hands, "I didn't bring you here to get you hammered, you mean more to me than that, more than I thought you possibly could. If you let me, I'll always keep you safe, Allie," he whispered.

I couldn't argue with that. He was opening his heart to me and in return, mine was bursting with feelings I no longer wanted to contain. He was plugging the cracked hole inside me that Kalen had cruelly created. I was ready to move on, and he needed to know exactly how I felt before I was to lose him too.

"Zach...I've never been one for sharing my emotions, but you should know that when I'm with you, I feel a little lighter, a little happier, a little more like the old me. I want you to know that I'm really —"

"Yeah...hold that thought will you, I just need to sort these two prats out first!" he interrupted.

"Oh no wait, you need to hear me out! I need to tell you

something, it's incredibly important that I do," I urged.

"No, I can't be letting those two muppets get away without a warning, that's just asking for trouble. If I let them off the hook once, they will only go and do it again and again. I won't be long and besides, we have our whole lives for you to tell me...don't we?" he beamed before hotfooting it over to the twins who were now making a hasty getaway.

Standard. I was solely seconds from rupturing my heart open to him — to wholeheartedly revealing the deep desires I had within. But instead of the warm embrace I yearned for, I was left standing on my lonesome with a bloated chest. Saying that, I wasn't as alone as I had first thought, Coral made certain of that. Her eyes were never too far away from me.

If it wasn't her lawless self, gawping at me, it was one of her errand boys watching my every move. If I'm being straight, it was really beginning to grate on me. I was going to have to say something. I didn't need this hassle, not from her, not from anyone.

What irritated me the most though, was that smirk of hers. It was as wide as her ego as she basked in the awkwardness of my abandonment. I was never very good at occupying myself at the smallest of social gatherings. I would always over think the situation, never knowing how to stand, where to place my hands or how to interact. This situation was no different, in fact, it was worse.

To add to my growing embarrassment, her party people were actively congregating around her persons. There was not one individual near me. Was I discharging an unbearable odour? Or was I really that hideous or uncool, that no one dare stand in the same vicinity as me? See, there I go, overthinking everything and everyone again!

By now I had located Zach to my far right, but he was too occupied with bestowing a dressing down to the boys than to rescue me from my self-pity. I recognised he was disenchanted with the Mapleby Brothers, but surely the matter could have been resolved by now? I was in need of help, that dreadful cousin of his required restraining, but he was clearly far too busy to come to my aid. If he wasn't prepared to help, then I had to take matters into my own hands, especially as Coral was still stupidly eyeballing me!

Enough was enough, this had to stop.

"Deep breaths, girl," I coaxed. "You can do this, suck it up and have it out."

∞∞∞∞

Pounding the damp grassy soil, I marched furiously towards Coral.

I forced my way through the tight crowds of cavorting torsos that were bumping and shaking together in close proximity. With every step nearer, came a deeper more aggressive scowl from Coral.

Her men, registering my aim, instinctively slid in front of her, screening my access and blocking any sort of confrontation.

"Ooh…" I blurted,

That was odd!

For no reason at all, I had come across all peculiar and had found myself scrambling to regain my balance. I wasn't sure if it was the punch or the adrenaline, but I was beginning to feel a little woozy. I threw my hands to my knees, arched my back and sucked in a deep breath.

"Keep going," I ordered myself, throwing the feeling of giddiness to the back of my mind.

My little set back was not about to deter me, but it had awarded valuable time towards Coral's blockade and as a repercussion, the walls were now fully enforced. I couldn't reach her, I could only watch on as she paraded herself within her newly formed circle, swaying her hands in the air to the beat of the vibes.

Her men casually rocked around her, sneering my way as

they pathetically fussed upon her inflated ego. I was hell-bent on bringing her down a peg or two and with tenacity firmly on my side, I was ready to infiltrate her bubble.

To breach her protection, I would have to backtrack, skulk up through one side of the party and filter through on a blind spot. You're thinking 'genius' idea, right?

Wrong! My strategy was foiled before it had even been activated.

The men must have guessed my motif as there was no gap large enough for me to squeeze through. It was useless to thrust my way in, as they would easily catch hold of me and elbow me out. I was going around in circles, attempting to find a way to wriggle through but with every plausible bid thereafter, the circle grew tighter and tighter.

"Yes!" I quietly squeaked, seizing my opportunity and squeezing my way in via a fortuitous opening in the ring.

∞∞∞

Having found himself involved in a spat with a tanked-up guest — Ike had left his post wide open. The guest in question had consumed far too much of that sinful punch, and as a result, had wobbled his way into Ike one too many times. The outlook for this kid was not sunny, but the same could be said for me too, as my achievement was also short-lived.

Axel registering my arrival, grabbed Coral by the hand, twirled her around and pulled her in close to his body. Her claws suggestively pawed through his tussled hair, throwing his head from side-to-side as she took control of his body.

She forced him onto her poison filled neck, which he duly smothered with his lascivious lips.

Knowing I was watching, she rolled her head back in sheer ecstasy. Where was her self-respect!

As my frustration increased, so did the music. The volume had intensified to an unbearable level, becoming louder and louder until my ears could take no more.

Loose soil, stones and rocks pulsated with the reverberations. Acting like mini-missiles, they made it difficult to walk on. Once more, I began to feel a little bilious and took the sensible decision to leave rather than continue my feud with Coral. She was by no means worth it, and I was in no fit state for a squabble, but unfortunately for me, I may already have been too late!

The woodland floor was instantly sieged by partygoers, hitting the exact same area I was currently occupying. I had found myself in the midst of a rave! Hair was tossing, hips shuddering and hands fist pumping as the revellers danced berserkly to this one galling track.

I needed air!

Desperately, I nudged my way out of the crowd and back towards the location of Zach.

To my relief, he was still in place, and the business between him and the boys appeared to be cleared up, although it was now me that he seemed less than impressed with.

Briefly, he threw a glance towards me and then to his watch, an expression of gloom washing over his face as he did so. Had I disappointed him by wandering off — for trying to confront my issue? Or did he feel I was wasting valuable time in my quest to seek retaliation, when I could have been with him?

He must have witnessed my failed struggles, but I had to do something. The situation needed to be addressed if I was ever going to be accepted by her. In addition, don't forget that it was him that had left me to fend for myself! But whatever it was that was burdening him, I'm sure we could sort it out.

"Za...ohhhhh," I shrieked.

Unexpectedly, Heath had grabbed my wrist from behind and without asking, chucked me over his shoulder.

"If Zach won't ask you to dance, then I sure will!" he livelily shouted.

"Woah, woah, wait a minute," I screamed.

My chances of making amends with Zach were quickly being hampered, but Heath didn't care. I was suspended over his shoulder like a saggy rag doll and heading face first onto the makeshift dance floor.

Zach watched on, he didn't respond, he didn't say a word. He just let me go.

I flung my open arms out towards him, playfully begging him for help, but he didn't come. He stood there, arms folded, blurring into the crowd. He was making his feelings widely known.

Like a blunt axe, Heath's laughter challengingly split through my core as he carried me against my will into the centre of the floor. The same floor I had fought so hard to escape from. As you know, I was no dancer. I didn't know my left from my right, and I very much intended to make a run for it at the first opportunity.

Heath oblivious to my displeasure, dropped me roughly from his shoulders with my feet clumsily smacking the dirt. I readied myself to bolt once stability had been regained, but he was quicker than me, snatching my hand and twisting me around.

"Very nice! Come, show me what that body of yours can do!" he hissed.

His eyes lewdly fixated on my hips as he rotated me around like an incompetent ballet dancer...again...and again...and again.

Heath's pitch and demeanour towards me had notably changed, he was coming across over friendly and bordering on perverted. I in no way felt comfortable!

Alarmed at his unusual personality overhaul, I hurriedly swept the edge of the dance floor in search of Zach, praying he could see the distress I was in.

"Allie, Allie, Allie...I hate to be the one to have to tell you this, but my boy over there, really isn't that into you!" pointed out Forrest, who was now shimmying his way through the crowd towards us.

"You do realise you're pining for something that's never going to happen, don't you? It's like I said earlier, you're not his type, people like you don't belong with the Zach's of this world," he confided.

Forrest offered his hand to me, beckoning me to dance. I timidly shook my head, I didn't want to dance, and I certainly didn't want to believe what he was saying was true.

"If you don't trust me, then let me show you," he replied, guiding my eyes towards Zach who was now stood on the out-skirts of the heaving dance floor.

I caught his attention, my eyes pleading for him to come for me but as so bluntly pointed out, he didn't. He lowered his head, screwing his face in frustration as he point-blank re-fused.

"Take it..." Forrest continued, holding his hand out re-lentlessly.

He was right, Zach wasn't interested.

For some reason, he no longer wanted to know me, and I had no clue as to why. Though if he thought I was giving up that easily, then he was wrong! Oh no, I would at least show him what he was missing!

I threw my hand into Forrest's clasp.

"Now we're talking!" he rejoiced as he triumphantly punched the air.

Wrestling me off of Heath, he successfully sucked me into his suffocating arms.

After his brother's odd behaviour, I thought Forrest would be the better option, but the truth was, they were just as bad as each other. They used me, roughly sharing me back and forth like a regurgitated piece of meat.

Their bodies gyrated up against my rigid back, their groins rubbed against my hips in vulgarity whilst their wan-dering hands fondled every available piece of skin.

On and off, I conspicuously switched my eyes towards Zach, in the hope he would be hit with a pang of jealously, intervene and rescue me from my self-infliction, but my plan was futile. Instead, I was left feeling ashamed and a little violated by the twins' obscene conduct. To top that off, he now had what I would call 'unwanted' company heading his way.

∞∞∞

Erratically, she swished her way through the woodland floor with her men in tow. She was too self-absorbed with her admiring glances to acknowledge anyone else other than herself and of course her Zachy.

She spiralled over to him, fondly whispering into his ear and summoning him to dance, and like the good disciple he was, he did as he was told. I felt humiliated that Zach could be so easily led by another, and to add insult, it was by her and not me.

Coral knew exactly what she was doing, she knew she was flicking my buttons and that her actions were adding fuel to my rage. Her campaign of degradation against me was far from over as she led Zach by the hand to a space on the dance floor directly in front of me. Her men followed closely behind and once again positioned themselves around her and Zach. She giggled vindictively as she pulled my date — her relative, close up against her body!

"I see you've downgraded my cousin," she crowed, as she jabbed the blade further into my severely severed emotions.

My heart tightened, the blood rushed to my head and the anger she broiled, heated my bones. Her spiteful grin would be forever etched in my memory, as would her heartless hollow eyes as they bore into mine.

"Does she realise that's her cousin? Aren't there laws in place for that sort of lewd act!" I openly bitched.

Forrest's face was one of shock and disgust. My comment was potentially a little too close to the bone for his liking.

"Please! They're cousins, nothing more, nothing less. They have a tight bond, he's like a brother to her. Ask before you assume next time, Allie!" he snapped.

"Sorry. I wasn't aware. I don't have cousins or siblings of my own. I opened my mouth before engaging my brain."

Of course I didn't agree with that for one second, but I needed to keep Forrest's temper at bay. It was true, I had no close relatives of my own age, but I was smart enough to know that this sort of behaviour shouldn't be exhibited.

No sooner had we exchanged words than did things really begin to grow weird as Coral indecently winded her body around Zach's, slowly blowing into his ear as she pulled him in close.

She was stirring him alright — his body tense, his face hot, sticky and flustered. This steamy little scenario here would be any boys dream come true but not for Zach, he didn't seem to be exactly enjoying her public display of affection. Something wasn't quite right between them, and by the look on his face, there was more to this than he had originally let on.

Uncomfortably, Zach stood motionless, allowing Coral to explore her way around his complaisant body. Up until this point, I thought I had lost him to some incestuous extra curriculum activity, but as our eyes accidentally met (courtesy of one of Forrest's violent twists), I knew all was not lost.

Zach held my gaze for longer than Coral would have liked. It was obvious we had unfinished business to discuss. I had to win him back. I had to find out what had gone so wrong between us. No doubt Coral was behind all this, voicing her vicious feelings and fabricating untrue rumours about me to him. As a consequence, spitefully poisoning his heart against mine. I needed to talk to him, to make him understand that I wasn't the person she may have made me out to be.

I could make him happy; I knew I could. He just needed to notice me....

Twenty-One
JEALOUSY, INITIATION & LIES

As the wind gathered momentum, so did the stench of evil as it wafted through the crowd. It could mean only one thing — Coral and her men were edging in closer!

Determination in full swing, I frantically wriggled my fingers and successfully liberated my crushed palm from Forrest's grip. I was free!

Keen to act fast, I stomped my way towards the direction of the disreputable scent and into the presence of my chosen subject.

With my balance resting on my tip toes, I picked up my heels and gave a firm tap on his oversized shoulder.

"Oi, 'Muscles', fancy a dance?" I pushfully asked.

This was sure to make Zach sick with envy, as he himself had pretty much declared he despised the very ground they walked on. Without question, this would be my best shot at provoking an emotion or two.

My unsuspecting target was Axel, the biggest, gnarliest-looking of all three. Slowly, he twisted his finely crafted physique around to greet me. This was shortly followed by his full-bodied hair which came to rest sexily on his broad shoulders.

Loathsomely, he looked down upon my quivering body as I geared myself up to make my next move.

I had taken a big risk, granted it was a stupid one, but it was all I could think of to do in order to win Zach back.

Assertively, Axel took a step towards me, and placing one hand on my waist, he growled, "that's if you can handle me, 'Bones'!"

His eyes locked onto mine as he flicked my flimsy frame back into the centre of the crowded dance floor. His wide hands wasted no time in working their way around my body, moving me into position after position. He was lapping up every second of my uneasiness.

His grip was tight, forceful, bordering on painful, but any discomfort I had was short-term as the ache quickly evolved into pleasure — my plan was beginning to pay off!

The twins were first to acknowledge my stunt but blatantly pretended to not have viewed my public display. Continuing to dance, they shuffled their feet from side-to-side, all the while keeping a strict watch on me from the corner of their eyes.

Zach had too taken notice. His lips locked tightly, his fists pulsating as his jealousy flowed onto the dance floor like a casual stream.

At last!! I finally had his attention; his emotions were stirring, and a reaction was forthcoming. I needn't carry on this farce for another second, as it was obvious I had Zach exactly where I wanted him. Axel, on the other hand, was not as obliging to cease our spontaneous liaison.

Oblivious to my ulterior motive, Axel continued to toy with me, gradually becoming more and more aggressive. He also took it upon himself to invite extras into our one-on-one — pushing me up against Mace and passing me on to Ike like a baton.

Back and forth they flung me, reeling me in and out, playing with me for sport. Ike finally brought the turbulence to a close by tigerishly releasing me into the midst of their circle.

Disorientated, I hit the floor arse first. I'd messed up.

All three of them sneered down upon me. Their combined heavy breathing resembled a pack of panting wild dogs.

This situation I had stupidly found myself in was far from

my own doing. It was extremely odd, heated and not what I had anticipated at all.

I had the overwhelming urge to make my excuses and run. One of them I could likely handle but all three of them... well that wasn't what I had signed myself up for.

"Ok, chaps, thanks for the dance but I think I've had enough excitement," I edgily exclaimed.

The men wickedly grinned at one another, their eyes wide and shifty. They were buzzing off my jitters.

"Gents, don't mind if I cut in, do you?" the voice rhetorically asked.

He never gave them a chance to answer — barging his way into the circle and snatching away my hand.

"Thank you," I bashfully mouthed.

In all honesty, it was about time Zach had made his move, but better late than never I suppose!

His timing actually couldn't have been more apt. The men were starting to give me chills and not in a good way. This scenario was all but perfect if it hadn't had been for old 'Muscles' throwing himself firmly onto my wrist!

Axel wasn't the type of man to just let me go, and I hoped Zach wasn't either. I was in a twisted tug of war, yanked from left to right, my sides groaning in pain with each obstinate tug.

Zach and Axel invasively concentrated into one another's eyes, fiercely demanding that the other back down.

"Me and 'Bones' here are in no way finished. I suggest you step back and wait until I'm done!" roared Axel.

"Would the pair of you just let go!" I yelped, to no avail. "Let go, let go, let go!" I screamed.

Despite my pleas, both boys refused to relent, acting as stubborn as the other! They were proving impossible to please.

"Ok...let me finish off here with Axel and then I'm all yours, Zach!" I flimsily suggested.

Weak? Yes. But it was the best negotiation tactic I had to

offer right now, and apparently, I was not the only one with little faith in my reasoning. As although the grip on both my over stretched limbs had been loosened, it was clear that neither men were about to give in.

"This is ridiculous, one of you has to be the bigger person and back down!" I frustratingly shrilled.

My plea annoyingly went unheard as they remained firm, unwilling to compromise.

∞∞∞∞

Unsuspecting, I ejected a tiresome cry from my emotionally drained lungs. However, this abrupt yelp of mine was not in disgruntlement but rather of shock as Forrest and Heath piled into the stand-off.

Much to my surprise and relief, they had rammed into the altercation, bulldozing me from the grips of both boys. The unexpected force combined with their incredible strength was totally unforeseen by all of us.

"Operation Allie, executed, sir!", saluted Heath as he stood to attention before initiating another one of his boisterous high fives.

"Good drills, my man, good drills," jeered Forrest.

He was most pleased with their efforts and made no attempt to hide it.

"Thanks guys, I really appreciate you helping me out there!" I breathed, with ease.

Plucked from their hold, I was still within view but thankfully out of reaching distance. They could carry on their 'my balls, are bigger than your balls' match without me!

"No worries, happy to help a damsel in distress, but next time do me favour, and pick your dancing partners a little more wisely," bit Forrest.

I couldn't agree more. I was highly embarrassed about the whole saga but what was done was done. I just hoped I hadn't caused too much trouble for Zach.

"Now, as you're not otherwise engaged, I suggest you owe me the rest of our dance," he forcefully added.

"I'm so sorry, that was downright rude of me. The truth is, I only ever wanted Zach to notice me," I explained, hoping my reasons would suffice. "He didn't seem the slightest bit fazed with me dancing with you two. I had no choice but to bring in a threat!"

The twins stared at me in amazement, they didn't have to say a word for me to know they were unimpressed with my scheming.

"Well…it worked, didn't it!" I rejoiced.

I was met with yet more silence and the added bonus of a double disapproving shake of the head. This was insane! I was now pleading my innocence to the very two people who hadn't exactly been angels on the dance floor or with the punch! If I recall, they were all fingers and no manners!

They continued to remain silent which of course intensified my guilt, making the whole situation ten times worse than it needed to be!

"Why is Zach so threatened by them? Tell me!" I demanded.

I was engulfed in frustration, completely spent with this whole cold shoulder routine.

"I'll tell you what! I am sick to death of hearing you gush about Romeo over there! Any issues you have, lie with him. He's accountable for his own actions, not us!" ranted Forrest.

He meant what he said, and with nothing left to say, he grabbed me by the arm and flung me back onto the dance floor.

The music was deeper and darker than before, and the moves thrown by Coral's guests were lethargically draining to watch. They were blunter, fiercer and worryingly unhinged.

The twins instantly joined in, swivelling their heads around into the motion of a circle. Frantically jumping on the spot — they were out of control!

Meanwhile, Zach had finished his stand-off with Axel and

had now found himself in an angry confrontation with Coral. His finger wagging harshly in her face as he expressed his annoyance.

Coral was stood rigid, focusing deeply into his eyes. She appeared to be soaking in his every word like a dirty old sponge. Unfortunately, the music was far too overpowering and disorientating for me to lip-read a word he was shouting!

Heath thudded the floor to the beats as he moved in closer towards me. His grubby hands wrapped around my neck, moulding me tightly into his body. Every attempt to catch the attention of Zach was scarpered by a twist, twirl or a pass to Forrest. It was almost like they were intentionally causing diversions.

"Dance!" grimaced Forrest, yanking me around the floor and ordering me to focus.

I could understand his anger completely. I was acting up, being a nuisance, behaving a little possessive perhaps. He was taking his routine very seriously. He meant business and was not inspired by my slapdash moves. He was in time to the music, hitting every beat and executing each move with splendid precision. He was intent on letting his feet do the distracting, and if he didn't have my full attention before, he certainly had it now. I had no idea he possessed such moves. This, however, was not the only event to astound me...there was more!

"What the..." I breathlessly gasped.

I had been so engrossed by the competency of Forrest's toes, that I had failed to acknowledge everyone else at the party dancing in sync to the same step.

"Glad you finally noticed, Allie! This here is your initiation dance," ecstatically beamed Heath.

"Initi...what!" I choked.

I didn't have a chance to fully release my horrified gasp before he filled me in on the ludicrous truth. Apparently, it was an unwritten rule that if any 'fresh meat' were to find themselves present at one of Coral's selective parties, then they were obliged to take part in an inauguration. This came in the form of a dance. It was Coral's 'thing'! She saw the dance as a bond — us being the grateful abiding subjects and her, the accommodating and generous ruler.

This one night of uninhibited frolicking would tie us together for eternity or thereabouts. Anyone not performing to her standards, showed a lack of respect and commitment towards her. They were extracted immediately from the evening's proceedings by her heavies, never to return (as I was about to witness).

Ike bounded his way over to a meek blonde-haired girl, whom was dressed as a bloodied bride. Her moves were a little muted compared to that of her peers but nothing that warranted a booting out. Her performance, however, was not acceptable in the eyes of Coral, and she was removed promptly.

No one had ever broken the bond from non-engagement, but there was always the chance of removal if you were underperforming. Everyone bar me was well-rehearsed, adamant not to put a toe wrong for fear of expulsion.

Impressive was not a strong enough word to cover the bumping, winding and grinding of dance unison that I was beholding.

"Oh right, well I best dance then!" I nervously laughed.

Imagine the joy Coral would receive if she had the golden opportunity to banish me.

Well I can tell you, she wasn't getting that satisfaction from me!

I moved in step with Forrest. I gave it my all, and to be honest it wasn't that hard to pick up. They were simple steps choreographed from a simple person!

Coral and Zach were the only two not to be dancing, still locked in a debate of some sorts.

"Shame she's exempt from a barring," I hissed.

"Allie, pack it in! Coral's party. Coral's rules!" Forrest snapped, unimpressed by my catty outburst, but in my defence, it was well justified.

Head back down, I focused on my footwork, keen to blend in.

Left foot forward, right foot back, wind the body and shuffle three steps.

Easy! And this coming from the girl who wouldn't, couldn't dance. However, my newly acquainted skill was soon to be abolished when my concentration was swiftly broken.

∞∞∞∞

"Get off!" I barked, as I was roughly plucked away from Forrest by my old friend 'Muscles'!

Forrest noting my alarmed expression was quick to re-assure me that this was all part of the initiation, "it's all change Allie. It's part of the routine. Go with it!"

See, as I was the 'fresh meat' (the one and only might I add), it was custom to be selected for a dance by one of the men, and unluckily for me it was Axel who had decided to take one for the team.

"Told you I would finish our dance, didn't I, 'Bones'!" he grunted.

Crikey, this was not the best of situations, but rules were rules, and at least I wasn't being marched out!

Slipping back into routine, I copied Axel step for step.

Left foot forward, right foot back, wind the body and shuffle three steps.

You know it wasn't so bad after all, which was mainly down to the fact his hands weren't pawing the length of my body!

After a few minutes of toe tapping, the music began to change tempo. The rhythm unmistakably slower, with an eerie echo filtering through — filling the woods with a bone-chilling yet inquisitive feel.

I knew I had heard this disconcerting sound before. I couldn't quite recall where...but it wouldn't be too long in the night before I was to remember....

Coral's guests swayed with the pace, rocking from side-to-side, positioning themselves shoulder to shoulder and in the formation of a ring.

They appeared dazed, shuffling in a zombielike trance. Had the sugar overload finally taken its toll? Seemed that way!

"Look at me, princess," squawked Axel.

I couldn't. I was too embarrassed by the level of famil-iarity he was flaunting towards me, and I wasn't the only one to notice. All eyes were now firmly on me as Axel rotated our embraced bodies into the middle of the ring.

Violently, he grabbed my chin and pulled my face toward his.

"Dance! Unless you're aiming to be pulled from the party before it's even started!" he snarled, with hostility baring through his pearly white teeth.

"Keep calm and ride it out," I quietly ordered myself.

In any other situation, I would be too proud to walk, but the more Axel growled at me, the more I realised this wasn't worth the fight.

"Give me your attention, girl!" he spat.

That's it! I didn't care if I was eliminated from this party and any other party that involved Coral and those bitch boys of hers. I quit!

I rapidly jerked my hand with the full intention of leav-ing the party (and his grasp), but there was no give. He had me firmly locked in his hold.

He reeled me in, rolled me out and reeled me in once more. He was making it known, he could do whatever he wanted with me, and there was no way I could resist it — he was strong, unnaturally so.

Every attempt of breaking free was met with a tighter

squeeze of the hand. There was no choice for me, but to dance.

"There's a good girl, dance nicely and I might even let you suck my lip!" he drooled.

"You have to be joking, you're just a nice haircut and a good set of teeth, nothing special!" I scoffed.

I was repulsed by his blatant arrogance.

"Pfft, tell me...what is your type then, 'Bones'?" he jeered.

I would have thought it was obvious. I had practically spent most my night pining for him — secretly begging for him to save me.

With Zach on my mind, I turned towards him, only to find him looking straight back at me.

Signalling with my eyes, I took the opportunity to ask for a little help, but once again, was met with that demoralising sigh of his. Where had my cheeky, brave, confident soldier gone? He was barely recognisable, and to add another blow, he was joining the ring with Coral.

He wasn't bothered in the slightest that I was nuzzling up to 'Muscles', not like before anyway. He was now too besotted with that maggot-infested cousin of his to care.

"Well, well, well, I should have known he was your type. Tragic! Well know this, 'Bones', you're not his type, never have been, never will be!"

His words ricocheted through my body, colliding with my vital organs and targeting the heart for maximum impact.

"Like you would know!" I bleated.

I was suffocating in my own sick with the amount of people presuming I wasn't the right kind of girl for Zach!

"Hah! He doesn't do girls like you, especially scrawny ones!" he bellowed.

I was hurt. Just a girl was I! A meaningless insignificant girl? Did he not see me as a woman? I had always been told by Nan I was wise for my years, so his words hardly rang true. His sentiments were cowardly and a pathetic attempt on influencing me to back off.

"He only wants a woman, does he? Sees me as an immature girl, does he!" I squeaked.

Now was probably not the right time to rant in full view of Zach, but I was spilling over with animosity.

"Did I actually say those exact words?" snapped Axel.

"Well, no, but it's what you meant," I sadly mumbled. "Why's he not into me? Surely he wouldn't have invited me if he wasn't interested?" I prodded.

I needed answers, and as much as I hated to impart on 'Muscles', he was the only one telling me how it really was.

"Can't you work it out already? You're nothing but a girl, why would he —"

"Don't mind me! It's all change, and this time I'm taking back my date!" Zach declared.

Not only had he severed Axel's sentence, but he had cut off his hold too. Leaving him to crawl back to a miffed face Coral, whose eyes were now firmly tapping into my skin as Zach pulled my hands into his.

"Heeeey," he whispered, almost apologetically.

"Hey," I half smiled, struggling to remain solemn at him.

Soft and drawn out, I could tell he was sorry for the way he had acted by the way in which he greeted me.

"Took your time?" I grumpily groaned. "Don't suppose you want to tell me what's been playing on your mind all night now, do you?" I quizzed.

I was after honest genuine answers, and Zach was now wise enough to know I wasn't about to take any nonsense from him.

"You're right. It's Coral. She's hard work. You have no idea what I'm up against," complained Zach.

I could, I really could! After all I had been swaying around to this induction nonsense for more than five minutes now!

Left foot forward, right foot back, wind the body and shuffle three steps.

We continued to dance in step, back and forth, round and

round with the thrum of the music failing to let up. Despairingly, it didn't seem to want to end anytime soon. On and on, it freakishly hummed, sending me into a state of drowsiness. Frankly, it was taking its toll on me. No wonder Coral had chosen to drag out the initiation. It certainly would weed out the weak from the strong.

"What's her problem? Is it me? What were you arguing about? Why all the secrets?" I yawned.

"Because...because it doesn't matter. I'm here. She's over there. No one's bothering no one, so let's leave it be, shall we!" he commanded.

"I know you're lying, your nostrils are flaring!" I blurted.

"My what? Stop obsessing over every little detail, will you!" he shot.

I had studied that face of his for weeks now and could confidently detect when he was lying or not. His nostrils gave him away, flaring out when he was hiding the truth. I first noticed this cute little trait of his a week or so back when asking for the last sweet from his packet of sugary goodies.

"None left," he replied, his nose flaring as he deviously lobbed the last chewy centred toffee into his mouth.

They were only white lies. The kind I didn't mind, but I refused to be lied to when it came to the big issues, like my easily bruised heart for example! I wouldn't be treated like second best. He had his chance to confess but had thrown it all away for her, and I wasn't going to entertain this crap anymore.

With a glint of sadness in my eyes, I resolutely asked Zach to escort me home. If it hadn't had been for my appalling sense of direction, I would have stormed out those woods like the independent woman I likened to be. Nonetheless, a night lost in the dark, creepy-crawly woods didn't quite appeal to me.

"I can't. I'm sorry...it's too late!" vetoed Zach without reason.

"What? What do you mean it's too late?" I appealed, stamping my feet like an overtired toddler.

By now, Coral's men had already stepped out from the initiation ring and were worryingly edging in closer towards me. With little time to change his mind, I had to act fast.

"Zach, please? I want to go home. I've had enough. Take me home, I beg you!" I wailed.

Talk about awful timing. I was not at all happy about having to change partners again, especially when I had only just reconnected with Zach.

With the men in reaching distance, I glanced at Coral's remaining guests in the hope that one of them had left enough space within the ring for me to break free. Still clearly brainwashed by my inauguration, they continued to do exactly as expected of them, following the script wholly.

Clasping hands, they step by step closed the gap which had been left in wake of the men. Unfortunately for me, the circumambient ring was now tighter and smaller than ever before — I was trapped!

With the insufficient breath I now had escaping me, I was feeling horribly claustrophobic and slightly lightheaded. Zach didn't look too perky either!

Knowing he didn't have long left, he hurriedly leant his body in close to mine.

"What, what's wrong?" I prompted, in response to his shifty demeanour.

Cupping my ear, Zach gently whispered, "I've not been entirely honest with you..."

Twenty-Two

TOE-DIPPING

Viciously, he prised my arm away — my fingers scraping against Zach's bones as I was mercilessly hoisted away.

"All change, Zachary," growled Ike.

"Zaaach! What do you mean?" I screamed, daunted and confused.

Zach stared vacantly at me, his lip quivering. I could see he wanted to speak, but his words were unable to flow. Instead he crumpled, the floor taking the impact of his eyes as he sheepishly sloped off and out of view.

I now had the overwhelming sense that this was NOT and had never been an initiation test. Something was brewing and it involved me at the forefront. Things were not as innocent as they had once seemed.

Gravely, I was now smack-bang in the middle of the circle with Ike griping durably onto my shuddery hand. It was like he had the strength of a hundred men within that one and only limb!

Mace not wanting to miss out, sternly took ownership of my free hand and led me into the formation of the ring; with Ike following up at the rear.

On our entry, the circle expanded, opening up and allowing me to breathe. The relief of confinement quickly escaping me as I proceeded to follow Mace, hand-in-hand, in a circular anti-clockwise motion. It was at this point that a dozen or so of Coral's guests immediately began to systematically drop out from their allocated spaces within the ring.

Bizarrely, they proceeded to prance around solely in their own little world on the outskirts.

Those that did remain, promptly opened up their area, loosely stretched out their connecting arms and enabled themselves room to dance. Once in place, the step quickly turned from a shuffle into a gloomy skip.

With myself firmly positioned within the ring, the likelihood of me breaking free was slim to none. I was going absolutely nowhere!

Coral who was of course one of the solo hoofers, spiralled her delicate frame into the heart of the circle. Drawn out and over dramatic, she was making her arrival well-known.

Once satisfied with her entrance, she cut back into the flouncing ring and situated herself next to Axel, which also happened to be directly opposite myself. With her highness in full flow, the creepy ritual continued.

The pace of the music was beginning to increase as did the speed of dance. The skip had switched into a nippy side-step, and we were now directly facing one another, rather than staring at the back of each other's scalps!

The smiling faces that were once looking back at me, bar Coral and Axel, were now distorted, ill-boding flickers. Undeniably, all eyes were on the sport — aka me!

Faster and faster we bounced, my legs dragging as I fought against the exhaustion. I appeared to be the only one in difficulty as I struggled to keep up.

Oddly, my fatigue happened to coincide with a notable change in music. Let me make it clear, I wasn't sure exactly when it happened as I was far too busy trying to breathe than pinpoint exact timings, but the beat of the music was no more.

It had slowly crept away, leaving only that familiar eerie wind chiming mewl to weave through the circle. The malignant shrill pouring from Coral's trap and the intermitting whoosh formed from the whisk of our cavorting bodies, were the only two noises to infiltrate the sound.

"Enough's enough now, boys!" I flapped, though my words had fallen on deaf ears.

Ike and Mace failed to react. Instead they continued to focus straight ahead, dedicated to the music and dance in hand.

∞∞∞∞

As darkness loomed above, the bleak grey clouds swelled, streaming in the same direction as our circle. The Willow trees frenziedly swayed from side-to-side, lashing the air with their agitated branches. The once placid lake churned and bubbled, threatening to flood.

Me? My head was heavy, and my heart was pounding at a dangerously slow rate. I willed myself to wriggle free, but the signals I sent from my brain were incapable of reaching my limbs. Powerless, I was trapped in a never-ending ring of blurred faces and demented leaping.

To top it off, the skies had violently opened, saturating our heaving bodies with what felt like a month's worth of rain. The dreary sky, the autumnal woodland and the assembly of multi-coloured bodies collided collectively as we spun at velocity — blending as one.

There was one thing though that remained unchanged. It was as clear as day when everything else was blurred, and it went by the name of Coral.

Incontestably, it was just me and her — those hate filled eyes glaring back at me. She let out a cackle, her head rolling back and forth in glee. She was having the time of her life.

I tried to scream, hoping someone would hear my distress, putting a stop to whatever it was that this was, but the words never came.

With my motion paralysed, I had accepted it was all but

my eyes that had failed me. They were still by my side, show-ing me what needed to be seen. They knew I had found myself in an antagonistic situation and had watched as Zach jilted me, leaving me to fend for myself.

I had so many unanswered questions! What was happen-ing? Why me? Who exactly was Coral, and what was Zach's game? I thought I meant something to him, but he had proved me wrong in the most spiteful of ways.

I'm not even sure if having my sight was a positive thing after all. Yes, they couldn't lie to me — especially my heart, but neither could they sugar-coat the harshest of reality. Yet worse than that, they were about to open my eyes to a whole new world, a world I could've never imagined existed.

At first, I thought my imagination was tripping from that earlier slurp of punch, but now I wasn't as convinced.

It all started with a small crack, no bigger than a dent which had taken shape on the muddy earth within the middle of the circle. Coral's guests hadn't seemed to notice, or if they had, they didn't seem fazed and continued to pound the floor regardless, causing its length to double in size.

Slowly but surely the crack widened, and as it did, the floor ultimately began to shake, resulting in a steady flow of tremors shooting through my tensed joints. With every trem-ble that impacted my body, the stiffness in my legs began to weaken, leaving a wobbly feeling, much like jelly.

It wasn't ideal, but hands down I would take the feeling of pliability than suffer another second with the wooden beams I had become conditioned too!

With a lack of hysteria escaping the mouths of Coral's guests — it appeared I was the only one reaching for the panic button! Unable to communicate, I had no way of verbally at-tracting their attention or alerting them of our arising pre-dicament.

I couldn't be sure of the actual cause of cracking, but the possibility of adverse weather conditions couldn't be ruled out. We could well be dealing with the beginnings of a sinkhole but yet here we were provoking the probability.

To my alleviation and that of the turf, the pace of the dance was thankfully beginning to diminish, although the damage had already been set. That small dent had amplified, exposing a gaping hole the size of a large, rounded, family-sized trampoline. The ground had finally yielded — gradually crumbling away from the irresponsible behaviour of Coral and her regime!

I shunted my head forwards and down, positioning myself to peer into the depths of the crater to view what lied beneath.

My presumption was unbelievably dumfounded, as I half expected to view a soiled interior with a tunnellike quality, which would perhaps lead me to Lucifer's dwell! I wasn't a churchgoer, and to tell you the truth, I wasn't very religious. I did, however, believe there was a heaven, so surely there was the possibility of a hell?

I didn't need to worry about a burning fire pit though, as the wretched smell of evil seeping from its core was more than ample.

Contrary to a dirty great big hole, a never-ending tunnel or the satanic abode I envisaged, I was instead met with a vision I would never have considered.

What was left from the disintegration of trampled grass and flaking soil was a pitch-black backdrop. I could see no tunnel or indeed how far the cavity had spread.

The profoundness of the pit was masked by an occult blanket of darkness, encompassing thousands of twinkling dots that resembled nighttime stars. They drifted effortlessly within, swirling at the same pace and in the same anti-clockwise direction as the ring.

As beautiful as the sight of these stars were and as much as I wanted to dip my toe in, I had a daunting feeling that if I went in, I wouldn't come back out.

And worse than that, the hole appeared to be lined with the presence of gushing indigo-metallic water — the Baltic type, the type that would blister your skin just by spitting on it.

I wasn't naive, I knew there was something not quite right about this glitzy crater, you would be delusional to think otherwise.

Never had I heard of such stories as the ground opening up to reveal what looked like a watery universe, but it had happened, and like I previously mentioned, my eyes didn't lie.

I figured there could only be three possible reasons for what was occurring.

One, I had unintentionally found myself mixed up in some sort of cult — witches perhaps? I wouldn't put it past Coral, she was the biggest hag of them all. Oh, and the signs were all there weren't they...nasty piece of work, awful cackle, not to mention her appearance from off of 'Hags Alley'. Maybe she was related to Blythe, what a twist that would be! This was certainly the top runner but seemed a bit farfetched.

Then there was possibility number two...sinkhole! An abnormal amount of water had been drenched upon not only me but on our earthy centre stage, and in such a short space of time too. Couple that with the effects of our combined weight and this ridiculous dance ritual and you had yourself a weak platform.

The curious lining of blue polished water — I could kind of explain...but the sparkly void? I simply couldn't process a reason for its existence! So, number three, my favourite and overall winner — the dreaded drugs!

I could well be fantasising the whole episode, concocting this elaborate fantasy as I went along my night.

Coral had most likely paid those twins of hers to slip an illegal substance of some sort into my punch. I had felt woozy not long after the juice had splashed upon my lips. This would definitely give reason for the twins sudden strange behaviour and as to why Zach was keeping his distance from me.

For all I knew, I could have been making a right tit of myself and not to mention him. It was no wonder he had backed off. This was decidedly the likeliest of all three options, it therefore had to be right. The disorientation, the drowsiness, the distortion, the hallucinations...it all made sense. I was drugged!

Reassured, I rolled my head and dropped my eyelids. It was a huge comfort to know I wasn't insane. This right here was all in the mind, there was no tedious choreography, no bottomless pit and certainly no special effects. Surely it wouldn't take much longer for these unpleasant side effects to dwindle and for my ordeal to finally be over. No more illusions, no more dancing and no more ghastly Coral.

I had to admit, I did feel extremely alert and focused for someone who had unknowingly been stoned, but I carried on regardless, pressing on with the consequences, ultimately waiting for this nightmare to end. Though I couldn't help speculate if my reactions, thoughts and feelings would remain as intact as they were? I'd never so much as touched a drug before, let alone considered the side effects, so your guess was as good as mine!

With my sense of awareness on heightened alert, I was questionably quick to notice that I wasn't the only person transfixed by the generous glitzy wet hole. Coral had also been carefully watching events unfold and more to the point was now firmly glaring at me again.

"Ready to take a little trip?" she crowed.

Even though I had convinced myself I was fantasising, I refused to stand still — denying her the chance to place me through any sort of ordeal — make believe or not!

I thrashed my shoulders, desperately attempting to release my palms from the claws of Ike and Mace.

"What's the matter, Allie...a little stuck, are we?" she cackled.

I was seriously beginning to question if drugs were genuinely at play here. The sense of fear and the throe of pain seemed all too real to be anything else. I was in this moment, living this misery and though my body was no longer mine, I at least had control over my own mind.

Coral, on the other hand, was firing on all cylinders. She had full power and I was the worthless putty in her hand. The sight of her ever-increasing smarmy face driven on by my circumstance made me feel sick to the stomach. The more I dwelled on the preposterous situation I had found myself in, the more aggravated I became.

My face, ruby raw with anger was a prime example of the disappointment I had for myself. It brewed within and all for what…!

All for a boy, that's what!

Not a man. A boy! An egocentric deserter who couldn't care less about what was to happen to me. A boy that used, lied and discarded me. A boy who had failed to find his backbone, denying me any sort of intel on what this was all about!

If I had the means to speak, scream or even shout — I wouldn't bother. To waste my precious breath on Coral or on Zach for that matter, was a breath not worth having.

Twenty-Three
WHAT THE!

Dangerously close to the edge of this abominable hole were my average size six feet. I had always considered my hooves to be of an adequate size. Never cared for them smaller nor had I required them bigger. That, however, was until they had found themselves peering over the edge of a disastrous-looking pit! I was crying out for a dainty size four right about now, heck even a five and a half would suffice.

I could actually feel the lumpy particles of gravel breaking away beneath my heels as the circle continued its cycle.

Coral's guests happily stomped the ring. They didn't wobble, jiggle or jerk or show any signs of angst. In addition, it appeared I was the only one to be unnerved, the only one bar Coral that was aware of my anticipated fate.

This whole situation felt increasingly all-too real for me not to take it seriously. I knew I needed help!

I darted my eyes towards the twins, who were opposite and several bodies to the left. They would surely be able to offer me some sort of comfort, right?

Wrong! Their bodies continued to skip to the rhythm of the motion. Their focus coldly gnawing at my skin, transfixed on me as I begged with my eyes for them to remove me from this dicey situation.

See-sawing from brother to brother, I longed for one of them to register my inner screams of help, yet nothing! Their optics were dead, empty shells, oblivious to my plea of desperation.

I inaudibly grimaced as my foot slipped on the fast collapsing brittle soil.

Of course, no one had heard my feeble whimper apart from Coral, who was pleasurably licking her lips at the sight of my left leg skidding towards the grave below.

Haplessly for her, I had mustered enough fuel in my belly to drag my blundering limb from up and out of the danger zone.

"Next time you won't be so lucky, and by the looks of things, you don't have much of that time left!" she chomped.

She was right, there wasn't a considerable amount of time to spare before the ground was to cave in from underneath my toes and swallow me up whole.

"Goodbye you cruel, cruel world," I softly grizzled.

I was nowhere near ready to leave this earth. I had my entire life waiting for me and to end it in these macabre conditions...well, it would be a bloody waste.

Then there was Mum and Nan to consider! What would they think of me? Would they automatically assume I had selfishly run away with Zach, without so much as a farewell? Or thinking the worst, would they conclude I had been kidnapped and murdered, my body dumped, never to be traced. Maybe one day, when time had passed, they would eventually stumble across the grizzly truth and discover I had been consumed to death by a pitiless crater.

They would have no remains, no body to grieve, no explanation — no peace.

At least with Dad, we had our answers, we were able to mourn for him, but I couldn't put them through the turmoil again. It wasn't fair to leave them behind, to weep for me and all for the sake of a boy.

My eyes welled with hurt, grief and most of all confusion. I couldn't understand how a simple attraction had led to this.

"Awwww, poor baby girl, you need a hanky? Or do you want my Zachy to come and kiss those snivelling tears of yours away?" she derided.

"Don't you dare cry!" I inwardly screamed at myself.

Stark determination was now all I had to get me through. If I was going to die then I would go with my head held high, no tears, no shame. I took one last deep breath and stared proudly into Coral's cutting glare. I wasn't afraid of her, never had been but it was time to accept my fate. I braced myself.

∞∞∞

Bottling my breath, my lips had become rigid — stunning my airways into a state of fleeting dormancy.

Unbeknown to me, the internal panic I had anticipated on releasing, was instead exchanged for a welcoming sigh of solace. Escaping my lungs, it allowed the warmest of smiles to defrost my misgivings, spreading light and joy across my cheeks.

If you had thought I had found peace with the situation or that I had devised some genius getaway with minutes to spare — then you would be wrong! No, this was far more superior, this was a sighting of a familiar face from days gone by, and for those split seconds, I had all but forgotten the danger I was in.

My body was overcome with affection, relief seeping through me as I was blessed to view his perfect face one final time. Never had I felt as appreciative as I did right now on feeling his warmth against my skin.

Had I confused him with another? Was I delirious from the shock my body had been thrust into? Or had I forgotten the pain that man had put me through? Nope, nope and nope. I wasn't confused at all.

With the dance still in motion, it felt like the world and everyone within it was still spinning apart from me — and him.

He had come before me and held my gaze, allowing those

deep and meaningful eyes of his to burn through mine. We were static. Locked together within the moment via a spiritual connection, and although I was aware we were still moving, I felt very much removed from the ring.

He was one of a kind, and I knew he would try his utmost to fight for me, even if there was very little he could physically do.

"It's you," I whispered contently.

My dear Baxley had returned and at such a pivotal time too.

With one last admiring look and a puff of his chest, he signalled it was time — battle was about to commence. For someone so small, he was incredibly brave and twice the man that Zach would ever be. Unlike my traitor, this one cared enough to throw himself in front of me, no matter the danger that lay ahead.

∞∞∞

Wasting no time in assisting me with my frightful plight, he took to the stage, expanding his exquisite wings to their full potential. Doubling in size, they were in their most powerful of forms. I was in awe of him. Charmed by his beauty and blessed by his courage.

The odds though were not in his favour, but whatever the outcome, I at least knew my special friend had tried and for that, I would be eternally grateful.

Baxley blasted himself into the heavens above. Generating speed, increasing in excess the further he flew. Once enough momentum had been gathered, he took a U-turn, catapulting himself down towards earth. His wings elegantly coiling into a glorious diamond shape as he plummeted at a rapid rate. The target was the circle, and with his location pinpointed, he made every effort to hit it.

He somersaulted in, erratically beating his mighty wings

at as many gormless guests as he possibly could. The thrashings were extraordinarily potent, so much so, those who were battered scowled in distress, their concentration splintered. Baxley had created enough turbulence to disrupt the ritual, slacking down the speed and causing the ground to regenerate.

Grit by grit, the hole leisurely began to close back up upon itself.

I couldn't believe my eyes, my brave friend who was nothing more than a delicate butterfly, was by all accounts saving my life. By pummelling Coral's guests, he had crippled the rings strength. They appeared to be the link that held the force in place, and without them, it dwindled.

The power the ring held over me began to waiver too. My body was more responsive and my voice was louder and clearer. I was now mine to control.

I hurriedly soaked in my surroundings, eager to plan my next move and to keep a track of Baxley who was dashing around left, right and centre. I needed to be there for him — like he had been for me. I wouldn't let him down, not after all he had done.

On my quest to protect, I caught sight of a dark figure lingering over Coral's shoulder. I could just about make out a silhouette — it was definitely male. He vaulted towards the ring, fearlessly head-locking men and women from behind, and dragging their obedient torsos from out of the circle. As soon as one individual was forcibly removed, the remaining docile guests would seamlessly close the gap — and one by one they fell.

Down went the phonies.

Down went the Mapleby brothers.

Down they all fell, and although we were not as erratic, we were still moving at some speed, which made it near on impossible to focus. I was, however, more than certain that this dark blurry figure belonged to Zach.

Baxley's determination continued to astound me. His

strength inspirational as he persevered, stunning the ring into disarray. With Zach as his accomplice, he took on the role of Captain Brawn, bringing in the extra manpower and shutting down the party. These two were a dangerous yet marvellous partnership, moving from person to person until the circle was disabled of all its supernatural ability.

From the corner of my eye, I caught sight of Coral's strained reaction to the arrival of the unexpected cavalry. Kicking up a huge fuss, she was clearly unimpressed by Baxley and his rather dashing ally — her cousin Zachy.

Untouched from the scuffle, she released herself from the ring with an almighty roar.

"Why involve yourself in this you interfering pest!!!"

Her words sprayed like pungent skunk scent as she vented her fury in one sharpshoot.

Overstretching her arm, she angled her hand sideways in the direction of my tiny saviour. Then, with the back of her palm, she slapped him. Baxley's petite frame didn't see it coming. He was pelted towards a robust oak tree, his body recoiling as his wings crumpled on impact. He was no match for that type of force.

"No, no, no!" I shrieked in torment.

The blood-curdling squelch of his dainty body smacking the chipped husk flipped my stomach. He was sent toppling onto the terrane with shards of broken bark raining down upon his maimed form.

"Why! Why him!" I sobbed.

He didn't deserve to die, not like this, not for me!

To lose Baxley would be a massive blow, and his death was one I wasn't ready to accept.

I wanted to scream these woods down in his name, but the words didn't come, just as they hadn't before. I was pathetic, unable to express my heartache, unable to move, unable to cradle him. I was useless.

This was no drug-induced shambles, this was real life and I needed out. I rammed my eyelids shut, hoping, wishing, this had all just been a good dream gone bad. I wanted to wake from my hellish nightmare, never having visited 'The Locust Lounge', never having attended this party and never having met Zach full stop.

∞∞∞∞

"Hey..." he whispered with a muffled tone.

I didn't answer, I didn't want to. I refused to acknowledge him.

"It's ok, I'm here now..." he faintly soothed

I shook my head in defiance. It was too late. I didn't want or need his help. The damage had already been done — no thanks to him.

Baxley was my friend, and I didn't have many of them, not special ones anyway. Yes, I had Mollie, but we were hardly best mates. We just happened to meet up once in a blue moon, which as you know would normally coincide around our birthdays.

Baxley, he was different. Yes, he was a bug, but he was one of a kind. He meant more to me than most and now he was gone.

He had proved with all his heart what he was capable of, but there was no way his feeble body could survive a brutal attack such as that. I had seen the aftermath, there was no stirring, only a lifeless corpse in place of his once sprightly heartbeat.

This was all Zach's doing! His egotistic, cocky, self-righteousness was to blame and now he had the audacity to suddenly turn up and 'help'. I wanted to lash out at him, to scream into his ears until they bled out through the pain. It's not even half of what he deserved, but I knew if I ever wanted to leave here alive, then I would have to cooperate.

"At least look at me, will you!" he barked, his voice now clear and stern.

With the enthusiasm of a sloth, I clamped open my eyelids and complied with his demanding tongue whipping. The last thing I wanted to do was to set eyes on a coward, especially one that I thought I might have meant something to. I would never forgive him for selfishly disposing of me to what can only be described as 'demonic worshipping cretins'.

Now I know you're probably thinking, "come on Allie, he's here now. Yes, what he did was wrong, but let's play fair and at least give the man a chance to explain?"

Well if that's your mindset, then stop, stop right now and rewind! If, on the other hand, you're on the same page as me, then let's continue....

I wasn't in the most pleasant of moods, so a glare was all I could muster, it was that or nothing to be honest. Considering I had spent most my evening tracking Zach's movements, it was now ironic that I could no longer bear to look at him. I did, however, meet him halfway and shuffled my eyelids up towards his shins. Ok, it wasn't quite halfway, but it was the best I was willing to do at this precise moment in time.

So here he was, he had managed to penetrate the ring, which was by now a pitiful circle — still intact and only ten persons wide. A mix of relief and disappointment trickled through my veins as he ripped me from the loosened grips of the ogres on either side of me.

Still zoned out, Mace and Ike were of no fit state to retaliate and so had let me go with ease.

Sweeping me securely into his arms, he placed one hand tightly around my waist with the other hand supporting the undercarriage of my legs. The charge for freedom ensued.

I was relieved he had finally plucked up the courage to come to my aid, but it stung me to the core that he could ever allow me to get into a situation like this in the first place.

Cradled in his arms, I took one last look behind. I needed to know it was over, to ensure we were free from danger, and thankfully it seemed we were. The fight, however, continued without me, and there bravely battling the remainder of Coral's goons alone was Zach.

Zach...!

What the! If I was here and Zach was there, then who the hell was holding me?

Twenty-Four

THE OUTLAW

Guardedly, I inch by inch rolled my eyes up the length of this mysterious stranger. He was hooded and cladded in a black leather, zipped jacket. With his mouth and nose shielded in a matching cloth bandanna — he barely gave much away. His eyes were the only part of his body to be unveiled.

What with the blurry arrival of Zach — or so I had thought, and the untimely death of my courageous friend, I had no reason to believe there was anyone else involved. The burning question, therefore was — who was he? What was he doing here and why was he trying his utmost to fight my corner?

Resembling a brooding outlaw, he peered down at me as he continued his mission to free me from my horrendous ordeal. Our eyes momentarily locking — I was glued, unable to take my gaze off him. It didn't help that his virile physique towered over my depleted body, making me feel vulnerable and gushy in his grasp.

"Alllllie!!! hollered a distracted Zach.

Having abandoned the fight with Coral's men, he was now directly behind us and yelling for me to stop.

As requested, the outlaw casually swivelled around on invitation, dropping me abruptly to my feet.

Zach seizing his moment — aggressively tore me away from the outlaws' side. His grip twisting my skin and searing my flesh as I unresisted his control.

"You're hurting me," I screamed.

Little did Zach know but this mystery man wasn't prepared to just hand me over.

Firmly shooting out his hand towards mine, our fingers instantly entwined on contact. The arduous jolt was such the surprise, that it forced Zach into releasing his tightened clamp from my aching wrist. The strength of this shrouded intruder and the pull from Zach sent us both tumbling to the floor with a clumsy *thud*.

Zach winded in the fall, strived to regain his composure, but finding it hard to recover, he struggled to peel himself from off the sodden turf.

There was no mistaking it, we were in the company of some kind of lout. I, on the other hand, was perched on my arse, a little ruffled but unharmed. I could now do nothing but watch as the outlaw casually swaggered towards me. Every step was filled with self-appreciation.

The outlaw, lout or whatever you wanted to name him, empathically tilted his head from side-to-side as he coolly crouched himself down beside me. He wasn't as feral as expected, he was actually far from it. Under all that bravado, he appeared to be genuinely concerned for me.

Did I know my masked man? I could hardly tell with all that fabric shielding his face, but there was something about him, something I couldn't quite put my finger on.

Breathing him in, I proceeded to scrutinise him from top-to-toe. He was pumped and his shoulders were delectably broad. His shapely legs were adorned with the cosiest pair of leather trousers. They skimmed the bottom of his waist, revealing a glimpse of his clearly defined obliques. His hands were dressed with perforated driving gloves and firmly clenched shut as they rested on his crouched knees. His ensemble was finished off with a pair of well-worn laceless ankle boots. His overall look screamed trouble, and it certainly caught my attention.

Quickly realising I was admiring his spittle inducing physique for far too long, I swiftly traced my gaze back up his edible body and on to his eyes. This idea was not much better as they too were dreamy. Although, I could barely see them through the secretion of his hood and the screen of night, but once the moonlight hit their core, they instantly captured my tongue.

Kiwifruit green, they were the colour of the Amazon Rainforest — dense and never-ending. I figured I may as well lose myself within them whilst I wait for him to do whatever it was, he was planning on doing.

I'm going to be upfront with you here, this situation was unquestionably frightening. It really was, but in an awkward way, I found myself slightly aroused by the way his over-powering presence intimidated me. It felt a little dirty — a little naughty — like I wouldn't object to his sweat-stained chest pressing up against my quivering body....

Was there something wrong with me as I can't recall ever feeling this excited with Zach or Kalen? This was pure filthy animal magnetism. He was bad and bad was clearly what I desired right now. To add to my giddiness, he began to add in the element of touch, which I can assure you, was about to send me over the edge on the flirtatious Richter scale.

Using his index finger, he sensually stroked the skin from the tip of my nose to the plump of my bottom lip — teasingly resting his finger there for no more than three seconds.

Hot and bothered by his antics, was what I was, and it hadn't gone unnoticed by him — the glow of the moon paraded his misted eyes as he pleasingly absorbed in my weakness.

As he stared at me longingly, I could sense we had the same burning thirst for one another. I could tell he wanted to touch my lips with his, to feel what I was feeling, and gosh, did I want to feel him on me too!

Unfortunately for me though, he quickly appeared to be disturbed by his own conscience, promptly removing his finger from my begging lips and dashing any hopes of a heated passionate clinch.

"Take it," he softly encouraged, offering me his hand with a glint in his eye.

Preposterous! I couldn't just aimlessly take off with him, a stranger and without good reason! As easy as he was on the eye, I had no idea who exactly was under that veil and what he would do to me once he had a hold of me.

Of course, there was the dangerous side of me that wanted to throw caution to the wind, to see what could potentially develop, but I couldn't deny that he was also coming across a little menacing too. Plus, I had encountered enough groping tonight to last me a lifetime. All I really wanted to do was to go home and sleep tonight's events off!

"Ah, erm...it's ok, I'm quite capable of making my own way home from here," I blurted.

Much to my joy, my voice had finally returned, allowing me at long last to be heard.

"It wasn't a request. You're coming with me!" he growled.

"Zach!!!!!" I bellowed.

I didn't much like the sound of his tone. I knew I needed to disengage and fast, but the only other person I could turn to was otherwise engaged! He was still no use to man nor beast. Bent over on all fours, Zach was having serious difficulty steadying his feet.

What was I going to do? Yes, I had strangely accrued feelings for this cloaked stranger, but I wasn't stupid! I wasn't going to just allow him to lead me off into the unknown.

Did he think he could lure me in with lust and expect me to fall head over heels? This smelt like a deceitful trick. It had Coral written all over it, and I wasn't about to fall for it that easily. Even out of view, she was still as conniving as ever, wasn't she!

Perched on the floor and with shaky hands, I frantically rummaged through the soil. I was searching for some kind of object to at least beat him off with.

"What are you doing?" he amusingly questioned.

I didn't answer, I didn't dare. God only knows what he would do to me if he found out my exact thoughts. Instead, I carried on about my business, much to his merriment. Although, I could see a slight twang of concern beginning to creep through his subdued demeanour. He needn't worry, as he would soon find out what I had in store for him!

A rotted lump of wood? No, way too small, it wouldn't even make a dent. A handful of lumpy soil and a gathering of puny stones? No, definitely too pebblelike, more laughable than anything! I needed something substantial, something weighty, something that would hinder but not decimate. I didn't want to annihilate him!

"Yes!" I triumphed.

All that grappling had paid off as I sneakily held the adequate sized rock in the palm of my hand. This little fella had been unearthed from its snug duvet of dirt and was about to launch itself as my ticket out of here!

"What are you up to?" he snapped.

I may have been a touch too vocal in my delight as mask boy was now onto me.

Success was smeared across my face like the spoils of those greedy piglets scoffing at the buffet table. That type of evidence was hard to wipe clean. As was my attempt to hide the tightening of my grip as I battled to conceal my weaponry from him.

With my plan about to be rumbled — it was time! I raised my right arm above my head and clenched the rock with fierce determination.

Gung-ho, I swung my arm back, preparing to fire. All I needed was a clear shot at his face.

"Alanna, no!!!" he boomed, throwing a hand up to his face...but rather than take cover, he ripped the mask clean off and rammed it to the floor.

That tormenting pace of slow motion had returned, drenching me with dread as I observed my hand edging nearer and nearer towards the freshly revealed identity. I was in a state of shock and horror as I peered on at the unmasking before me. It was a face I knew too well.

"Cover your eyes!" I painfully willed, but it was pointless, it was too late, he would never be able to shield himself in time.

I stupidly had myself believe that my ammunition was a safe bet, but in reality, there was every possibility that my one blow to the head would kill.

Why hadn't he told me sooner, what was he thinking! I was about to seriously injure or worse kill him in the most tragic and heart rendering of ways, and there wasn't a damn thing I could do to stop it!

"Arghhh!", he cuttingly howled whilst instantaneously charging towards me.

He snatched my wrist just as my fingers rolled back in readiness to flick the mighty rock. The pressure from his interception was ultra-tight, forcing the weapon from my clutches and buckling me to my knees.

The rock hurtled to the floor, kicking up a mouthful of dust as it pounded the ground — not once but twice.

I remained where I had fallen, eyes lowered to the dirt with the rock a foot in front of me and at a standstill.

I was too ashamed, distraught and overall sickened with my actions to meet his eyes. If it hadn't had been for his perceptiveness and his staggeringly quick reaction to my stupidity, then this could have ended very differently indeed.

Midst my embarrassment, the normal speed of reality washed over my remorseful body. I couldn't cower from the truth any longer — it was time to face him.

He too was now knelt down on the gravel, and I could sense he was exhausted not only physically but mentally.

Frigid, I took one straight look at him and instantly melted into those swirly mint greens of his. He though was angered, diverting his disgruntled gaze away from me. I could tell he was disappointed, but I only did what I thought was best.

Restless, he picked his body up from off of the ground, straightened his back and patted down his clothes, all the while adding in an accompaniment of unnecessary huffing and puffing. Meanwhile, I continued to focus on his bare face, absorbing in every feature like it was the first time — before plucking up the courage to say, "hello, you."

Twenty-Five
YOU + ME = LIES

More than anything did I want to be the one to tell you that I had no idea why he was here, but it was obvious wasn't it? He was here for her...he was here for Coral!

He had disappeared all those weeks ago, without so much as a passing phone call or a cordial goodbye. So, bumping into me tonight had all just been a very unpleasant coincidence for him. Not for a split second would he have imagined that I would be at one of Coral's parties, but as it happened, here I was. Surprise!

I can only assume the guilt of briefly knowing me and perhaps the sudden ditching of me had twisted his arm into actioning a full-blown rescue.

Funny though, I hadn't noticed him all evening, and I'm pretty sure I would have clocked him — mask or no mask...unless he was intentionally trying to avoid me?

He offered his hand.

I shook my head. I knew better than to fall for his promises again.

It's what I had always wanted, wasn't it? But it all felt a little too late. Yes, he was here and offering me a way out, but he had left me once and he could well do it again. I didn't need him, not now, not ever.

I jumped to my feet and shuffled off, ignoring his barrage of pleading calls. This evening was the first time I was able to admit to myself that I was finally getting over him. So why now would I want to drag up the past and add more sorrow to my already shattered heart?

"You can trust me, Alanna, you know me, you always have. It's only now you see me for who I really am," he declared.

My steps stalled as I digested the dribble that leaked from his gums. He was impressive with his chatter, I'll give him that, but he certainly had to do more than plaster me with sweet nothings if he wanted to make me quake. I turned to face him, to hear him out. One last time I told myself and then it ends — once and for all.

"Forgive me," he said, "I messed up," he said, "I need you," he said.

Wave after wave they came, thick and fast, rupturing off his tongue and marinating me with his monotonous current.

I'm the first person to tell you that some things in life should be left in the past. If the memory was good in the first place, then that's it, keep it as a gooey loved-up memory. Why change it? You may live to regret the day you ever tried to bring your recollections into the present.

Time ticks on, people move on and they may not be the person you once thought they were. You might not be the person you once were. Best to leave it behind where it can't be tampered with.

These were actually the wise words of good old Nan, passed on to me in case one day I needed to take heed from them.

I always got the impression that Nan was speaking from experience. Like she was harbouring a magical encounter that she refused to relive, for fear of destroying what she had treasured so dearly. She was adamant that you didn't mess with a good thing! Nan was a wise woman, a sensible soul and for that notion alone, I would apply the same reasoning here.

'Carry on walking, let it be and forget him', I urged myself. Although, there was one minor issue...I didn't have a beloved memory of him. The ones that prevail in my mind involve rejection and bleakness.

If you recall, he upped and left me, leaving a storm of woe in my desolate heart. As much as I wanted to walk away, I owed it to myself to gather the answers I so desperately needed to hear. I had to stay, to find out why he did what he did, and at least then could I finally close the book on us. I had no tender memories to damage, there was nothing to lose. With hope and belief on my side, this chapter could have a reasonable ending.

$$\infty\infty\infty$$

"Not a day went by that I didn't think of you, Alanna. I would imagine you a thousand times over, remembering that one moment we had and how it was supposed to end," he soothed.

My foot edged in closer, I pined for more of the same.

"When I was gone, it was your vision and yours alone that comforted me. You lingered on my yearning body like the sweet scent of lavender.

In time, I will explain to you why I left and why I am the way I am, but first of all, I beg of you to come with me. Can you do that? I promise I won't ask anything else of you," he voiced.

Trust is what he asked of me, and with words seeming so honest and pure, I didn't have the heart to say no. Besides, there really wasn't any other option open to me right now, and I hadn't the foggiest idea where I was.

Trustingly, I stood before him and presented my hand. I expected him to scoop me up into his arms and whisk me away. Well, that's what I thought he was insinuating, but no, it didn't play out that way. There was no swipe of the hand, bundle over the shoulder or sweeping me off my feet moment. Nor did he scoop me into his arms and passionately embrace me. No, instead of the romancing I had hankered for, he buffaloed me with the oddest and most ill-timed of requests.

"Your necklace, Alanna. Pass it to me," he softly demanded.

"Sorry, what?" I spurted in confusion.

"It's quite simple. The chain from around your neck. I need it. It's what I require before we are to go any further," he ordered with a now brusque tone.

"I'm afraid I can't do that. This was my nan's, it's precious and I won't be parted with it — not for you, not for anyone!" I spouted.

"I must have it; you know I wouldn't ask if it wasn't important," he pressed.

What deserving reason did he possibly possess for needing my necklace — any necklace for that matter?

Oh...oh wait, I see, it all made sense now...the munchies at 'Hawkers Cavern', the disappearing act at 'Blossomvale', the continuous secrecy and now the need for expensive items! This all stunk of a dirty drug habit, and I can tell you now that Nan's necklace was in no way, shape or form going to be used as easy cash for his next hit.

The signs were all there, how did I not see them before? He was right, I didn't know the real him at all!

"Give me one good reason for why you need it!" I angrily barked.

I needed to hear him admit the truth with my own ears.

"I can't tell you. I just need you to do as I say, no questions asked!" he ordered.

I held the gem lovingly in the palm of my hand. Why was I even contemplating handing him my nan's dearest of keepsakes?

I don't know how, why or where it had come from, but all I knew was that Nan had wholeheartedly entrusted it to me with the sole purpose of treasuring. This if any was a substantial enough reason for me to protect it with my life. I may never learn the true meaning of the gem or know the framework of its past, but for whatever reason, Nan had chosen to keep a tight lid on it. Perhaps this was a secret best kept hidden.

His hand prompted for the gem once more, "I will look after you, you do know that, don't you?" he reassured.

Could I trust him not to abandon me once he had taken what he so dearly craved? He seemed genuinely sincere. Maybe it was finally time to hand over a second chance. Nan may not forgive me for what I was about to do, but I'm sure she would rather have her granddaughter home safe!

"Ok, you win, take —"

"So, this is the elusive Kalen that I've had the *not so* pleasure of hearing about. Don't be fooled, Allie, he won't look after you, not like I can!" Interrupted a breathy Zach.

His words halted me in my tracks, ceasing me from administering any drastic action. I couldn't see him. I could only hear him. He came from behind, brushing through the darkened shadows. He stopped inches away from my body, his hot sticky breath licking at the hair follicles on my neck.

"Well, look who has finally decided to join us! You know you're really starting to grate on me, boy," growled Kalen.

With mettle, Zach hauled me from the forefront and roughly placed me behind his body.

"The gem, Alanna. I won't tell you again," raged Kalen.

He was no longer playing the oversensitive, Mr. caring role. That chap had long gone! The desperation he had for the gem was palpable, and I was beginning to think he would do whatever it would take to get his grubby paws on it!

Zach, on the other hand, was bubbling with animosity. His back was pinned straight, his chest puffed, he was ready for a ruck. His reasons for deserting me at the party were still unknown, but I couldn't help feeling a little devotion for him as he stood in front of me, protecting me like he always should have.

My feelings right now were an amalgamation of confusion. In all honesty, I didn't know who to believe, who to trust or what on earth had gone on this evening. I was throwing myself into a right tizzy, I needed to sit down. My head was spinning in circles, faster and faster until *thwack*, I came to a sudden stop.

Slumped forwards, I found my hand unintentionally looped around Zach's firm waist. It was the first thing I could find to grab on to. I felt unbearably faint and needed assistance in holding myself up.

Zach flipped his head to the side, laying his gaze upon my intimate hold. Of all the places to hold him, why did it have to be there? I really didn't mean to stir any feelings, but something moved for us — we both felt it.

Feeling somewhat awkward about my blunder, I fumbled to push myself off of Zach. He didn't flinch, instead, he appeared a little crushed as he watched me move away.

"Allie painted you out to be quite the dashing prince, can't say I see any resemblance myself," needled Zach.

Kalen's exasperated expression tightened as he seethed from the malevolent words tumbling off of Zach's tongue. Though, I couldn't actually recall ever bleating on about Kalen to Zach? Gushing about your crushes wasn't really the done thing to do...unless he had sourced his information from the likes of Coral, which was highly possible in this case. It would certainly have explained his sudden shift in behaviour towards me this evening.

"Now like the lady has already pointed out, she does not wish to give you the gem. It's best you back up and 'move out', don't you think, boy!" Zach sarcastically snipped, whilst shoving Kalen's right shoulder blade.

Kalen's torso twisted with the force, plummeting him back towards the remnants of a once grand tree. Try as he might, he was unable to regain his balance and toppled over the squat stump in true clownlike fashion. He hit the floor with an almighty *smack*. Humiliation dripped across his brow like the sweat of a succulent pig. It was safe to say retaliation would not be far away.

"Fool, you should not have done that!" laughed a loathsome Kalen.

He was furious and ready to engage.

Zach was prepared, rolling his head from side-to-side and dancing from foot to foot as he limbered his body up for the onslaught. Kalen, on the other hand, stood calm and collected, his hands loosely balanced onto his waist. He watched Zach with intrigue as he displayed an array of warm-up techniques that seemed best suited to a boxing ring.

Having seen enough, he smugly grinned and summoned his opponent towards him with two slow flicks of the finger.

Zach welcomed the challenge with open arms, boldly throwing both his hands down the length of his body in a presumptuous manner.

I couldn't stand by and let these two rip shreds out of one another, I had to interpose and fast.

"Stop!!!" I screamed in frustration. I was exhausted by their belligerent behaviour.

I had grown terribly fond of both boys, and to have to endure them prepare to fight one another was excruciating.

"Take it! Just take the blasted gem, Kal," I sizzled.

It was the only way this nightmare would end. Give him what he wanted, even if the price to pay was too unbearable to stomach. And as much as it killed me — it had worked! Caving into Kalen's demands had stunned both the boys into submission.

"But once you take it, you never come for me again, you hear me!" I cried.

Kalen was silenced, he couldn't even bring himself to speak to me, which of course infuriated me even more. If I was prepared to sacrifice my nan's most valued of heirlooms (for what looked like a quick high), then he could at least have the decency to show some sort of gratitude or acknowledgement at the very least. To say nothing at all was possibly the worst insult he could have delivered.

"Did you hear me!" I squawked, patience not being one of my strongest attributes.

It was obvious Kalen had heard me alright. My screeching

appeared to have snapped him back into action, whilst soften-ing his previous angered expression.

His eyes catching sight of me, noticed me — like they had done all those months ago in that frosty old corridor of Elder-crest College.

Well, I can tell you this, his smooth-tongued routine wasn't about to work on me again. I tugged on the gem, the force straining to snap its delicate chain — one more tug should do it!

With his eyelashes now blinking upwards, he took a double glance — aware of his four-leaf charm, he seemed al-most surprised that I would still be displaying it. But let it be known, I wasn't wearing it for him, contrary to what the glow of bliss filtering through to his face would have you believe.

"Wait! You've got this wrong, you've got me all wrong!" interrupted Kalen, replying to my thoughts as if he could read them.

"I have so much I want, no — need to tell you...but I can't, not here!" he added.

"Oh, don't tell me, are these the same 'dark, deep things' you've already previously failed to tell me?" I sarcastically laughed.

Zach with arms folded, stood his ground firmly, shaking his head as Kalen slowly approached me with his hand held out.

"I will tell you all, that I promise but now is neither the time nor the place."

I clutched lovingly to my necklace as his words pierced my skin.

"The gem, Alanna," he pressed.

My slender fingers oscillated the gem between them, al-lowing me to take in the beauty of its swirling thistle and teal hue one last time. I slipped my index finger under the chain and carefully lifted the necklace from off my unsettled chest.

"Don't do it, Allie. If you give him what he wants — he's won, you owe him nothing," urged Zach.

It was never about winning or losing for me. If anything, it was always about trust. I thought I knew Kalen, and even though he had treated me badly in the past, I never thought he was capable of doing the things he was doing to me now. How I had once allowed myself to lust after this wicked manipulating bully, I do not know.

It went without saying that after today's events, Nan would never be able to trust me again. She would be distraught to learn I had forsaken the memories of a past she greatly valued, and all for a boy whom I barely knew. For that, I wanted to forget I had ever laid eyes on him.

To think I had wasted countless amounts of money on cans of fizz, not to mention the back up of tooth decay I had encountered for him! If I wasn't so drained of emotion, I would have sobbed my eyes out until they were parched of life, incapable of shedding one further tear for him.

With Kalen accepting the role of an emotionally unstable thug, Zach was auditioning for the part of the spurned lover. He was livid with Kalen for showing up unannounced and spitting his demands out to me. But what really outraged him was that I was about to accommodate him. Zach didn't have the right to play the wounded lover, considering he had left me for what seemed like dead only a matter before.

Zach saw my compromise as pandering to Kalen's needs and confirming I was under his control, which he thoroughly detested. With Kalen acting in the manner he was, I was already heading over and beyond him, but Zach unable to see past his own ego — failed to acknowledge this.

Kalen's smirk had now taken on a slightly sinister presence. Never had I seen him like this. It was very out of character, and one I was becoming increasingly wary of.

Straightening his posture, he clenched his fists and advanced a step closer to Zach. He was practically on top of him. Their heads were millimetres from brushing into an explosive bout. Kalen had snapped — I was sure of it. He was about to blow. With his patience evaporated, he was determined to finish what he had begun.

"You couldn't stay away could you, you had to involve yourself in my business! I've tried to play fair, to turn a blind eye but you've given me no choice. You have forced me to behave in this way!" snarled Kalen.

"Don't you dare threaten him, Kalen Snow! Your drama is with me, not Zach. If you want it, then you're going to have to come and get it!" I courageously offered — immediately regretting the hunt I had now incited.

Patience was all that was needed, and he would have got what he had come for. However, his pure greediness and offensive behaviour had wound me up too tight. I now no longer felt like playing ball. If he wanted the gem that bad, then he would physically have to take it from my neck. I would fight my hardest to defend my possession — for Nan and for her past.

"Give me what I want before it's too late. This is your final chance. I suggest you take it!" roared Kalen, slapping Zach in the chest and hammering him effortlessly to the ground.

His gateway to me was now open, there was no obstruction, no confrontation. He saw his opportunity and he took it.

Kalen storming towards me as I frantically backed up was the last image I captured before slamming my eyes shut. With shallow breath, my grip tightened around the gem. I braced myself for the incoming attack.

I prayed it would be over quickly. I didn't want to feel the ache or experience the agonising lead up to my unfortunate death.

I waited and waited. Those seconds felt like minutes as my thoughts took the lead.

Vividly, they whizzed around my mind as I awaited his contact. I pictured my dad waiting for me — reunited after all these years, and although the impending pain would be hard to bear, there would be a wonderful adventure awaiting me on the other side.

If, however, I survived this ghastly attack, then unwillingly I would have procured a mental scar that could never be healed. To learn of the suffering my dad would have tolerated before passing was a sensation too far.

People tell you what they think you want to hear, they try to ease the blow, to make a sad situation a little easier to accept. Strangers told me, the paramedics told me, even Mum found it in her heart to tell me that Dad never felt a thing. Apparently, the impact from the car had instantaneously knocked Dad into a state of unconsciousness. They promised the accident had happened at such a breakneck pace that Dad would never have had a chance to feel the pain. He had gone peacefully or so they thought.

I, however, knew different, and I know this as I had broken free from the clasp of Mrs. Genevieve Louise Snook. She couldn't keep me away — not from my dad. No one could.

No child should have to witness what I did that day, and no child should ever have to lose their daddy in such horrific circumstances. That day I did what any other child would do — I cuddled him, begging him not to leave me.

It was me who helplessly clung on to his limp lifeless hand — waiting in the blistering cold for the paramedics to arrive. It was me that was squatted on the floor, begging him to wake as the purest of snow turned into a red slush beneath his vacant torso. It was me who wiped away his blood-sodden brow with my tears as each and every bystander looked on, pitying my grief. It was me, the one that didn't let go of his cold clammy hand as the paramedic pronounced his time of death. No, not a stranger, not a paramedic and certainly not Mum. It was me and me alone. So how would they have the faintest idea if Dad had suffered or not? He wasn't gone and for those cruel seconds, I and only I knew that. Knowing of the pain he felt was not something I was prepared to live with.

∞∞∞

"Allie, MOVE!!!" bleated Zach as Kalen's presence towered above me.

I thrust my eyelids open, but overcome with shock, I was once again unable to move.

Zach realising my difficulty — manically gathered himself up from off the floor and sprinted in at an electric speed.

From behind, he lassoed his muscular right arm around Kalen's broad shoulders, sliding his fist up and into his target's throat. Using the weight of his body and the tightening of his choke hold, he successfully capsized Kalen onto his back.

"Get your pathetic self off me now, boy!" bellowed Kalen — buzzing with rage.

Zach was nowhere near finished as he successfully flipped Kalen onto his front, straddled his body and pinned his face down into the dirt.

"Tell her what you are!!!" spat Zach.

His fiery head was practically touching Kalen's as the sweat dribbled from his weeping pores and onto his captives flushed cheeks — antagonising him even more.

"What are you babbling on about, imbecile? You've picked yourself a right one here!" blasted Kalen.

"Tell her who you really are! It's your last chance!!" reiterated Zach.

"You've no idea who I am but trust me when I say you will. Mark my words — you'll find out! Now get off, or I will throw you off!" raged Kalen.

Zach grabbed Kalen by the tuft of his hair, pushing his face up and sideways towards mine.

"Allie, look at him, what do you see?" ordered Zach.

"Ignore him, Alanna," spoke a significantly calmer, more contrived Kalen. "Can't you see the boy has lost a marble or two. He's not right for you, and I will do everything in my power to remove him!" threatened Kalen.

As the threats and insults began to flow, the tighter the pull was on Kalen's scalp. The strain was evident on his face and no amount of play-acting could disguise that.

"Allie, that thing you lust for is nothing but a savage, deceitful, backstabbing FAIRY!" splurged Zach.

I spluttered in amusement at the drivel I had been spun. "A fairy you say?" I questioned with stunned breath.

"Seriously! A dinky fairy? Is that the best yarn you can spout!" laughed Kalen, hysterically.

"Yeah, laugh it off all you want, but you know damn well what you are, and I'll prove it!" Zach shouted in defiance as he released his hold but not before pushing Kalen as far into the ground as physically possible.

Even with a mouth full of soil and shrubs, Kalen still continued to laugh, only this time there was an air of nervousness to his hysterics.

Confused at Zach's assured claim, I started to query his sanity, perhaps he had taken one too many chugs of the old goblin punch too.

What I needed was a rational answer from Kalen on this outrageous allegation and not the edgy out of control giggle that I had actually received. With no words spoken, I could only assume he was as confused as I was at the unfathomable statement, and unable to react seriously to the situation in hand.

Picking himself up from off of the gravel and seemingly spooked, Kalen finally responded to the charge, "don't be so farcical. I've never heard such nonsense. I hope you don't believe the spiel he's feeding you!"

In all truthfulness, I didn't know what to think...a fairy? I mean come on! They didn't actually exist — did they? Plus, they were minuscule, near on invisible to the naked eye. Completely opposite to the strapping man that stood before me. I knew Kalen had always been a little different, but I put that down to him being a quirky individual. Not at any point did I conclude his traits being relatable to a mythical creature!

Zach's outburst was quite insane. Most people would accuse their rival of adultery but to imply Kalen was a supernatural being was a bit farfetched for even the most fanciful of people. He most likely had acted under pressure, keen to sway me away from Kalen's beguiling talons, but in truth, his shaming was unrealistic, irrational and most of all unhinged.

"He's nothing but evil, dangerous and damaged! I've had my eye on him for some time, and he's far from the human he makes out to be!" burst Zach.

"I only brought you to this blasted party to keep you safe from him! Why on earth do you think me and Coral have been having heated conversations and whispering in darkened corners for most of the night."

"Well that's obvious! Coral has a deep hate for me, always has. It was clear she didn't want me anywhere near you," I argued.

"She doesn't hate you! She hates that I'm protecting you and risking my life for yours!" he confessed.

It still didn't add up.

I can remember Coral taking a real dislike to me from the very first day we met, which happened to be outside the doors of Eldercrest College. I had been running unusually late, my hands were strewn full of books and I was soaking wet from the onslaught of rain.

"Hold the door, please!" I exhaustedly shouted, fumbling up the path, desperate to make the bell.

Coral turned and glanced. Inconvenienced by my plight, she callously released her hand, allowing the double doors to smack me directly in the face! This ladies and gentlemen was the start of a lengthy hate campaign, directed at me by his 'oh so delightful' cousin.

Anyway, if anyone should know of Kalen's bizarre secret, then surely it would be Coral. After all, she was the one who had stolen him from me, and as much as the thought repulsed me, maybe it was her that I needed to speak to in order to seek out the truth.

∞∞∞∞

"Who exactly are you, boy?" demanded Kalen, vexed by his outlandish declaration.

Zach sauntering back over to Kalen, edged his body in as close as he possibly could and shrewdly whispered, "you don't want to know!"

Kalen's face was screwing, he was just as mystified as I was at Zach's behaviour.

It had dawned on me that for this ordeal to be over, I would have to choose between one or the other, and the outlook wasn't looking good. With a toss-up between a fickle fairy and a cocksure loon, it was never going to be a win-win situation! For starters, I couldn't even believe I was contemplating the idea of Kalen actually being a fairy, but on the other hand, I hadn't put Zach down as a nonsensical liar either.

Kalen was by no means your average day-looking fairy, but if there was truth within the madness, then had our two worlds actually crossed? Had our paths been thrown together in a weird twist of fate? Perhaps, I was crazy to even consider such a notion, and maybe the truth lie within Zach! Was he just mentally unstable? Had I not been aware, or had I subconsciously chosen to ignore this? There was much speculation to be had, and as unsettling as both were, one of these options would ring true.

With my heart breaking, my head firmly told me to point the finger at Zach. He had to be disturbed to fabricate a tale this farfetched and fictitious. Fairies were a myth, dreamt up to feed the desirous imaginations of little girls and boys. I should know, I was one of them!

It was Nan who would spend many a summer afternoon spinning me the most amazing tales of dainty toed, pointy-eared, little-winged people. With the sweetest of tooth, bundles of energy, a creative flair and a mischievous streak, they were enough to derail the calmest of humans.

As a child, I believed every enrapturing word, but as the years passed, so did the magic and little by little the belief ebbed away. I had assumed these were just tales to open my mind and explore my creativity, but now I wasn't so sure.

"You both have no idea how difficult you're making this for me," I puffed. "If I have to choose, then fine, I choose —"

"Watch your step, Alanna!" warned Kalen, as Zach concurrently pulled me away from the clutches of unmistakable danger.

Twenty-Six
MUD SPLIT

It wasn't the sight of them but more the noise they created that signalled their impending presence to me. It was an unfamiliar noise. A crackling hiss. A sound that only if you had heard it many times before would you know exactly what it was. This was the tune of compacted mud splitting, the very mud that we were standing on.

All three of us stood there — our eyes transfixed on the wet clay below.

The split had ceased at the tip of my toes, trailing back as far as the eye could see and into the hovering mist.

Unlocking my eyes from the muck, I peered into the vast dense vapor and gasped, "there…there's something there!"

I turned to Zach and Kalen in the hope that they had witnessed it too.

"What? What's there?" queried a befuddled-looking Kalen.

"I don't know exactly, it's too far away, and I can't quite make it out, but whatever it is, it's watching us!" I squealed.

"I think you're mistaken," advised Kalen.

"No, it's right there!!" I adamantly informed as I turned back towards the hazy mass to indicate its location.

"It was there, I swear it was!"

Whatever it was, that was watching us, had vanished, and within only seconds of me diverting my attention! I couldn't believe the boys hadn't seen it! Surely one of them had?

"Zach, you can back me up, can't you?" I elicited.

Zach shook his head; he too dismissed my sightings.

"There it is!!" I squeaked as the vision abruptly re-appeared and this time in full view.

There were three visible yet slightly blurred silhouettes, stood rigidly side by side, directly facing us from the onset of the split.

"Alanna, there's nothing there," echoed Kalen.

Agitated, I rubbed my eyes.

They had definitely been there; I had seen them and would bet Nan's gem that they were up to no good.

"You're stressed, tired and emotional. Your eyes are play-ing tricks on you. Rest is what you need. I'll take you home!" soothed Zach.

Kalen's face creased at the notion, but he continued to hear him out.

"If you care for this girl as much as you say you do, then leave this for another day!" Zach implored.

"I care for her more than you could ever know, but you have to understand, I need that gem, I can't go without it!" Kalen argued.

Zach liberated an unpleasant frown and proceeded to in-form Kalen in no uncertain terms that he would be leaving empty-handed. There would be no gem and definitely no girl by the end of this farce.

Yet again the coals had been stoked, and the boys con-tinued to row with one another. Though less heated than be-fore, it still made for uncomfortable viewing!

I forced my body in between the pair of them, slamming my palms on each of their throbbing chests. I tried my abso-lute best to prise them apart, but I was no match for their strength. Instead, I couldn't help but admire how delicious they both were when incensed.

The feel of their hot, feisty well-defined abs withstand-ing my touch was enough to make me bite my lip and blush.

Spitting flames of ferocity, they were equally as hot-tempered as the other. The protectiveness of Zach and the unwavering want from Kalen was sending me into a giggly mess. Again, this was clearly not the time to fantasise and quickly I averted back to the moment in hand.

"Stop it, stop it now! You'll end up killing one another and for what? There's no need for all this aggression, let's see if we can't compromise somehow!" I argued.

Silence fell.

I did it! I couldn't believe it, they had actually quit snapping, and all that was needed was a stern word from myself to fix the brakes on their bickering.

"Now isn't that better, I can actually hear myself think! A little calm makes even the darkest of situations more bearable!" uttered a rather smug me.

Oh, and boy was I smug, I was totally impressed by my own interpersonal skills and was raring to continue on my path to civility.

Now, wouldn't this have been a sufficient ending? Well, it would have been if it had of actually been my words that had shocked them into silence, but in fact, I had nothing to do with the lull.

You see, whilst I was in the middle of my lecture for peace, I had actually missed the commotion that was occurring all around us. The lads, however, were not and rather than preoccupy themselves with me, they instead were fully focused on what was about to happen next.

I watched with uneasiness as their heads slowly gravitated towards the direction of the mist. Now, it was not the mist itself that they were captured with but by the ground that lay beneath it.

Together they intently monitored the movements of an unknown existence. Their eyes slowly synchronising at the same pace as they tracked its askew route until — *Bang! Bang! Bang!*

Explosions of grass, weeds and shrubs inexplicably burst from their grounded roots — rupturing mid-flow. The remnants of vegetation shooting in all directions as the dirt continued to violently erupt underneath us. It was a war zone of foliage as earthy bomb after earthy bomb detonated left, right and centre of us!

"Ouch!" I bleated, rubbing my bruised scalp.

Don't ever underestimate the power of a terrain attack until you find a clump of moss hitting you square in the back of the head!

"Look!" I gasped, motioning towards the cloudy film — the pain subsiding as my attention was plucked.

It was them!

Yes, them! The source of destruction was visible, and this time they didn't appear to be going anywhere.

Slowly they rose from out of the soil like a triple-headed creature from a horror movie — their bodies twitching as their feet reached surface level.

Flakes of mud crumbled from the tip of their fractious heads, avalanching over their stiffened bodies before resting on the disturbed gravel floor below.

Not stopping to catch a breath, they automatically flew with speed towards Kalen. You heard me...they flew, but I guess that's no more surprising than grown men surfacing from beneath the dirt!

These grown men were now clearly unmistakable. They were Coral's men and they were definitely not human! They were hungry for blood, and they were surrounding Kalen — rowdily forcing him to the ground.

His body caved in as his face impacted the soil with a sickening *thud*. Vulnerable, muted and dazed, he was pretty much out cold — sprawled face first into the soil, with that pack leering over him like a freshly cut leg of lamb.

Kalen's cheeks had all but drained of colour, and although disorientated, he was just as aware as we were that he was about to receive a pounding.

Zach saw this grievous bashing as a superb opportunity to escape, and he took his chance.

"Gently, Zach," I creaked as he snatched my hand, heaving me along with fervor.

The pressure of his grip didn't ease up, and the pain soared through my veins like a raging bull. I never thought the aching would end or if he would ever stop running, but I knew with time one of them would eventually have to give.

∞∞∞

Zach dragged me along with clout, pelting with briskness towards a tight entanglement of 12ft thorny Rose stems. These stalks were sharp to the touch but minus the beauty of the Rose. Nasty things they were and ugly to behold! They stretched for miles, from left to right, back to front, ruling out any other possible route.

We had no choice but to power on regardless, and Zach had no qualms in continuing to yank me through the compact prickles.

"Ow!" I winced.

The stems spitefully snagged at my clothes, pinching my skin as I moved gingerly through the maze of obstacle greenery. There was hardly any room for movement, what with that carcass of a Rosebush wrapping its vicious stalk around every visible tree, weed and shrub going.

Then there were the monstrous dewy cobwebs — revoltingly hanging from branch to branch, threatening to asphyxiate me if I dared to cross their path.

The lonesome tweet of the nocturnal barn owl sliced through the damp smell of mould as it lingered in the night air.

Soggy leaves slapped against my cheeks, stinging my already chapped skin as the spindly twigs poked and prodded against my bruised ribs, badgering me to give in.

I wailed. I couldn't face another second of this horrendous ordeal.

The pain soared towards my head, overpowering my mind and forcing my legs to wobble.

"Don't give up on me now, you're nearly there!" Zach incited, as he took one final thrust, yanking me through an opening in what seemed like a never-ending wiry bush of jumbled up cable ties.

SMACK!

I toppled to my knees as I landed on a grassy carpet of pear shaded needles and sepia toned cones.

I was encompassed by a three-sided parade square of rigid sky-high trees. These fine soldiers stood to attention, reporting for duty to the supreme stars above. Loyally, they were guarded by a thicket of identical Brambles; girdled with terra-cotta wild mushrooms, they furnished the bereft deer track paths.

We were still well within the woods, and although I was surrounded, I at least now had room to move and most importantly breathe.

I hugged my chest and patiently waited for the pain to slowly shrivel away. Even if Zach wanted to carry on running, he had no choice but to stop — my body was crippled in agony.

"Zach, you really hurt me, you didn't need to hold on so tight. I was coming with you!" I panted, dropping my head in exhaustion.

He kneeled before me and lowered his head in order to catch my eyes. He apologised profusely but was so staunchly focused on pulling me to safety, he hadn't realised his own strength. I could forgive him for that, it was easily done, and I couldn't really grumble as he had just taken me out of a volatile situation. I know he didn't mean to hurt me — he was simply carried away in the moment.

I took a few moments to compose myself and inescapably found myself reflecting on the wretched situation we had but marginally escaped. Though it didn't take too long for reality to set in and the panic to break out.

"Kalen, we left Kalen!" I wailed.

I had deserted him, he was alone, attainable and at the mercy of Coral's men. Even though Kalen was not the man I once hoped he was, my heart still cared for him. We had to go back for him, it was the right thing to do.

"Stop it, Allie! Lover boy is old enough and clearly strong enough to sort out his own battles! He's rubbed too many people up the wrong way and like I have been trying to tell you, he's no good!" snapped Zach.

Whatever Kalen was involved with was certainly not above board and neither was Coral's men. I didn't want to know nor did I want any part of it. However, if I liked it or not, he had taken a piece of my heart with him, and I could not — would not see him harmed.

"Come here, you're shaking," eased Zach, his strong arms beckoning me in.

"You're safe with me, I promise, and I'm sorry I lied to you. I should have been upfront from the moment I knew, but I thought if I told you, there was no guarantee you would have accompanied me tonight. I knew what he was and what he was up to. I've known for a while, and I vowed to myself I would do whatever it takes to keep you alive."

This all sounded bizarre!

I was utterly confused and a little hurt that yet again I had misread the signals. This was and had never been a legit date. Zach had only ever invited me along to keep me safe. He thought he was doing me a favour! What really stung though, was that he had known about Kalen and me all along, yet chose not to say a word.

"I want to go home! Let me go home!" I toilsomely cried,

shrugging off his gestures of comfort.

My tears like my heart were on the brink of exhaustion. All I wanted to do was curl up into a ball and sleep this nightmare away.

Zach never one to give up, rested his fingertips on my dried-out lips. He pulled me up from out of my huddled position and nestled me into his chest. Manoeuvring me with ease, he showed no signs of a struggle. I was light in weight, but still, he must have been as shattered as I was, or he was just very good at hiding his exhaustion!

Effortlessly, he carried me towards the settlement of an overgrown spike-jutting bush and gently dropped me to my knees. I was hidden from the naked eye and away from any lurking danger.

"Now Sshhhhh," he cooed. "I will get you home, but first I need to ensure Kalen has gone. This is a dead end, there is only one way out and it's back the way we came. Kalen will kill you if those men haven't got to him first! You have to know that," he urged.

"Wait!" I screamed.

Kalen was no killer, and as ruthless as he appeared, he in no way had it in his veins to slaughter me. There was, however, no point in me declaring my plea of endorsement to Zach as he had already made his mind up about Kalen, and no amount of evidence would change his verdict.

"Woah, keep it down, Allie, do you want to get us both killed!" shushed Zach.

"Sorry, I'm sorry, but if you must go at least tell me how you know so much about Kalen?" I beseeched.

Zach had acquired some damning intelligence on Kalen, it was the type of knowledge that wasn't so easy to come by and frankly surreal. If I was to trust Zach's despicable accusations of butchering, then I needed proof to back up these elaborate fairy claims.

"OK, I know this must all sound like complete twaddle, but I have very good reasons for knowing what I know! Why can't you listen to what I say, digest it and believe in me!" he flapped.

"Well, this is a pretty messed up situation, don't you think! Never in my wildest dreams could I have imagined the night I have experienced. So, forgive me for wanting a simple straight forward answer!!!" I bellowed.

I was congested with rage and no amount of shushing was going to quieten me down!

Zach's face was flushed with the colour of beetroot as hundreds of tiny blood vessels shot to his head. The frustration button had been firmly flicked!

I needed a legitimate explanation, not excuses and no skirting around the issue.

Was Zach actually a sick man or a compulsive liar? I needed to know!

"Zach, you have got to see how this looks from my point of view. You do know your behaviour tonight has been questionable, don't you? And as for these fairy comments...well they're not the words of a sane person, are they?"

I tried to empathically advise, but my tongue had other ideas. Like a shard of glass, my words left a steely cold scrape in their absence. He needed to be told, and I wasn't in the mood to dance around the subject.

Zach hesitantly crouched his body to the floor. He knew full well he had to provide me with a decent answer, that's if he ever wanted me to trust in him again.

With defeated breath, he proceeded to splurge the information I craved.

"I know what I know...because they took him from me! Ok? Is that the god damn simple answer you were after, Allie!!!" he emotionally burst.

Well, it was an answer alright, but maybe not the simplest of ones I was hoping for.

"They took who? Who are you talking about?" I awkwardly asked.

Zach was ashen-faced, his skin the colour of dirty dishwater as years of suppressed hurt rippled through his body. The valve had finally opened, and he was about to let me in.

Twenty-Seven

'IT'

His voice cracked with pain, splintering his words as they fell from his dry lips, and like an unexpected Tsunami of fallen ice — they surged!

"September 1st, 2007 was a date I'll never forget and one that has been etched in my memory ever since. Not only did we experience a scorching freak heat wave of forty-two degrees Celsius, but it was the day my brother Sol turned thirteen years of age. I can't tell you how he had impatiently longed for the day that he would become a teenager. He truly believed that this was the age the boy became a man. He was my big brother, my friend but most of all my hero. I idolised him."

Zach's eyes glistened with adoration as he spoke fondly of his sibling. I couldn't help but feel moved by his sentiments.

"I can remember that day like it was yesterday, and no matter how hard I try to forget, I simply can't.

I was young at the time, a ten-year-old boy with the world at his feet. I was afraid of nothing and nobody. Each day was a surprise, leading anywhere I wanted it to.

However, this day was unlike no other! As I said, it was the morning of Sol's birthday, and he had woken as the man he always said he would be.

Confidence, authority and protectiveness oozed from beneath his blue pinstriped pyjamas, as he coaxed me from my slumber with a doting ruffle to the hair. Once fully awake, I was ordered out of bed and sharpish. We were on the hunt to find ourselves a little adventure, and it was *here* in these very woods that it all began.

I agreed to play his favourite game of 'soldiers' — as I had done on so many occasions before.

Dressed in matching combats, we would smear mud across our chubby youthful cheeks. We were every inch the mini action man, fighting for our Queen and Country, with patriotism soaring through our tiny veins as we geared ourselves up for combat. We didn't have a care in the world, and it showed as we freely frolicked the morning away."

A glint of excitement glazed across Zach's tear stained eyes as he re-lived his childhood exploits.

"It sounds like you and Sol had the most wonderful of times here. How come you never mentioned you had a brother before now? I had assumed you were an only child?" I queried.

As warm and gooey as his reminiscing was, I had to ask the question. I wanted the truth, no more secrets. Zach took a few seconds to ponder my query — but refused to respond. Instead, he continued on, as if he had never heard me.

"I was full of fantasy and excitement back then. The enemy was stored in the innocence of our imaginations. It was all we needed to enjoy ourselves, none of this materialistic mumbo jumbo that kids have today.

We created our opponents. Sol was particularly good at this, and I instinctively played along."

Zach told me that when his back was turned, his brother's favourite trick was to lob a medium-sized stone into an opportune bush.

The aim was to disturb the mark aka Zach by creating a shuffling noise from the leaves shifting on contact. Zach knew the bush was a decoy, but it didn't stop him from feeling petrified each and every time. With young Zach on edge, Sol would emerge from out of view and throw his brother to the ground in the most heroic of somersaults. They would then lay in hiding until the coast was clear or until Sol had decided they would make their escape.

"Autumn was a particular favourite time of mine, mainly due to the fact we were in conker season!

My brother would take a fallen branch and bash as many Horse Chestnut trees as he could."

Zach said that the vibration of the swipe would penetrate the existing branches, sending the green spiky encased nuts plummeting to the dirt. Sol would then go on to declare that they were the recipients of a grenade attack and cover was required pronto!

According to Zach, his brother wasn't always responsible for the special effects. Oh no, he had the unpaid labour of gratuitous wildlife to thank for that. A scurrying squirrel, bombing through the open trees in April, and the sporadic burrowing of a hare into the dewy soil of spring — provided the perfect shape and sounds of a direct attack. With an open mind and a little inspiration, a world of daydreaming was born.

Although autumn was ranked highly on his list, it was the months of winter that he cherished the most.

Smothered in their matching oversized knitted scarves and hats, they would wait patiently for the snow to fall. On the rare occasion that it would, they prayed it would settle overnight.

Pure white, untouched, virginal snow was what they craved. Zach told me how fresh snow lost its appeal once touched by the human foot. It seemed spoiled. Like it had lost all its purity and beauty in that one print.

Zach's words eventually tailed off, leaving a heartfelt sigh in their place. I could sense he no longer wanted to disclose, but he had already said too much for him to stop now. I had successfully demolished at least one of his barriers and was in far too deep to terminate the conversation now. If anything, I needed to know what happened between him and his brother.

"Sounds magical, you're lucky you had someone to share these moments with. I wish I had," I enviously said. "Erm, I don't mean to pry but what became of you and Sol?" I gently asked.

Zach nodded, obliging this time to my request, with little to no resistance.

"We thought the woods would provide a welcome shield from the blazing sun, but we couldn't have been more wrong. The intense rays took every opportunity to bake our skin through the waving gaps of towering overhead trees. It was uncomfortably hot, sticky and close, and we found ourselves excessively panting and tiring more quickly than usual," Zach uttered, before pausing.

"Go on..." I gestured.

"As my brother rightly said, he had become a man that day and man had to go it alone at some point, so it was decided we would become enemies of war. It was one-on-one combat, and we would fight to the death or in our terms, until the other one was caught!

Joining my hands, I extended my arms and pushed my index fingers together. This was to be my trusted imaginary rifle, my companion, my weapon of destruction. Sol, on the other hand, opted for a large tangible rotted old stick!".

Zach inwardly chuckled to himself as he revived his brother's antics.

"Fire!" Sol would bark as his rifle pretended to release a magazine of bullets across the woods. Berries, acorns stones, snails, mud — you name it — he flung it. They would shoot from his hand as he mimicked the spray of a machine gun."

Zach would gleefully gallop past the bushes, arms swinging from side-to-side in search of his foe, whilst Sol pounded the ground, armed and dangerous in search of his prisoner.

They raced on with their fictional weapons, their cheeks flushed a shade of maroon as they dared to ignore the extensive heat of the sun. Sol had the added bead of sweat as he hammered his body through the trees.

The sound of sweet boyish giggles was no more, instead, they were replaced with the sound of their makeshift rifles:

'pop pop', *'pow pow'*, *'pew pew'*.

Zach was struggling to continue, his words stalling as they declined to escape his tongue.

Grabbing his hand, I tightly squeezed his fingers. I was here for him, and I hoped from my touch he could sense he was able to confide in me.

His heartbroken expression stared me squarely in the face as he reciprocated my squeeze.

He understood.

∞∞∞

"It was…it was when we were alone that I saw them. We must have been separated for at least fifteen minutes.

I was on the brink of dehydration and was in need of a five-minute breather. I had pinpointed Sol's location but was in no state to carry out a strike, instead choosing to hide behind the nearest shrub to recuperate.

Whilst in standby mode, I caught sight of these shifty figures, there were three of them, lurking in grand bushes near to Sol's stakeout. They were young adults, male, no older than fourteen years of age — if that!

Dressed head to toe in dark clothing, they edged towards my brother's territory, careful not to alert him to their oncoming approach.

The next thing I hear is a piercing shrill directly squalled from Sol's location.

My eyes automatically darted towards his hideout. I was petrified as I watched the leaves from his bush frantically tremor. He made no other sound apart from his initial scream. The woodland was muted, his position was static. I immediately turned to the site of his shady-looking neighbours, but they were nowhere to be seen. Deep within my gut, I knew something was wrong."

My heart sank for Zach as he re-lived the ordeal as if it

were happening in real-time.

He told me how he had dashed to his brother's refuge, expecting to find him cowering within the shrubbery, afraid, shaken but alive.

Sol, however, was not there. Zach insisted he would not have been able to leave without him noticing. It would have been impossible!

Zach slammed his hands into the bush, manically ripping the abundance of twigs and leaves from out of view. He desperately hoped to find his brother curled within a ball, those carefree grassy greens peering back up at him, but it wasn't to be. His brother was gone, vanishing into thin air. The blood-soaked scratches from his desperate manhunt were all the proof he had of his brother's disappearance.

"They viciously took my brother from me, and I didn't do a single thing to stop them. That's how much of a man I really am, Allie!" he wept.

"You were only a boy back then, what could you have done to stop them and three of them at that!" I protested.

"My brother would never have let them snatch me away, but me? I happily allowed them to take away the one person I loved to death. So, there you have it! You happy now? You got your story!" blasted Zach.

In a bid to console him, I placed my head against his. I had pushed him too far, opening a wound that was incapable of healing. But as callous as it was, I had to place his emotions aside. I was still in need of answers and resolute on probing a little further, no matter how much it would hurt him.

"Please know, I appreciate you feeling comfortable enough to recount a personal tragedy as harrowing as yours. I really do...but what does all this have to do with Kalen?" I meekly asked, for fear of further upset.

"Allie, isn't it bloody obvious?" he bleated.

Well...actually no, it wasn't but I knew I had to tread carefully if I was to ever retrieve the truth.

"Those suspicious boys were and are Coral's men and

your precious Kalen is very much a part of that clique, can't you see?" he stated.

"Coral? Your cousin Coral?" I repeated, perplexed.

"Yes! How many Corals do you know!" he bit.

"She's your cousin, Zach...you're telling me your own flesh and blood is involved with the men responsible for the whereabouts of your brother...?" I quizzed, in confusion.

"That would make Sol her cousin too!" I snorted, dismissing his claim.

"Well, no...not exactly.... I need to be straight with you.... I only told you we were related in order to lure you to the party. We're in no way connected, blood or otherwise. Sorry," he shockingly revealed — like it was no biggie!

"Are you freaking kidding me!" I flipped.

How on earth did he think it was acceptable to lie about something as big as this, and how hadn't I realised it was all a sham? This preposterous fib was no insignificant little white lie — it was astronomical and not easy to hide!

"Those vile men are fae!" he affirmed.

"Fae?" I asked baffled.

"Fairies, Allie! Eves, pixies, imps — y'know — creepy little arcane people! As are Coral and her herd of sweet-toothed guests! If they're not of her kind, then they're definitely under her spell.

The party was a trap, and I'm sorry to say, you were the bait. I had to gain your trust, to bring you here so that Coral would eventually grant me the opportunity to access her world.

It has taken years of betrayal to find myself accepted into their ring. If they were to find out who I really was, then not only would I be dead but so would you," he blurted.

"Zach, you realise how crazy this all sounds, don't you?" I burbled.

"I know! That's exactly why I didn't tell you. I know how absurd this must all seem, but you experienced yourself the capability of their powers, didn't you! That there in the ring was no elaborate magic trick, and that goblin punch wasn't your average bowl of fruit and liquor either.

They're after you, like they were with my brother! The only difference is...they caught him," he voiced sternly.

"Why me, what have I got to do with all this?" I nervously asked.

"You, Allie, have something they want, and I can guarantee it lies around the nape of your neck!" he unfavourably announced.

As much as I hated to agree with this utter folly, it was kind of beginning to make sense. Oh, and as for that punch, I knew it had been laced with more than just a glug of booze and a handful of blackberries!

"Once they have what they want, they will kill and dispose of you and all without a second thought. Most likely feeding the remains of your carcass to an undergrowth world of vermin—never to be traced. Their world is not like ours, an enigma, protected with secrecy, above and beyond the life of any human," he sinisterly confessed.

The more shocking the details, the more I contemplated the possibility of all this actually holding some sort of truth. I could but not reflect back to the party: the suspicious potent punch, the sudden disintegration of the ground and that bizarre dance ritual. This was weirdly followed by the mud split and the unexplainable growth and speed of those three curious men. Plus, now added to this mix of peculiar events was the revelation of Sol's disappearance.

All these incidents had one thing in common, and it was clear that 'thing' was Coral!

Zach had insisted his brother had not moved from his hideout. He was convinced he was swallowed into an unexplainable pit. The exact one that was responsible for my near on death.

It sounded like a scene straight from a paranormal movie, not the type of occurrence that you would expect in a sleepy little village like Eldercrest.

"There was no footage, no marking and no concrete evidence to prove my wild allegations. Besides, who in their right mind would accept a witness statement that appeared to be unbelievably fabricated and divulged from a child!" he added.

"And Kalen...what does he have to do with Sol?" I urged.

"I screamed for him to quit playing around and to take me home at once. It wasn't funny anymore. It was past lunch time and Ms. Crumpling would be bulldozing the house down in search of us. If anything would shock Sol into revealing his location, then the mere mention of Ms. Crumpling's name would do it.

Sol never responded, and it was then I knew he was gone," he sniffed.

Gosh, I hadn't heard that name in years! Ms. Nora Crumpling was a very affluent and well-known lady in Eldercrest. She was a little on the podgy side, under 5ft and in her early fifties.

Bitter-face, strict and impassive, you would be lucky to see her cry, let alone crack a smile. She wore the drabbest of ill-fitting blouses, calf-skimming skirts and never was she seen without her trademark stained pinny adorning her clumpy hips.

Her hair was fashioned into a loose messy bun onto the crown of her head and was the shade of a bleached plum. She had the beadiest of button eyes and a voice that screeched like a dry chalkboard.

Children loathed her, but to the rest of the community — she was widely respected.

Unable to conceive a child of her own, she turned her back on men and chose to live a life of celibacy. Registering as a foster parent, she opened her home to any child in need of a warm bed and a hearty meal.

"My biological parents placed me and Sol into care when

we were very young. I was only seven months and Sol was only three years old at the time. Mum got sick and Dad couldn't cope. It was only ever meant to be a temporary measure, but as the months passed, the visits dwindled, and the contact eventually stopped." revealed Zach.

"Credit to Ms. Crumpling though, as she was there for us when no one else was. It was then a whole year after losing Sol that Frank finally arrived on the doorstep and registered to adopt me as his own."

My heart reached out to him. His childhood was tainted with unbearable sorrow. In the absence of their parents, Sol had taken on the role of a father figure. Understandably, he was a major influence on Zach and a great loss in his life.

"Those men stole my brother; they took the one thing I thought would never leave me. Do you have any idea how it feels to be left so alone?" he raged.

"No, no I don't," I sympathetically replied, "but I lost my dad too, remember? You're not alone."

I tried to ease his pain, to relate to his grief in the only way I knew how.

"I'm hurting, Allie. I have been ever since that day, and I will not rest until he's found!"

Zach was deadly serious, he needed to know his brother was at peace before he himself could start living again.

The thought of Sol's decomposed corpse scrapped and forgotten, didn't distress Zach half as much as the thought of him being out there in captivity and living a life of torture did!

I knew now that Zach's self-confidence was all a facade as inside him hid a broken man. The strong shell that had been harbouring a tragic spirit was slowly beginning to perish.

"You did all you could and look at you, you've never given up. You're definitely the man your brother always wanted to become. He would be proud."

I meant it. Every last word.

"But...Kalen?" I reminded.

Zach rolled his eyes to the back of his head before continuing.

"It was here, this summer that I first saw your treasured fairy boy. I was searching for Sol as I always did, praying that today would be the day he would jump from out of the bushes screaming, *'bang-bang'*. Faith is everything to me, Allie and the world would be a very melancholy place without it," he declared.

He made a good point. Faith was something I had lost the day my dad died. Since his passing, I vowed never to trust completely in anyone or anything ever again, as you never know how long they actually plan to stay around. Life from that moment on became increasingly dull, miserable and lonely for me.

Only once had I since made the mistake of falling into the trap of complete trust, finding out via the hard way that not even your mum could be relied on. Her lack of empathy and support since Dad's death was nothing compared to her hidden trunk of bits! Forgivable, yes, but forgettable, no.

When I first saw Kalen, he was alone and sniffing around these woods. I thought it was a tad strange to be lingering around here of all places, but I couldn't exactly judge considering what I was doing. He seemed distant, almost as if he was meditating. His body was present but his mind elsewhere. Out of curiosity, I followed him, which is how he led me to you!

"Huh," I was flummoxed, as far as I was aware, we first met at 'The Locust Lounge' and then later over a tin of spam at 'Crocker and Sons'!

"Where?" I interrogated.

I needed to know how long exactly this farce had been going on for!

"I tracked him over to your house, keeping a close watch as he effortlessly enticed you over to 'Blossomvale'. You were too busy salivating over his every word to notice me! You practically needed a bib," he enviously scoffed.

My cheeks stung with embarrassment as he delivered a blow-by-blow account of my thirsty antics. I knew I had felt someone close by in 'Hags Alley', but I couldn't recall the same feeling inside 'Blossomvale', but then again, I did only have eyes for Kalen.

"I waited and watched, hoping to find a vital clue and prove my suspicions correct, but with your unexpected arrival, any potential activity of a scandalous nature was halted.

Hours of monitoring with nothing to show, I decided enough valuable time had been wasted in preoccupying myself with lover boy. So, I left.

After a further hour or so searching Eldercrest Woods, I decided to call it a day. It was too dark for me to do much more, and I promised myself I would revisit again first thing. I headed out of the woods, towards 'Hags Alley' and home, and that's when mine and old Romeo's paths crossed again.

Instinctively, I dived behind the nearest hedge, hoping not to have been seen, and that's when I caught sight of Coral. From the moment I saw them two together, I knew there was something suspect about them. My gut told me to follow them back into the woods, making sure to keep a safe distance.

At first, I had them firmly in my sights, but the further into the woods we trekked, the harder my self-appointed task became. I struggled to track them — it was pitch-black, and they were exceptionally fast on foot. Their distant figures fading into the shadows of the night as if they had never been there in the first place."

His words chugged away like a steam train, building in motion, reaching for climax. I knew it was inevitable, but still, I was unable to step out the way of the oncoming cabin.

Kalen had left with Coral, that I was sure of, but wrongly, I had assumed they had gone back to hers...not into the open visibility of the woods. Classy she was not!

"To catch him, I had to keep a vigil — returning day after day. It was only a matter of time before he would show again. I kept a low profile, hidden from view — with very little possibility of being spotted.

I had spent years honing my hide and seek skills, so that not even the unparalleled of sleuths had a chance of finding me. Day and night, the faces passed. Young and old. Happy and sad. But none of them resembling Kalen.

Children in full on tantrum mode, accompanied by frazzled parents on impromptu family strolls, would pass by obliviously to my presence. Groups of rebellious teenagers stumbled through, unaware of my existence as they guzzled half empty bottles of piss-flavoured cider. Wheezing joggers pounding the same early morning route before their commute to work were always none the wiser.

My only weakness was the continuous flow of dog walkers and their inquisitive breeds. It wasn't uncommon for these hairy mutts to sniff me out, but still, I remained undetected, with not one of them able to communicate my location to their master.

I waited and waited, days passed — one after another in quick succession, but still, none of these faces were Kalen. I was on the brink of losing all hope and ready to abandon my post...but then the twenty-third day arrived.

I was drained, weak and cramp was setting in at an uncontrollable rate. I was starved and hankered for anything sweet and sugary. It was all I could think of. Leaves, grass and berries no longer cut it, and the thought of eating soil, snails and bugs was most definitely off the menu. Unwashed and ridden with filth, I smelt and looked like an old weathered tramp!" he whined.

"Sounds horrendous! You exposed yourself to some awful conditions...and all on a hunch? That's mental!"

"Mental? No, Allie. I was determined," retorted a defensive Zach.

"I won't lie, I was in the process of acknowledging defeat,

which by no means was easy for me to admit. Then fate decided to step in," Zach said, adjourning as he proceeded to grin from ear to ear.

"Well, what happened on the twenty-third day? Don't keep me in suspense. I need to know!" I nagged.

If Kalen's name was to be dragged through the mud, then I had a right to know why. We did have a past of some sort, and it was only fair I should hear the truth about the man I'd once involved myself with.

"Easy, I'm getting there!"

Zach had no idea of the undue distress he was causing me, yet he knew full well he was about to trample on the memories, the feelings and the love I once had for that boy.

Delighted he was! The enjoyment oozed across his face like an overfilled jam doughnut.

I urged him to enlighten me, and after several pleas later, he complied, spewing the details I so eagerly craved.

∞∞∞

"I was about to up and leave when a warm gust of wind breezed through the woods, kissing my skin as it passed. Within seconds, the temperature had increased by a whopping ten degrees. The heat was sweltering, overpowering and unbearable, just like it was on that day in September, 2007.

I knew I needed shelter and to find shade, but before I could make my move... 'it' showed itself to me!"

Zach disclosed to me how he witnessed this unexplainable thing appear through thin air, blind to his presence of only a few feet away.

Zach shuffled over onto his stomach and peered through a gap in the foliage. Rubbing his eyes, he assumed he was delirious from the heat and lack of sleep, but the sighting remained unchanged.

"In front of my eyes, it began to form, to evolve and take

shape. I hadn't a clue what I was seeing. Allie, I'm not playing games with you, and I'm not withholding information to make you panic or over think. I can only tell you what I saw, and it wasn't of our kind."

How Zach knew the way I felt, I will never know, but he seemed to just 'get me'.

"This thing showed itself as a glittering shadow, formed from a magnitude of stars. It had no features, no gender — it was transparent and faceless, and with the rise in temperature came its baffling spectral growth.

I watched in astonishment as this mysterious being effortlessly extracted and absorbed the fiery heat...the very heat that was blazing through the woods.

The overbearing flames of warmth were sucked through via the core of this thing — oozing inside like liquid lava and swiftly circulating throughout its body.

The severe temperature began to disseminate, resulting in the growth of cells, blood, muscles, bone, skin and hair. The facial features were the last but most important piece of the shadow to form, and as they came together, 'it' transmitted an enigmatic stroboscopic light, signalling the evolution of its human structure."

"Is that even possible? You sound daft! Can't you just tell me the truth about Kalen and leave all this other nonsense out!" I angrily scoffed.

"Is it really that daft? After tonight's events, do you really think my so-called tale is that hard to conceive?" he responded. "All I can tell you is that this thing appeared from out of nowhere and transitioned before my very eyes. If you choose to believe me or not, then it's your call, but I know what I saw," he argued.

"It's not that I don't want to take your word for it, but it's hardly realistic!" I doubtfully laughed.

"Life isn't always as straightforward as it seems. There are things that the eye cannot see, things that go on beyond the limitations of our imaginations. Although you may not see it

—doesn't mean it can't exist," he disputed.

Ok, he had my attention, and I was willing to hear him out.

"You, like the many other ignorant individuals out there, don't want to believe in the unknown, unless it's handed to you on a plate," he fumed.

I was hit with pangs of remorse. Here Zach was promulgating the hardest moment of his life to date, and there I was unable to take him seriously. Those wasted years injected into his search for Sol had clearly sent him delusional. He needed my help, not my ridicule.

"Right, so what exactly is it that you are trying to tell me, and when does Kalen make an appearance within all of this?" I pushed.

"Are you really that naive that you've not worked it out? This thing, this 'it', this 'inconceivable' character is KALEN!" blasted Zach.

"Not this again! It's not possible and you know it! Kalen is as real as me and you, how could he be anything but?" I snubbed.

His words slapped me full throttle in the face. He wouldn't let up on the mysterious ways of Kalen, but the more he insisted, the more I believed, even if I didn't want to admit it.

"I know what he is, and yes it's hard to believe, but he is one of them!" Zach sighed.

It was clear Zach cared for my wellbeing, and I was touched he didn't want me to end up the same way as Sol. Besides, who in their right mind would think up such a far-fetched story if it wasn't real?

"If I can't find out what happened to my brother, then at least it wasn't without trying, but most importantly, I will have managed to save you from the same fate. I could have walked away from you that day, left you to learn of your own destiny, but when I laid my eyes on you, I knew I never wanted to leave you. Allie, you were never mine to protect, but I'm in too deep to walk away from you now."

He was either an impressive liar or he truly meant every word.

"I care for you, Allie. I wish you could feel that, but with Kalen around, I'll never have your full attention, will I?" he stressed.

I couldn't give him the answer he wanted, not yet, but I was swaying more towards him than I ever had before. Maybe there were things out there that I didn't understand, but like Zach said, it didn't mean they didn't or couldn't exist. I only had to revisit 'Blossomvale' and her curious little creatures to know that!

If Kalen was what Zach believed him to be, then I sure didn't want to find the truth out for myself. I was therefore inclined to do or say whatever Zach wanted from now on — if it meant escaping these woods alive and away from 'it'!

Twenty-Eight
ESCAPE & EVASION

Zach's orders were loud and clear....

"If you stay here, you'll be safe, you're completely out of sight! Neither Coral's men nor Kalen will find you — unless you move! So, don't move, and we will get through this!"

"Whoa, what are we doing here, we're an easy catch, let's make a run for it!" I panicked.

Using my arms, I leant into the soil and heaved my knees up from off of the ground. Only my shoulders were instantly met by the force of Zach's palms, directing me back down and into the damp dirt.

Crouching down beside me, he placed his rigid index finger onto my pursed lips.

"Baby, do me a favour and sshhhhh, you need to stay here and stay low. I'll get you out of these woods, but I need to make sure Kalen has definitely gone before we make our break. Even with a head start, he will sniff us out and hunt us down.

To him, I'm already a dead man, and he won't think twice about killing a pretty little thing like you, no matter what you think you two had. He's not like us, he's a different kind of species altogether."

Zach had no qualms in making Kalen out to be a heartless monster. Like he was inept of any feelings with no morals or emotions. Was the soft-spoken, reserved Kalen I once knew, really capable of killing me in the cold of night? Not even if I pushed him to the brink, could I imagine him hurting me!

There was always the likelihood he could bruise or slay Zach, but to execute me, surely not?

Zach compatibly digested my expression of hurt and confusion. It was clear he was concerned for my state of mind, after all, he was the one responsible for delivering the blow that had begun to crush the world I knew around me.

"Looking back, the signs were there, they probably were for you too, but at the time I chose to turn a blind eye. Something had felt odd, I had sensed it, but stupidly I chose to ignore it. That decision will haunt me for eternity as it cost me dearly, it cost me my brother, Allie." he whimpered.

The pain in his eyes was apparent as he unexpectedly informed me of the odd set of events that led up to Sol's disappearance.

"Unlike any other time, the woods had always felt like a second home, but on this occasion, they had felt very different. We were stalking one another's positions when queerly this sinister chiming tone wafted through the trees. It weaved into every nook and cranny before slapping my skin with a layer of goosebumps."

Zach must have been referring to the same eerie tune I had heard down 'Hags Alley' and come to think of it… throughout Coral's initiation ritual! It ambushes you from behind and entices you in. You know deep down it feels wrong and unpleasant, but you follow the sound regardless, you can't help but not.

"Why didn't you tell me any of this before?" I asked bewildered.

All I knew was that it was a blistering hot day, there were a few dubious characters prowling the area and Sol disappeared. The end.

This little revelation was quite big in the grand scheme of things. It gave more insight into the shape of that day but most importantly it related a little to my own experience.

Zach told me he didn't want to burden me with too many details but thought it was about time I knew the precise ins and outs, as I might actually take our current situation seriously.

He said he had bellowed out to Sol, asking him if he knew where this woeful sound was coming from and if he could see who or what was causing it?

Sol popped his head from out of hiding and shook it confusingly from side-to-side. He either couldn't hear what Zach was hearing or wasn't fazed by it. If his big brother didn't consider it an issue, then neither did Zach and so it was dismissed.

Zach very much felt they were not alone that day and although he could not see them, he could sense their eyes watching his every move. He spent the day constantly scouring over his shoulder, in order to catch a glimpse of whoever or whatever it was that was creeping up on them. Sol, on the other hand, was inattentive. He was having the time of his life, and Zach wanted to make sure this was exactly how it would stay for his brother.

In hindsight, he should have addressed the issues earlier on with Sol or even made the call to leave when he felt as wary as he did, but unfortunately, when you're young, you see no, feel no fear and regrettably, he failed to react.

Sol was charging through the woods, kicking up dirt with his wet boots when for no reason at all, he was stopped dead within his tracks. It was as if his feet had been slammed and pinned to the gravel mid-run. His body stood still, apart from his head which slowly and creepily rocked from side-to-side. He had heard it, and this time his attention had well and truly been caught.

Sol had entered into a trancelike state, lasting only a few seconds but it was enough to have had the desired impact on him, and as soon as the effects had worn off, he headed towards the suspect bush. Coincidently, this was the last time

Zach saw his beloved brother alive.

"I know in my heart that haunting chime and those ominous young boys were connected," he growled.

"If you know all this, then why haven't you done anything about it? Seems that Kalen's not the only one that's been cosying up to Coral!" I tutted.

It didn't add up, why hadn't he addressed the issues before now, and why socialise with the very people you believe are accountable for your grief?

"Try to remember, these people aren't strangers to me. I've cleverly wormed my way into Coral's circle, befriending her — way before you and I became a 'thing'. I've seen things you couldn't imagine and bided my time for when the moment was right. What's the point in actioning an attack before I have the proof I need! Coral has no place in my heart. She means nothing to me. But I need her. Like, I need you," grimaced Zach.

After all that had happened tonight, I simply took Zach's comments on board. Nothing could shock me any more than it already had. I had seen more in one night than some had seen in their entire lifetime.

"Ok, I hear you," I sympathised.

"Allie, you don't know how remarkable you are!" gushed Zach as he tenderly stroked the fallen wispy strands of hair from off my brow.

"You and I — we're the same. I know we are, and tonight I've realised how lucky I am to have found you."

The ruggedness of his gravelly tones kissed my muddled heart, convincing me once and for all to put my full trust in him. Those affectionate words of his had toyed with my indignation — twisting my hurricane of emotions and pouring into my overcrowded thoughts.

However...I couldn't deny that the whole Coral and Zach 'thing' hadn't niggled away at me. There was definitely more to their relationship than he let on, but I wasn't quite willing to express my doubts and worries with him just yet...though he already seemed to know.

"Are you ok, Allie? Whatever it is, it will probably feel worse if you keep it locked away," coaxed a concerned Zach.

Should I tell him what was eating away at me and risk hearing the unpleasant truth? If I didn't ask, then I would never know, and maybe he had a perfectly good reason to back up his behaviour.

"You and Coral, what's the deal? If you're not cousins, then how have you managed to wriggle your way into her clique? If I know her like I think I do, then she will most definitely want something from you." I blurted.

The sheer ampleness of chemistry that rocketed between those two as they greeted one another at the party, hadn't gone unnoticed by me. It did make me feel incredibly uneasy and slightly nauseous which gave me reason to question their relationship. I had originally assumed they were just overly friendly individuals with a deep family bond, but then as you know, I would be lying if I hadn't thought for a split second that they were the fuel for some sort of dirty incestuous affair.

If Coral was not a cousin of Zach and instead part of this 'fairy cult', then how exactly had they come to meet and how close were we talking?

"She's massively fond of me, Allie, to the point she hates you for being in my presence," he admitted.

"She knows we're more than just friends though, doesn't she? You have told her?" I pressed, expectantly.

"Eh, yeah she's aware but let's put it this way, if it wasn't for that chain around your neck, you wouldn't be standing here," he whispered.

"Huh?" I gasped.

"I told you! Kalen wants you for one thing, and sadly for you, it's not your body. Your nan's necklace is what he desires, it's what Coral desires, and he will do whatever it takes to retrieve it for her. If it wasn't for that, there is no way Coral would allow you near me. Like I said, she's rather fond of me."

"So, you're telling me, you're part of this sick plan too? Tricking me into thinking this was a date when all you really wanted was to please that scruffy cow!" I snapped.

"No, well yes, well erm, it's kind of complicated!" he babbled.

"It's one or the other!" I indignantly directed.

"Ok, ok! Yes, Coral believes I tempted you here for her, for the gem, but like I told you, I brought you here to protect you from Kalen. He would kill for that glitzy pendant, but at least with me by your side, you have a chance of living. Coral doesn't know my past, she doesn't know the real me, not like you do," he promised.

"Oh my god...I'm this present, aren't I?" I screamed in realisation.

It was obvious and judging by the expression of guilt slapped across his face — I was right!

"None of this makes sense!" I wailed.

"If I had told you the truth, you would have laughed. Like I said, you wouldn't be with me now, would you? You're safer here than on your own at home, believe me," he continued.

"If that's the honest truth, then why leave me if your intentions were only ever pure?" I demanded.

"It looks bad, I admit that, but I had no idea the lengths Coral would go in order to get what she wanted. I never once planned for any harm to come to you, but what happened out there was above and beyond my control," he pleaded, his arms wide open, hoping for forgiveness.

"I sussed early on in the evening that Coral was becoming increasingly suspicious of my intentions for you. I had to keep my distance, disguising any genuine interest I had for you as detest. As far as Coral was concerned, I had completed my mission by bringing you to the party, and my services to you were no longer required.

You must understand, I had no choice but to play along. If Coral had learnt of my true agenda, then I would have been of no use to either of us," he convincingly muttered. "And no, we're not dating, we're not fooling around, not like that," he sharply added.

Yet again, Zach knew exactly what I was thinking. It was either a lucky guess or he was infiltrating my mind.

"I have been close with her for my brother's sake, in the hope that one day she would open herself up and lead me straight to him. I thought if I told you we were related, you would feel less threatened by her testy glances and sleazy behaviour," he confessed.

As much as I didn't want to, I could understand where he was coming from and the lengths he would likely go to in order to reunite with Sol.

"The moment I saw her, I knew she was trouble, she absolutely reeked of it. You only have to watch her with her prized men to know she's not as innocent as she would like to portray!"

He was right, she ruled those boys with an iron rod, and they obeyed her demands like the dogs they were. The leader of the pack — they were owned! She ordered — they followed, but how far they were actually willing to go was yet to be seen....

Twenty-Nine
THE WATERY GRAVE OF THE RED-HAIRED NYMPH

Her body lay limp, lifelessly floating within the woods notorious lake, known gruesomely as 'Suicidal Waters'. Anyone who knew of these watery fables would never consider venturing into the lagoon, let alone dip a toe within its tempting liquid. A sensational vision to view, yet it held a dark secret, responsible for luring many a misinformed visitor into its glorious embrace.

'Suicidal Waters' was well-known for becoming the resting place for anyone that dared to take a paddle, soak or swim inside her.

Funnily enough, it was only ever the men of Eldercrest and beyond that weakly caved in at the sight of her luscious turquoise waters and the intensifying vibrancy of her cushioned green Lily Pads.

Once enticed, they would lower their thirsty bodies into the deceptive sea-green lake, only to be dragged under seconds later. Their hands frantically beating against the slip of water as they grappled to stay adrift.

No one ever did.

"Coral was a vision of deliciousness, an enthralling temptation. She took my breath away. I was transfixed by those curves, her pale snow-white skin and that sultry slick of red hair as she floated effortlessly across the waters. Her body gracefully bopping on the surface as the breeze danced with her figure," he gushed.

Insufferable bile churned violently inside my stiffened throat as he fondly recalled his stimulating encounter with her. My temperature bubbled, breeding from within the pit of my stomach and culminating within my aggrieved cheeks. I was sick with relentless envy as he spoke of Coral with passion and zeal.

It was becoming more and more apparent that I was nurturing feelings for this boy. Yes, I knew I liked him but not to the extent that his besotted words for another would bludgeon away at my already frail heart. I had bestowed a piece of myself to Zach without even realising, and it was now too late to ask for it back.

Too engrossed in reliving his perverted fantasy, Zach was completely unaware of the effect his throwaway comments were having upon me. He was literally drooling with excitement as he reminisced over the gentle flow of water that elegantly trickled across Coral's slender legs, shapely waist and perfectly perky breasts.

"A beautiful scintillating honey glaze was left in the wake of crystalline water, forming across her bare body and glistening within the light of day," he slobbered.

"BARE, you say? As in naked? You're telling me she was stark naked and afloat?" I choked.

No wonder she had his attention! I was screwing inside, absolutely livid at the thought of him ogling her unclad body!

"No need to get all uptight now, Allie, it's not like I could see anything, well not much that was worth seeing..." he saucily winked, whilst inappropriately rounding up his crass remark with a dirty guffaw.

From the outline of her curves, Zach could tell Coral was in the nude. Her modesty kept only intact from this peculiar shimmer-based coating that had unexplainably reacted with her submerged frame.

"Come on, I'm a young red-blooded male, it's only natural I'm going to have a sneaky peak," he pointed out.

I supposed so, but still, it hurt knowing that at one point

344

he had eyes for that trampy tart.

From the moment Zach laid eyes on Coral's exposed body, he automatically knew she was not like me or you. He had, of course, caught a glimpse of her at 'Blossomvale' with Kalen but had decided to give her the benefit of the doubt, accepting not to prejudge her until now.

"God, I wanted to join her, the water looked delectable… as did she!" he swooned, licking his lips.

"Marvellous!" I sarcastically quipped, knowing full well it was more the latter that excited him.

Zach was still very much unaware of the green-eyed monster he had unleashed. It had tossed and turned within before cracking through my ribcage in rage. Regardless of this, Zach continued on with his stomach-retching account.

"From out of nowhere, I had this uncontrollable urge to move out from beneath the rustle of the trees and into the vulnerability of the openness. Abandoning my unlit hiding position and revealing myself to this mysterious temptress.

I was very familiar with the rumours of 'Suicidal Waters', but at the time, any concerns I had of such hearsay, simply waned away.

In full view, I made my gradual descent towards her. One by one, kicking off my boots whilst simultaneously fumbling to pull my head through my T-shirt. Impatient to join her, I couldn't unrobe quick enough — the irresistible want to touch her appetising skin was huge! I decided by this point that I didn't care if I was to enter with or without my jeans on," he brazenly confessed.

Zach's moment was fast approaching. He was about to gallantly slip inside the waters of the murderous lake and inspect the swamp-rat for signs of life.

She had been lying on her back motionless for quite some time, and Zach, ever the gent had become quite concerned for her wellbeing. He said he had a moral duty to ensure she was breathing and would do what needed to be done to ensure she was alive.

Who was he trying to fool? He had been bleating on about her allure for long enough, that I was quite familiar with the fact he wanted to do more than just check for a pulse!

"I was stripped down to my waist, ready to dive in when I was met by an unwelcoming occurrence," whispered a now more serious speaking Zach.

He explained that at the time of the incident, the desirable turquoise waters encasing Coral bled with raw blood. The unfavourable fluid seeped from her open pores, diluting itself within the unadulterated lake surrounding her.

With the grisly change in water, came the accompaniment of an irritating humming sound, similar to a swarm of aggressive bees. This being the queue for her 'guest' to make its melodramatic appearance

BOP!

It had risen from the depths.

"At first, I couldn't quite make out the identity of the object but soon realised it was the appendage of a limb — a human limb, and it was alive."

Disturbingly, Zach continued to watch, observing this 'thing' as it manoeuvred itself from its enclosed watery grave to the surface of the lake.

Slowly, this 'thing' circulated its way around Coral's flawlessly crafted feet — the fluid sliding freely down the shaft of its fingers.

"For some unknown reason, I failed to react in the slightest to this highly abnormal situation. I didn't even attempt to warn her of the potential danger she was in. Shock or perhaps curiosity had intervened, and I hastily retired to the safety of my previously darkened corner," admitted Zach.

He confirmed that Coral didn't respond or remotely flinch to the touch of the unknown hand as it began to do more than just revolve around her feet. With index finger poised, 'this thing' positioned itself on the tip of her daintiest toe, before sensually trailing its way up the length of her knee.

On the arrival of her cap, the remaining fingertips joined in, slithering up her sculpted thigh and caressing her pierced navel and petite waist. They pawed at her svelte arms and grazed against the sides of her heaving breasts.

BOP!
BOP!

Two more unidentified hands fisted through the film of the chilling blood-stained waters. They too locked onto her stripped body and proceeded to fondle her seducing skin.

"Weirdly, 'this' had now become a 'they', and after several minutes of intimate stroking, they one by one withdrew fully from out of their murky graves," recalled Zach.

The hulking arm connected to each one of these hands gradually and menacingly erected themselves from out of the lake, bringing with them the rest of their herculean body and a heavy flow of downward gushing water.

Three bare-chested men were now displayed in full view, their waists and below remaining underneath the deathly water — much to Zach's relief.

Blood stained droplets of liquid trickled from their sopping wet hair, rolling onto their flushed cheeks and dripping over their chiselled chests. Oblivious to prying eyes, they carefully continued to feel their way around Coral's faultless body. No skin went untouched.

The taller of the three arrivals waded towards her expressionless features, while the remaining two continued to brush her inert body as she angelically slept.

He towered above her, confidently hovering atop her peaceful ripe mouth. He was careful not to touch her but close enough to arouse her.

Pearls of watered-down claret moistened her sumptuous deep red lips, trickling from his oily mouth to hers. These little globules of scarlet leaked through the cracks of her pouty pillows and drizzled onto her pulpy tongue, causing a prompt reaction.

Up until now, she had remained stationary, with Zach initially fearing the worst, but this was all about to change — her senses had been awoken!

"Throwing her eyelids wide open, she flashed her piercing jade-green eyes directly towards me. I thought I was undetectable, but she knew different," he said.

"What happened? What did she do?" I probed.

"Nothing, absolutely nothing! I could have sworn, hand on heart, she saw me that day. She stared straight into my eyes as if she had known I had been there all along. It's like she had gotten a kick knowing that I had been privy to her bizarre and seedy antics!" he blurted.

"What I don't get, is that if she's this secretive, mystical nymph that you say she is, then why didn't she do away with you there and then?" I quizzed.

After all, he had seen some weird shit, it's not the type of information I dare say she would want to unveil to the world?

"Go figure! Look, all I know is that I was spooked, and I fled. I was too scared to stay. Too afraid to confront them."

"But you went back, right?" I asked.

"Right. I was unable to erase her from my thoughts. Something inside me knew that the answers surrounding my brother lay with her, and the only way to bury the mystery was to face her," he informed. "A few days later I built up the courage to return to 'Suicidal Waters', and sure enough, there she was."

As Zach had hoped, Coral was wallowing in her pool of toxicity, but only this time, she was awake and alone. Bathed in a soup of Northern Lights, the lake was alive with bubble gum pinks and apple green tones — bursting with electricity, colour and charm.

"I've been waiting an impatiently long time for you. Come. Join me," she announced, summoning him into the still waters with her.

He did as he was told, hesitatingly undressing and waddling in with only his underpants for protection.

"She was all smiles with eyes as wide as the moon — illuminating with delight. Her cute girl next door persona did well to charm me," he enthused.

"What a treat," I silently mocked.

"I swayed my way through the liquid of vitality towards her as she gracefully stood to greet me. The water flowed off her body like a flurry of delicate feathers, revealing a magnificent nude gloss of encrusted diamonds that shimmered from every inch of her exposed skin. Breathtaking she was.... I was barely able to remove my eyes away from her sparkly sheen," he planted.

Pacing a step forwards, Coral brought her lips to Zach, trailing them down his quivering neck with her lizardlike breath. Her lungs could be heard heavily inhaling his all-male scent as he let her do the things to him that I could only dream of doing. Then without warning, she clawed her bitch nails into the back of his neck. Forcing him upon her exposed flesh as she hungrily chewed upon his bottom lip in true X-rated fashion.

Coral liked Zach, she had made that quite clear, most notably sparing him unlike no other that had entered her fateful waters. If I chose to believe it or not, she had taken a shine to him, introducing him to an unearthly life that neither of us could have known existed.

Never fully welcoming him in, he remained on the outskirts of her magical realm. Aware of her land but never setting a foot inside.

Coral had fallen for him, and as a sign of her loyalty, she entrusted him with her most precious of secrets — her world.

Zach never questioned her revelation as he wholeheartedly believed she was not of our kind. Instead, he openly accepted her with the personal aim of closing in on the search for Sol. In Zach's mind, Coral held the key to finding his brother. He admitted he had grown close to her, showering her with affection, 'playing the game' as he so crudely put it. He promised me there was never anything more than a little risqué, hands-on action, although he admitted Coral was intent on changing that.

"The men in the lake with Coral were those young boys — the boys that took Sol. Those boys are the men you met tonight. Coral is the heartbeat of their kingdom and as for Kalen, well he's cut from the same cloth," he angrily stated.

"I don't know about that…" I disputed.

"You know full well he has links to Coral. He is after that necklace of yours, as is she. Coincidence? I think not! Oh, and as for his woodland manifestation, well there's no logical explanation. He has to be one of them! They're all connected — a colony of sick and twisted, vile creatures," raged Zach.

"It's all just a little bit too out there for me, Zach," I expressed.

"Think about it, Allie, he's been manipulating you. The bloke is odd, you only need to look at the facts to know that!" he drummed.

Yes, he was a little different but a fairy, come on!

"I'll enlighten you then, shall I?" he offered.

"Please do!" I snapped.

"Well for starters, I bet you've not met any of his friends, other than Coral, have you?"

Well, no I hadn't, but we weren't quite at the meet and greet stage yet, besides it wasn't exactly compulsory to meet his besties now, was it?

"And how about look-alikes? Don't suppose you've noticed the odd Kalen shape replica cutting about, have you?" he drummed some more.

"No, why would I?" I asked, on the defence.

"It's a typical fae move. They will transform into whatever or whoever they need to be in order to survive, lie or deceive. You'll notice small similarities between the individuals, be it a larger nose, square jaw or tint of hair. The eyes though, they don't mislead and, in many cases, will remain unchanged."

Replica? Can't say I...oh...erm, come to think of it, you did have the three ginger ninja's at 'Hawkers Cavern'! I couldn't put my finger on it at the time, but now you mention it, all three had the same asparagus and coconut husk rimmed eyes — much like Kalen.

"And how about a sickly-sweet tooth or a passion for over the top bright colours? Oh, and let me guess, did he make you one of those 'sick in the mouth' home-made gifts? Oh wait, of course he did!" he smugly finished, whilst nodding towards my bedecked wrist.

Tick, tick, tick, he was spot on. Even the bracelet... which he had quite rightly clocked earlier on at mine!

I didn't need to verbally agree with Zach for him to know he was right, and I hated to admit it, but things weren't looking at all good for Kalen.

"His lot go undetected, rarely seen, hardly heard. They can pop up when you least expect them, but you have to be quick in order to catch them!

They'll follow you.

They'll hunt you!

You might even feel their tongue lashing the back of your neck as they mimic your every move."

There's no denying the helpless feeling of being watched that I had endured during my last day of college. Or those sinister words of warning that bled through the silence of those solid concrete walls.

It didn't take a genius to realise that Kalen had access to roam through the corridors freely, and I could only assume that I was originally right in thinking Coral was behind that menacing threat!

"They'll never enter into a home uninvited, nor will they take anything from you without asking.

Oh, and I can guarantee they'll know everything there is to know about you before you do! You wonder how they know so much and even consider the possibility that they can read your mind. Well, I hate to break it to you, but they most likely can.

And 'Blossomvale'... that right there is your doorway to his world!"

If what I was being told was the honest truth, then how had I actually found myself caught up in the middle of all of this, and what was so important about Nan's necklace?

Zach had unfinished business, a score to settle and in the process had created a very dangerous life for himself. If Coral was to learn of his actual agenda, then I would dread to think what she would do to him next.

Thirty
OWED

One thing that didn't quite add up was Ms. Crumpling and how she had seemingly given up on Sol.

"No, I don't believe you! Ms. Crumpling would never give up on a child in her care. She was many things, but she was never a deserter. She loved you kids. You're lying!" I loudly screamed, as I stood to leave.

"Sit down!" barked Zach.

"Excuse me! Don't you dare tell me what I can or can't do!" I retaliated.

Zach had heard all he needed to hear and promptly backed me up to the swollen thorn scattered bush behind me. It was triple my height and extremely uncomfortable to the touch.

With his masterful hands, he pinned my torso in place and proceeded to give me a stern dressing down.

"Now listen here, Miss Perfect! We searched high and low for my brother, for hours, days and months. There was no disturbance to the soil, no crime scene, and no clues to work with. An exhaustive amount of time, money and manpower had been injected into endless searches, but with no progress, the searches grounded to a halt. The media were the first to abandon us, swiftly followed by the doting public. Eventually, even Ms. Crumpling left, she too had lost all hope. I was the only one remaining! We were truly and hopelessly forgotten."

Some say the story was fabricated by Zach to hide the fact his brother had simply run away from home in search of a better life. They assumed Sol didn't want to be found and the only way to ensure this happened was to fake his own mysterious disappearance.

"In the beginning, the media were extremely supportive. They couldn't do enough for me and Ms. Crumpling, but as there was no proof or influx of clues, questions and accusations started to take flight. The media decided that fighting alongside the doubters was a far better option than to fight the corner of a 'tale-telling' boy.

It turns out that the ground opening up and swallowing my brother was a step too far, and one the locals of Eldercrest could no longer buy in to. I was no more regarded as the surviving victim to a cruel and unfathomable crime but as an attention seeking foster brat," he sorrowfully informed.

"And Ms. Crumpling…?" I reminded, determined to get to the bottom of this.

"Oh yes, dear old Ms. Crumpling, well she served the final blow, didn't she! She out of everyone knew that my brother and I were as thick as thieves. She knew the love we had for one another was unconditional, and the last thing he would do was leave without me.

Even with her inside knowledge, she chose to ignore the facts and instead join in with the vultures and their unjust character assassination of me!" he barked.

"Vile! I can't believe she would act like that," I grumbled.

"Believe it! She was a heartless cow and took it upon herself to treat me with contempt from there on after. The first I knew of her change in attitude was when I returned home from one of my many searches. Tired and hungry, I had found myself turfed out from the twin bedroom I shared with Sol — extradited from the upstairs living quarters and banished to the stone-cold embrace of the basement. This derelict dive remained my cramp sleeping quarters for the year until Frank arrived and rescued me."

Everyone had given up on Zach, it was heartbreaking to hear. He was only a boy, and the fear of isolation and betrayal he must have felt would have killed even the hardest of criminals. Still, he kept the faith, searching for dazzling rainbows in the grimmest of puddles.

∞∞∞

Frank, a local scaffolder, had heard Zach's plight. Taking pity, he adopted him as his own — no questions asked.

"We ended up fleeing to his second home, a lovely villa, several countries away. I was finally away from the hounding and ridicule, a second chance to rebuild my life. Frank saved me.

After several years, my tale was yesterday's news. I myself had grown, my appearance changing, my voice successfully breaking. I was unrecognisable from the worn-down boy that scarpered five years prior. With our heads held high, we returned to Eldercrest with the dream of beginning our lives again. Frank had selflessly given up his world for me, and now it was time for him to go home," he uttered.

"But my dad, I thought you knew him?" I questioned.

"I did. I wasn't lying," he reassured. "Look, we weren't complete strangers. Now and again we would return, visiting for weeks at a time before settling back here for good. Your dad was always on hand with extra work for Frank, he really was a saint, ensuring we could pay our way whilst here."

Makes sense and it definitely sounded like something my dad would do.

"I was sixteen-years-old on our return, a man, ready to start afresh. I tried, I really did try to adjust, but I was never quite able to pull myself together and away from the unsolved heartache of those woods," he whimpered.

The realisation of Zach's tragic journey impacted my heart. I felt an enormous rush of empathy for him. For a little man, he had taken on more than his shoulders could bear. I'm only grateful he had Frank by his side when everyone else had turned their backs.

"Words can't describe how sickened I feel for you, Zach," I soothed.

He was a child for heaven's sake! I was disgusted to the core of how he was treated by our own people.

"I owe Eldercrest nothing, but it owes me everything, Allie! My brother, my childhood — my life!" he declared. "As with everything, things can sometimes resurface, even if you don't want them to, that's life and that's what happens. Coming back here would always be a constant reminder of Sol and the life I once had. That's why I had to leave and that's why I also took the decision to sign up".

I understood.

"...and Ms. Crumpling, well she was a massive part of my childhood, no matter how she treated me towards the end."

"Ms. Crumpling has been dead a few years now, hasn't she?" I questioned.

Zach respectfully nodded in confirmation.

That deceitful woman had backstabbed and betrayed Zach, yet still, he vowed to honour her for all she had and hadn't done.

"Let's remember this woman took both us boys in when no one else would," he reminded.

"Sure," I remarked, unconvinced by his weak justification. "...did you attend the funeral...as I did...but I can't recall seeing you there?"

I personally didn't know Ms. Crumpling, but I had heard many a good word spoken of her. I had learnt from an early age that it was custom to pay your respects to those long-standing and well-respected members of the community. This was a tradition my dad had installed within me and one I would continue to uphold.

"I know you were. I saw you, and I can assure you I was there too!" he snootily replied.

There was no judgement on my behalf, just an observation but it seemed to strike a nerve with him.

Cause of death you ask? Turns out the old girl had acquired a severe sweet tooth, so much so, it had become the hideous death of her.

The year leading up to her demise had been a chaos of sugary fat sweetness. She had stuffed her little round face with tubs crammed full of giant cookies! Which were ungraciously slurped down with whole buckets of deliciously flavoured dairy ice-cream.

Pallets of milk chocolate and trays full of sticky iced cakes were guzzled and crunched, washed through with bottles of sugary fizz.

She was unable to control her appetite or her waistline and quickly piled on the pounds at a gastronomic rate.

Her heart felt the brunt, straining whilst her body struggled to control the stretch until she could take no more.

She was found dead in the bathtub, surrounded by scrunched up sweet wrappers. She was in a sorry state, with a mouth full of squidgy marshmallows bleeding through her gums and clogging her airways.

Ms. Crumpling must have been in an awfully unhappy place to eat the masses of sugary junk that she did. Some say she couldn't forgive herself for cruelly abandoning Zach, feasting excessively to keep the guilt at bay. Others...well, others say she was murdered! An act of revenge for her traitorous actions.

Zach had rubbished my unholy claim, assuring me that no harm had come to her — the coroner had said as much. Mind you, he needn't have been so defensive about it, it wasn't like I was pointing the finger at him!

"Stay a while, won't you?" I asked.

There was no rush in finding Kalen, nor was there to leave. I quite liked being in his company...though I had the feeling it was all about to come to an abrupt, grizzly end.

Thirty-One
DEATH.

Wrapped in a chilly blanket of watchful stars, I gazed blissfully upon the serene night sky. Hidden from oncoming danger, she had protected us well.

We must have been camped out for the best part of an hour, and although circumstances were not ideal, I was glad to have been given no other choice but to hear Zach out.

Undeniably, he had done well to rapidly change my perception of him and of those wild connotations of his. Maybe it was the sleep deprivation or the fear in his eyes that had begun to sway me, but either way, it didn't seem so hard to believe anymore.

I amicably placed his farfetched finger pointing to one side, allowing my fondness for him to thrive. The sudden surge in attraction was most likely related to the blood hurdling towards my head, as I rested comfortably in the dip of his lap. I was content.

Kalen had preoccupied my mind for such a long time, that up until now it had seemed wrong, almost unfaithful to even look at another man in the same way that I had done for him.

Truth was, Kalen was never mine in the first place. The more time Zach spent with me, the less my mind wandered in search of 'the one'. I had wasted precious days on someone I thought I owed my heart too, and in the process, overlooked what was staring me right in the face all along. Kalen's unexpected appearance this evening was no exception, in all honesty, he made me realise I had denied myself to another.

"Ready, Allie?" spoke a weary-looking Zach.

I poked my head from the enclosure of his secure lap and nodded with anticipation. It was time for me to leave our nest, and though I was unsure of how the next twenty-five minutes or so would unfold, I could honestly say I trusted Zach enough to at least try and lead me out alive.

Preparing himself to depart, he propped me into an upright position and verbally delivered me his plan.

"Listen carefully to my instructions, and do exactly as I say," he ordered.

I bowed my head in agreement.

"You are to remain here at all times, keep still and do not utter a single word. If you do as I instruct, we will get through this, but if you move and scream, then I can't help you.

Understand?" he sternly questioned.

"Understood...but...but what about you? Where will you be, and what do I do if you fail to come back for me?" I wailed.

"That's not an option, you have nothing to worry about. I need to make sure the coast is clear, and when I signal for you to run, you run — ok?" he enforced.

Before I could plead with him to stay, he was already gone. I wanted to shout his name, to call him back. We could wait until the morning, there really was no hurry...but I had made a promise and muted I remained.

It's surprising how lonely the world can feel when you only have your thoughts to keep you company. The mind can become a dark and dangerous playground when left to ponder... and ponder mine did.

It was deadly silent and too black for me to correctly

make out if any of the shapes I was focusing on belonged to Zach. A simple unkempt shrub was easily misconstrued into an ugly bone-crunching ogre, and the breeze through a leafless tree was the ghoulish outline of an intestine sucking zombie! If Kalen and Coral's men weren't enough of an enemy, then my thoughts would certainly rival them.

Minute by tedious minute fleeted away and still no call from Zach. I wondered how long I would be able to refrain from screaming or breaking down in fear.

I peered frantically out from the side of the bush, my mind on overdrive, producing horrific thoughts that repeatedly regurgitated from stomach to mouth.

Had Coral's men trapped Zach?

Was he hurt?

Would he end up the same way as Kalen?

What if Kalen was alive and had caught hold of Zach?

What if all four of these airborne ruffians were beating him to death?

At least if I was there, I could intervene and stop this senseless butchering. I could never forgive myself if Zach had come to any harm, whilst I pathetically lounged here chewing on my already gnawed fingernails. No, this was no good, I couldn't idly sit around twiddling my thumbs. I had to do something. I had to find him!

"Urgh!" I growled, paralysed to the spot and unable to move from the waist down.

I thrashed my arms in distress, hoping to propel myself into the sky like a ferocious jet-fuelled rocket, but it was of no use. My hearty attempts to shift my weight made no difference. I was somehow securely pinned in place by an unseeable force with no sign of let up. Something inside of me was demanding I stay put, to remain seated. With a significant reduction in mobility, I had no option but to obey.

SWISH!

A sharp short gust of warm air shot through the still of the woods.

I took it as a warning sign that something negative was about to erupt…and unluckily for me, I had front row seats.

Crack! Snap! Crack!

This was the alarming sound of heavy footprints cautiously trudging on the array of sprigs and crisp leaves of the woodland floor.

My senses, my body, my soul — froze. I couldn't breathe through fear. I knew it wasn't Zach. He would have alerted me to his presence. It was someone or something else, and it was making its way straight for me.

"Alaaaaana…oh…Alaaaaana. Where are you…?" sounded the perilous tone.

I knew that voice! It was Kalen. And he wasn't happy.

Part of me was relieved he was alive, but the other half was petrified of what he was about to do to me.

I pushed aside the leaves on the prickly buffer in front of me to create somewhat of a peephole — immediately, spotting his position, my suspicions were confirmed.

Out of control and crazed, the man I saw before me was not the laid-back version I used to know. He was on a mission, erratically darting from corner to corner. His boots kicking up dirt and foliage as they dug into the ground. The speed in which he raced was phenomenal. No human could sprint that fast — it was impossible.

Appearing as a bolt of brilliant white light, he reached his destination in supersonic time.

He was on the hunt, and I was his feeble prey.

There was no way I would hand myself over to him, not

without a fight. So, without hesitation, I made the decision to run. Zach would understand.

You're probably thinking, 'silly cow, did you forget the slight issue of paralysis from the waist down?'.

Well actually, I was fully aware of my own body, and the paralysation only happened to be a temporary restraint — coinciding with the arrival of Kalen. Come to think of it, that was probably the work of him too!

However, I was now faced with an altogether different drama which promptly stopped me from any further movement.

An excruciating pain had torn through the lean skin of my ankle, prompting a sudden screech of anguish. Reeling in agony, I clutched my foot in an attempt to block out the acute ache.

In my rush to escape, I had somehow managed to hook my foot into a web of surface roots. Tightly wedged, I was uncertain as to how exactly I had found myself entangled, especially as I had no recollection of their presence in the first place.

I violently shook my leg in a bid for freedom, but the more I tussled, the tighter the hold became. With both hands, I lunged, grappling with the coarse wood, attempting to wrestle the scraggly roots into submission.

Impossible! I was unable to break free and with Kalen closing in, my time was up. If anything, my unpredicted squeal was likely to have given my coordinates away.

Peering back through the bush via the makeshift hole, I faced my oncoming fear. As expected, Kalen had been made aware of my cry. He had halted mid-sprint with his head cocked to one side in an attentive manner. My whereabouts had been acknowledged with no more than five metres separating us.

Inhaling large chesty breaths, he sucked in the air, deciphering my feminine yet slightly perspiry scent from the stale wet smell of woodland growth.

Elongating his arm, he stabbed his noxious index finger out towards my surroundings. Trailing it along the rows on rows of identical bushes before stopping dead on my hideout.

"There you are!" he softly whispered, with a hint of threat.

Kalen aligned his head and locked his glare on to me through the peephole — he had found me. Wasting little time, his frogmarch towards me commenced.

I cowered behind the bush, eyes closed, body shaking. I had no doubt in my mind that this was my time to die. I had no way of escaping — I was trapped. All I could do was pause for the thwack, impatiently waiting for the burning sting to rush through my body like a fluent gunshot to the chest.

I was 'just' existing until that trickle of apocalyptic blood slithered across my guiltless skin, calling time on my overdue survival.

I waited and waited but not a single strand of hair on my stooped crown was scuffed. What was he waiting for? If he was going to kill, then I at least hoped he wouldn't be so cruel as to make me linger.

∞∞∞

Cautiously, I cracked one eye open and instantly caught sight of an intense lilac and white hazy flash of light.

This out of place burst was shortly followed by a large object falling directly above of Kalen. The collision concluded with an aggressive groan and copious amounts of mandatory ground writhing.

With both eyes fully swept open, I was astounded to see that this large object was in fact, Zach. He had returned as promised and thankfully just in time.

Clambering up onto a wispy old oak tree, he had balanced himself onto one of the sturdier arms, near to and alongside my location. I figured he had most likely been there all along, watching and protecting over me.

Knowing Kalen would track me, he bided his time, waiting for him to pass before triggering his attack. With accurate precision, he had tossed himself headfirst off the branch, landing directly on top of Kalen's unsuspecting body. Zach had not only hindered Kalen but had successfully used him as a crash mat to break his fall. Zach took one last dig into Kalen's ribs before buoyantly jumping off of his victims flattened torso.

Kalen sneered with rage, "you should not have done that, boy! If anything, I've tried to be patient with you for Alanna's sake, but there really is no helping you, is there!"

"Kalen! No! Please don't do anything stupid. Let's sit down as adults and talk this through. No one needs to get hurt!" I begged.

For a split second, I thought I had made progress as Kalen appeared to listen as he stared with affection into my pleading eyes. Deep down I knew he didn't want to hurt either of us, but it wasn't enough to stop him. This wasn't the Kalen I knew, and I couldn't make him see sense.

"What I'm about to do, is all for you, Alanna," he crowed.

With those harrowing words, he bolted upright from off the earthy pit, straightened his right arm and lifted his palm to the skies. Closing his eyes and with his palm still in place, he raised his head to the heavens above. He was zoning out.

The midnight sky no longer harboured a quilt of harmonious stars, their positive glow erased, much like my prospects for a happy future. Instead, we were varnished in a sheen of grey foreboding clouds. These dirty cotton balls of doom swirled furiously above our heads as he encouraged them to unite with him.

Adhering to his call, they descended, lowering their gloomy mass of condensed water vapour several feet above him. Then without warning, they activated, emitting a surge of electrifying light, shooting from their crux and into his pulsating palm.

The light was intensifying, bright and smouldered with electricity. It embodied an enormity of power that would easily kill on contact.

The palpitating stream of fire was intended for Zach and Kalen didn't miss.

He sharply flexed his palm, enabling a sucking mechanism to take hold of the inferno, and once absorbed, he closed his fist and steered it towards Zach.

With target engaged, Kalen opened his palm — releasing a throbbing torrent of golden flames onto his helpless victim. The force of this fiery hit smashed into Zach's body, rebounding off his torso and blasting through the colossal tree trunk to his left. The impact so deadly, it burnt straight through the wooden core, leaving a gaping hole in its devastating wake.

As for Zach, he was tragically engulfed, helplessly yelping in pain. His body instantly wrapped in a ferocious deep purple blaze, with only the thickness of black smoke to censor his barbaric execution.

The ball of fire escalated up through the length of his body, consuming him in its entirety. There was no way he could escape its torrid grip. It had taken control of him with speed before dispersing into the cool of the night.

Left cindered and scorched, Zach's cries of suffering shortly subsided, informing me his horrific ordeal was over.

I screamed in horror — devastated by what I been made to see.

Zach had been right about Kalen all along, he wasn't of our kind. He was a demonic winged creature with powers beyond our control. How he could do such a cold, inhumane act was beyond me!

I shielded my eyes, unable to look upon the burnt corpse that awaited to greet me. I could not bear to lay my eyes on Zach's charred embers, knowing full well the pain he had sustained in his final moments. His beautiful face unrecognisable, his soft skin eaten away to the bone.

∞∞∞∞

Thump...thump...thump...

Unbelievably, I could hear the footsteps of Kalen treading towards me. He was coming for me — with not a second given to grieve.

"Open your eyes!" he disrespectfully demanded, as he invaded my hideout — dragging my jittery palms away from my screened eyes.

"I'm sorry you had to witness that, I hadn't planned for it to happen this way, but your 'friend' had to be dealt with. Now you know what I'm capable of, it's probably best that you do as I say. I don't want to have to hurt you too," he coldly breathed.

I was shaking with dread, sickness and betrayal. I had no idea what to do for the best, but with Zach no longer by my side, Kalen's threat needed to be heard.

"Alanna...you're trapped?" he uttered in surprise. "How did you manage to find yourself in such a mess?"

I didn't answer. Stubbornly shrugging, I refused to make eye contact. It was obviously him and his goblin magic! He might as well cut the crap as I wasn't about to buy it.

Kalen visibly offended by my attitude and lack of response — raised his deathly index finger towards me as punishment. Unable to run, he had me cornered, and with a finger full of power, I didn't fancy a positive outcome. Though this time, I bravely glared back at him — waiting for my thrashing like the warrior I yearned to be....

With his finger still in place, he sharply sliced his fiendish hand down towards the ground in a diagonal motion. My body tensed, preparing itself to fight off the unendurable pain that was heading my way. Yet, there was no piercing agony, no crushing of bones, no singeing of flesh. Just a gentle sound of crackling as the root encasing my ankle crumbled into tiny pieces, liberating me from my shackles.

Kalen hadn't hurt me; he had freed me and with my emancipation came the introduction of a whole new bubble of confusion.

Holding out his hand, I dubiously accepted and there it was — that old familiarity — that fizz of adrenaline as his skin melted into mine. He pulled my hand closely into his chest, and all those suppressed feelings I once had, came rushing straight back to me. It was as if tonight had never happened.

∞∞∞∞

"That all you got, fairy boy? You should know I prefer my skin burnt not toasted!" came the unexpected chuckle.

Kalen's face was flabbergasted and mine wasn't far off as we turned to meet our inappropriate joker.

There he was! Bold as brass, breathing life and cockier than before — if that's possible?

Casually stood there, he patted down the few remaining flames that were romping upon his blackened clothes. His face and arms were smeared with charcoal. He hadn't baked or fried. He was perfectly intact, apart from the torched clothes.

How had he survived such a profound ordeal and without so much as a blister?

Full of energy and laughter, it was a miracle he was even standing.

"Zach!" I beamed from ear to ear.

I wanted to grab him with both arms and hold him against my body.

Was this for real and not some sort of twisted hallucination on my part?

"You still remember me then, Allie? It's just from where

I'm standing, things all of a sudden seem to be getting a little cosy with wing-boy over there," he knowingly winked.

Kalen was beefier, stronger, more confident than I remembered. It was hard not to be dragged in by his enhanced desirability. I honestly didn't expect to feel anything for him, especially after the atrocious act he had just despicably committed. I would have happily walked away, vowing never to lay eyes on him again, but my heart had no such intentions. It was playing a very perilous game with me and one I wanted no involvement in.

How could I still retain feelings for a man that was capable of these reprehensible acts? It wasn't right.

Kalen's bewildered frown had now transformed into a self-satisfied grin as he turned up the heat by playfully rummaging his hand through lengthy strands of my hair.

Orgasmic! I hadn't experienced a sensation like it. He knew exactly how to tease me and where, but I wasn't stupid. I knew full well that 'this' was Kalen's dirty little way of exhibiting to Zach that he was more than capable of making me weak to his very touch. It was bold, boastful and completely out of character.

"Mmmm," I dribbled.

What was I doing? I was tastelessly lapping up the attention, unable to control myself as he toyed with us both. I had waited such a long time for Kalen to touch me, the way he was touching me now, that I didn't want it to stop, and as inappropriate as his timing was, I couldn't help but revel in it. Why I was feeling this way after all that had happened — I do not know, but I couldn't rule out that there was a little fairy dust at play here!

Zach was disappointed in me. I couldn't blame him. He was bound to feel this way. This man? This fairy? This man-fairy if you like, had only minutes earlier attempted to kill him and now his girl was swooning all over 'said' assassin like a prized sausage!

I was as confused as Zach with no plausible excuse to

offer him. This wasn't me; I wasn't brought up to behave like this...but here we were.

Silence had fallen.

Kalen unaffected by the awkwardness he had caused, gripped me by my shoulders and slowly backed me into his body.

"Alanna, believe me when I say I'm not going to hurt you. The gem you have been bestowed belongs to me and my people. Without your cooperation, our very existence will cease to exist. I'm asking you to do the right thing, and hand it to me," he openly begged.

"Yeah, yeah, yeah, here he goes with the sob story. Just shout if you want me to get the violin out, twinkle toes!" chirped an unimpressed Zach.

Squatted comfortably on top of a tree stump, Zach began to heckle from the sidelines. Ok, he had finally allowed Kalen an opportunity to speak from the heart, but it came with a barrel of abuse.

"The truth is that, yes, I am a fairy," confirmed Kalen.

"Otherwise known as a man-fly!" sniffed Zach.

"Call me what you want, boy, your simple words don't harm me," replied Kalen. "I am not like you, Alanna. I come from another realm. If I had told you what I really was, would you have believed me? I'm a myth, and that's the way my family for centuries have sort to keep it."

His coruscating greens simmered into mine, drawing me in more and more with every snippet he spoke.

"Don't tar me with what you think I am, or what you have been misled to believe by uneducated simpletons. My intention is not to capture or to kill but to retrieve the gem that hangs from your delicate neck," he urged.

"Oh bravo, bravo indeed!" clapped Zach, unimpressed by his rivals speech and derogatory comment towards him.

Kalen responded to Zach's petty remark with a sharp tut. He was becoming increasingly tired of the constant interruptions and negative mockery that was batted towards him.

"Now hand me the gem. I can't physically take it from you," he requested, holding his open palm towards me.

"If you want it, then you will have to take it!" I snapped.

He was more than welcome to it now, but there was no chance I would happily hand it over to him. He was silly to think otherwise.

Frustrated by my reply, Kalen threw his head back and smacked his hands down onto his waist.

"Someone's getting their lacy wings in a twist!" chortled Zach. "Why don't you just trap her to the ground again and bore her into defeat..."

"Be quiet, halfwit! You know I had nothing to do with that...don't you!" retorted Kalen, as he struck a rigid finger in the air to shtum Zach — all the while keeping his focus directly on me.

"Mate! You're gonna want to do more than raise a finger to keep me quiet!" goaded Zach.

Kalen bit his lip and nodded his head in agreement. At least they concurred on something, even if it wasn't the friendliest of understandings.

"How about this then, boy?" smirked Kalen, rising to the bait.

He raised his clenched fist to his lips and blew a blast of freezing cold air into the pocket of his palm. Swivelling around to Zach, he extended his arm and unlocked his fingers.

The shot of air propelled through the woods, slamming into his mark.

Taking the full force to his chest, Zach's torso jutted backwards whilst his feet remained put, unfazed and firmly fixed to the ground. If Zach wasn't so flexible, I was certain he would have snapped in half from the weight of that one hit!

This debilitating puff of air wasn't only a weapon of annihilation but a barrier too! On contact with Zach, the glacial air expanded, snaking around his torso like crackling ice, before climaxing into a gigantic, frosted, frozen bubble — big enough to encompass a full-sized human body and intentionally removing the subject from the equation.

Zach had miraculously survived a fireball — it hadn't stopped him. Would he fare any better a second time around? Although not fire, he was physically contained, unable to reach us but still heard...if a little muffled.

Zach inconvenienced by his circumstances, rested his hands heavily on the invisible wall that encaged him. Although transparent, the slightest gloss of bubbles was evidence that the impediment was in place.

"Kalen, what are you doing! Can he even breathe in there?" I panicked.

"He's fine. He has at least an hour," Kalen informed with disinterest.

Rap! Rap! Rap!

Zach walloped his fists against the field, trying his hardest to break through. His beats although subdued were still detectable. There was no way Kalen could silence him completely. He had tried to kill him once already, and thankfully that attempt was a huge flop. I hoped this situation was no different.

"Give me a minute, WILL YOU!" hissed Kalen, as he tried to regain focus.

His acrimonious request was solely aimed at Zach.

"Now — enough, Alanna! Hand over the gem. It's easy. Unclip it from your neck and pass it to me. Nice and slowly now," he ordered.

∞∞∞

I had always found his eyes mesmerising, and like a drug, I was addicted to them, but right now they were an altogether different kind of pill.

Without reason, they menacingly began to alter their

form directly in front of me.

The first notable change was the growth, widening in size, converting into an almond shape with a minor upwards slant — similar to those of a sultry cat. The pupil, it remained unchanged with the iris bleeding into the milky white of the eye, creating a riveting magnetic shade of flamboyant parakeet green.

Occupied, I was unable to draw my head away as I watched on with intrigue. God, he was beautiful, what was I thinking, of course I would help him.

"I want you to have the gem, I do trust you and I will do whatever it takes to make you happy," I whispered in a slow drawn-out pace, with the words straining to leave my tongue.

The sudden urge to want to help Kalen wherever possible washed over me in waves, and I would do whatever was necessary in order to honour that.

"Stop!" hollered Zach, as he rattled his fists down the barrier. "Allie, turn away, he's working you, can't you see? You're better than that!" he screamed.

I had heard Zach perfectly well, but to me, they were just words, they didn't make sense, and they made no difference to how I felt. I was far from caring right now, too transfixed by Kalen's penetrative eyes to think of anything other than them.

Kalen, unlike me was versed in the art of multi-tasking and saved me the trouble of answering Zach by doing the deed for me.

Flicking his index finger towards the invisible wall, he expelled a surge of bright white light from his fingertip and slashed it up against the perimeter.

Zach felt the overwhelming power as the force bayonetted the boundary, cleanly knocking him off his feet.

Untroubled by their ongoing feud and the additional attack on Zach...I continued, discreetly unclipping the catch and lifting the necklace from off of my calmed chest.

With the gem now cupped within my palm, I no longer felt any of the emotions I once had towards it. It was no more than your average-looking chain with a glitzy stone attached. I had no qualms with handing it over.

"Now pass it to me," ordered Kalen, his pussycat eyes narrowing as they stabbed into mine.

"Pass it!" he badgered, infuriated by my sedate movements.

"Oof!" I mumbled, wobbling as I gently massaged my brow.

My concentration interrupted with what felt like an invisible jolt to the head, urging me to conform.

My surroundings were spinning, my vision was blurred.

Something didn't feel right.

I was a little lost, a tad dizzy, but I felt compelled to continue.

Holding my disorientated hand out towards Kalen, the chain dangled off my little finger, enticing him to take it.

"You've made the right choice, Alanna. You'll not regret this," he gleefully smiled, relief crossing his face as he approached the sparkling jewel.

"Oi, fairy boy!" provoked Zach, loud and clear.

"Why-oh-why won't you die!" roared Kalen.

Resentment slushed from his cheeks as his eyes flippantly reverted back to normal.

"Ooh," I groggily muttered in response to his sudden change in behaviour.

My eyes were quick to register his oddly altered appearance — the shock knocking me out of my stupor and back into reality.

As I came aware of my actions, my mind instantly powered up — my body quick to regain authority over its senses.

Realising what I was about to do, I snatched my hand

away, and clutching the necklace tightly in my palm, I began to back up.

"What now!" growled Kalen.

His patience had evaporated.

Unable to control Zach, he had aggressively lashed out and inadvertently broken the force field that had kept Zach contained. Much to Kalen's disappointment, Zach had been dealt a lucky hand and was once again free to roam.

"Let's end this now!" he declared, as he marched purposely towards Zach.

He was no longer willing to continue the dispute and was hell-bent on finishing Zach once and for all.

He had spared him thus far, and in reality, he could have disposed of him a long time ago. Zach was no match. He never was. He didn't stand a chance, not against the powers that Kalen possessed.

I had grown to love these two for very different reasons, and now they were actually about to destroy one another in front of me. Zach would never be able to compete, not against a supernatural being, and I feared with all my heart that he would be the one I would lose.

Subsequently, I would also have lost Kalen as no way could my heart cope with continuing to love the soul of a murderer.

"This has to stop! If you would kill for the gem, then you are welcome to it! If it means more to you than what I do, then take it, but you will never see me again, that I swear," I wailed.

As you know the necklace was of irreplaceable value, but what I would not, could not do was have the blood of Zach on my hands.

Where my nan had actually acquired this burdensome pendant from was beyond me, but it seemed to me, she probably knew more about it than she originally let on!

With my mind made up, the necklace exquisitely somersaulted into the air. Soaring high, the gem guided the way, the chain twisting and twirling behind in alliance. This sacrifice would give Kalen what he craved and provide Zach with the freedom of life...or so I assumed.

Turns out, I was delusional as my little sweetener was not enough to satisfy both lads. Most people would have patted me on the back and thanked me for my unselfish actions, but then most people didn't have to contend with the likes of these two did they.

Let's face it, they weren't your average lads. You had Zach, who was deeply troubled and utterly reckless...and Kalen—just your every day, run-of-the-mill fairy!

I thought I had reached a balanced decision, one that would benefit the pair of them, but I guess I was wrong, very wrong! If I'd asked you to put cold hard cash on it, I reckon you would have plumped for Kalen to be the one that was causing me some sort of grief right now. Well if you had, then you would have backed the wrong horse, as it was indeed our little outside runner that had abolished my sacramental offering.

Let me enlighten you on the teeny-tiny problem that was Zach.... Refusing to engage his brain, he decided from out of nowhere that he would dive into the direction of the plummeting necklace and take a stab at snatching it. He had no purpose for it, apart from severely annoying Kalen and perhaps trying to win me over with his 'have-a-go' hero routine. So rather than the instigated run of deliverance that I had expected him to welcome, he instead thought it would be wiser to rumble with Kalen for one last time.

Zach had been quick to start with, ejecting himself from off the ground the moment I bowled the necklace into play. Kalen had also risen to the occasion, darting after the chain in double the speed.

Like a plunging diamond carrot, they both dashed from opposite directions towards one another with hands cupped open. Their eyes firmly fixated on their twinkly pirouetting trophy as it made its descent to the dirt.

They were closing in, a fingertip distance away. Uncertainty of the successor rang pungently within the quietude of bated breath. Head to head, they dived, scrambling to catch the treasure as it fell in between their pilfering palms.

A deflated growl signalled the frustrated sound of the loser's call, and to my amazement, it came in the shape of a very beaten and embarrassed Kalen. He was initially too slow off the block, and his dive had come in too short, which didn't help his cause. He fell to the gravel, a defeated mess, his rage evidently on show as the enemy stood before him defiantly.

Zach had succeeded in plucking the gem away from Kalen's hungry clutches. His fist proudly risen above his head as he gripped the chain, the gem loosely swaying to a halt.

"No! It's not for the likes of you!" seethed Kalen.

Zach was becoming quite the match, which Kalen found hard to swallow, as by all accounts, he was the mightier force to be reckoned with.

"Guess wing-boy here is losing his touch!", sneered Zach. "It's quite the accolade to flaunt yourself as a fairy, but a fairy with shoddy powers, well your practically no good at all!" he taunted.

Zach couldn't help himself, he had to keep on prodding at Kalen's smouldering ego until *BANG!* — he finally exploded. The inner bull inside him was let loose, and it charged towards Zach with a whole lot of muscle.

Kalen's face was stocked with grit, his body poised — he wouldn't fail this time. Zach aware of what was about to head his way, braced himself for the full knock of Kalen's weight.

THUD!

As predicted, Kalen didn't miss. He ran headfirst, grabbing Zach around the waist and ramming him into the mud. Winded, Zach's grip faltered, inevitably releasing the gem. It hurtled to the dirt with a punch. For those brutal painstaking minutes, the lads had actually forgotten what they were brawling over.

Lunging into one another, they didn't hold back, raining blow after blow onto one another's already tender bodies. They made sure the other was fully aware of what they were capable of, and I was almost certain they would not stop until one of them was dead!

I slowly backed my feet up; I didn't want either of them clocking onto what I was about to do next. I figured there was no way back from this. I couldn't stop them, let alone make them see sense. The best thing I could do was to leave but not before I had scooped the pendant up from its newly housed, squelchy ditch.

My eyes firmly kept watch over events. It pained me to do so, but I couldn't be so ignorant as to pretend it wasn't happening. The pit of my stomach flipped as I witnessed Kalen chasing after Zach. He was literally on his heels and about to finish him off when Zach switched the situation. Unbeknown to me, it was Zach's intention to lure Kalen in, to make him believe he was winning.

He had run at speed towards the old oak tree, using its trunk as a springboard to backflip off of. He must have flipped well over six feet into the air, skimming the tip of Kalen's hair and landing directly behind him. Kalen was taken completely off guard, and Zach knew it!

Seizing his opportunity, he hooked his arms directly underneath Kalen's, and with a swift move, directly cast him over his head. Kalen smashed face first into the sludge with a squishy *thud*. Vulnerable, he rapidly twisted himself over on to his back and raised that dicey finger of his. Rather than continue the fight with his fists, he was going to take care of Zach in the only way he knew how.

Kalen with all his capability was an unknown quantity. I couldn't predict how far he would take this, especially as he had been so lenient before now. Zach, on the other hand, wasn't afraid of Kalen's presence. He was agile and strong. He didn't possess fear, and he thrived on danger. I wasn't sure who I should be more afraid of — Kalen for what he was or Zach for his erratic actions.

Enough! I could watch no more! I had taken all I could possibly take, and so I continued to back myself up, quickening my pace with every step taken, praying I would go unnoticed.

They were welcome to kill one another, if that's what they truly wanted, but I wasn't going to give the successor the audience they craved.

Thirty-Two

A STEP TOO FAR

One single foot was all it would take for me to be out of sight, out of mind. From then on, I would sprint as fast as I possibly could, no looking back. I had no idea where I was going or if I would even make it out of these woods alive, but anywhere right now was better than here. I guess I would rather die trying, than not try at all!

So far so good! They hadn't noticed my efforts to fade away. They were oblivious to my stealthlike movements. If I shouted for them to stop, would they have cared? No, they were too busy attempting to slaughter one another to keep tabs on me.

"Nearly there, come on, you can do it," I reassured myself. "One more step and you're free," I coaxed, carefully lowering my unwavering toes to the ground.

That all important step was the difference between being caught in the middle of a deathly catfight and living a life of ignorance. I absolutely did not need to know the outcome or have the desire to capture the gory details of their irresponsible duel for myself. Liberation awaited, but irksomely, so did something else, and it was insistent on halting me mid-step.

It came in the guise of a blood-curdling wail. Raining down from the skies and piercing the air like the prick of a pin to the gaunt skin of a rubber balloon.

Kalen and Zach had also heard.

Stunned from their affray, they temporarily terminated their butchering to investigate the sinister interruption. But with little to no interest in what was about to come our way, they disregarded the concerning squawk and resumed their bloody brawl. I, however, wasn't as confident and took it upon myself to scan the woods.

I frantically circled the spot in which I stood, searching for the curator of this grisly scream.

Nothing conspicuous had yet highlighted itself towards me. Although, there was one other place still to look and that was beneath the sparse leafy amber layers of the multi-storey trees....

I groaned in utter despair, as sure enough, perched upon the branch of a decrepit old Sycamore was the subject or should I say subjects responsible for the hideous shriek.

I'd hoped we'd seen the last of them, but of course, that was wishful thinking. Coral's men were adamant that not only would they be heard but they would also be seen.

Now, it's wise I fill you in on a key detail here. One that would have probably gone unnoticed if you had not been alerted to their presence and seen them with your very own eyes. They were still Coral's men, but they looked a little different, very different actually — in fact, they were an eighth of their size different!

The men had literally shrunk, they were the size of miniatures, resembling the tiniest of action man figures. They stood rigid, side by side, arms folded and ready for war. Blink and you would have missed them. It's no wonder I hadn't noticed them watching me before now — they were pretty much rodent size!

Zach really wasn't lying, was he! They too were fairies, although they didn't look like the type that could cause much havoc, especially at that laughable measure!

I didn't know whether to laugh or cry, after all, I had originally thought that this was all just overhyped twaddle. How wrong could I be! I had walked into a world that I only ever imagined lived in the pages of over-embellished storybooks, and I wasn't expecting to find my happy-ever ending at the end!

Urgh, there it was again! That spine-chilling squeal. The type of squeal that urges you to dive under the safety of your bed covers. No monster can get you there, it's the unwritten rule!

But I had no cover, I had no bed. I was unprotected — I was fair game.

With the squeal resurfacing and echoing through the woods, my senses were doused with an inflow of sickness.

One by one, these pocket-sized vermin hurled themselves to the gravel with spunk. As tiny as they were, they had no issues with their nerve or indeed projecting such a loud and gruesome noise from their minuscule lungs. If Kalen and Zach weren't phased by their cries the first time around, they certainly would be now.

The nearer to the ground the men reached, the taller, the wider they grew, and with both feet hitting the woodland floor, they didn't stop to recharge. Instead, they automatically walked in line towards their target, still growing in length with every heart-stopping stomp taken.

∞∞∞

Standing proud like a beacon of hope was the famous Redwood — the mighty giant of Eldercrest Woods. With the majority of his age-old heart carved out, he was my gateway to freedom. If it hadn't of been for Kalen's earlier fireball stunt, then the chances of me escaping through the density of these woods were undeniably zilch. Without realising it, he had thrown me a lifeline in the form of a fiery rebound.

The grandfather of the woods, he welcomed me in through the hollow of his man-made cinnamon swirl tunnel, and even with his thick and spongy bark splintered, his status remained unharmed. Feeling safe within the protection of his mountainous watch, I took that all-important step of evasion, but in reality, it was pointless — they were already onto me!

Coral's men had reached human-size by the time they had approached the ancient arc of wood. Face to face and underneath a marquee of bark, they ensured our fraught meeting was hidden from prying eyes.

Stumbling backwards, I gasped in shock at the unwelcoming sight of their mutated features. The unexpected fright forcing me to exit through the towering arch of timber.

These black-hearted, pointy-eared men no longer resembled three young men in their twenties. Bare-chested with ripped jeans, their physiques had swelled in size. With a strong back, shoulders hench, the veins bulged through their muscular arms — raring to snap me.

Their skin mottled a lighter shade of dolphin grey, revealed a scattering of patchy mirrored mosaic scales. These opalescent fragments of armour — inserted in place of their flesh, smothered their cold, martianlike frame with reflective light.

Similar to Kalen, their eyes were visibly slanted and larger than normal, except unlike him, theirs were pitch-black and soulless.

"Erm…ahhhh," I gurgled.

I was tongue-tied — unable to speak.

They glared at me with disgust as if I was inferior to their species. They didn't want me here; I wasn't one of them and I had an awful feeling they were about to rid me of their land. I now had no doubt in my mind that they were responsible for little Sol's disappearance and most likely his death. These men were scum, they oozed evil from every orifice and were hell-bent on serving me the same sentence as poor Sol.

Tonight, had been an absolute disaster with my life hanging in the balance. I was stumped as to what I should do next with the last of my hope petering from my very existence. With my expiry date fast approaching, I had almost accepted my demise, when unexpectedly, I was thrown an extension of serendipitous proportions.

There she was, staring straight back at me as I dipped my view sideways for what I thought was the last time. Somehow and with the aid of Zach, I had come full circle. She was in full view, drawing me in and although it was unlikely I would make it, I had to give it a go. I had to run to her. I had to run to 'Hags Alley'.

Boom, Boom, Boom!

I was running for my life.

Boom, Boom, Boom!

I was almost there.

Boom, Bo—.

"Arghhh!" I yowled.

With the flick of a switch — they flew! The speed undetectable by the human eye. Their bodies acting as a prism, discharging a rainbow smear through the twists of bark and leafy burnt orange hues.

I was surrounded — trapped within their ring of maleficent voodoo. With no way out, I was now theirs, and they wasted no time in finishing what they had originally started.

∞∞∞

Together, they sharply cocked their conniving heads to that familiar volatile sky above. Staring upon it in silence as they spurred their immoral punishment to take hold of me.

Those miserable clouds obliging to the call, began to moodily whirl, circulating faster and faster as the men's concentration deepened with intensity. They were summoning an evil presence and sure enough it came.

"Coral..." I frustratingly grumbled.

That poison faced, acid-tongued trout was back. Glaring down upon me as she projected herself through the clouds like a misted optical illusion.

Hideously, there was not one but five versions of her, each flaunting a different but equally grim expression as they spun overhead. If I hadn't already been battered with a thunderstorm of unexplainable details from tonight, then maybe a cloud shifting into the features of Coral's face would have been a step too far...but as it happens — it wasn't.

With the speed picking up the pace to dizzying heights, her replicated quintuples chaotically merged into one. Without a doubt, she frolicked with pleasure at my unfortunate entrapment and spiralling discombobulation.

Reeling above, her baleful shrill slashed through the unsettling silence, vibrating through my ears like the infuriating repetition of an early morning alarm. I wanted to slap her into oblivion, switch her off, deconstructing her into itty-bitty components, but what realistically could I inflict on what appeared to be a mirage of watery mass!

Not only did I have to contend with her overseeing gloating, but her deafening squawking had awoken the sinkhole of condemnation. This time though, it returned with vengeance — darker, stronger and fiercer than before!

Almost immediately and with the slightest of touch, the dirt surrounding my toes began to crumble away — the brittle earth bed sucked into the endless abyss as the formation of the cascading sinkhole or 'portal' (as I was now beginning to believe) took shape.

I shot a glance up towards Coral, appealing for pity. Would she reconsider and excuse me from this purgatory? I could only hope, but by the looks of things, hope was all I had as Coral was now nowhere to be seen. Her image evaporated from the louring fluff above.

Instead, I had found myself left in jeopardy, balancing on a small solid island of gravel with a trench of plunging emptiness surrounding me.

The men's sadistic game was working, and this time they undoubtedly meant business, taunting me as I horrifically waited for the ground to swallow me up. With the gap too wide, I was unable to step across the unravelling ditch for fear of slipping in and drowning within its murky downfall.

I would never make it across to secure land alive. I was stuck in the middle, isolated with no means of reaching safety, and with every second that passed, my rate of survival reduced significantly.

Coral's men relished in my predicament, slurping up every drip of agony as the island I stood upon became leaner and leaner, ensuring a jump from me would be less likely.

"I don't want to die, not like this," I cried, gripping tightly to the gem, the gem that was the cause of all of this!

The men had cleverly waited for me to be only inches out of view from Kalen and Zach before confronting me. They wanted me alone, with no outside interference, and they got precisely what they desired. I was exactly where they wanted me, and I knew that if I didn't act fast, it would be all too late. There was nothing left for me to do but to ask for help from the very people I was running from.

"Kaaaal!!!"

Zaaaach!!!"

My lungs bulged as I screamed their names from the top of my afflicted pipes.

I wasn't sure how much longer I had left in the company of Coral's handsome fiends, but I hoped my distressed outburst would have the desired effect.

And it did.

The soil beneath my feet began to tremble as the response to my cry of desperation was acknowledged. A flicker of relief bled through my chalky skin as both Kalen and Zach skidded through the wooden passage and into view. Within seconds of my wail, they had arrived, albeit filthy dirty and smothered in bloodied mud. Their faces locked with confusion, no doubt surprised to see me tucked away in a shady crevice, surrounded by all three reprobates.

Zach had marginally trailed in behind Kalen, instantly resting his knuckles upon his shaky knees as he tried to catch his breath. Kalen was the opposite — full of stamina and bounce. The beauty of me knowing Kalen's real identity was that I needn't question why he wasn't out of breath or even slightly panting. Dare I forget that Kalen wasn't mortal! The effect on his superhuman body was minimal compared to that of myself and poor Zach.

With both boys' present, I secretly hoped one of them truly cared enough to save me. But rather than oblige, they were motionless, a blank canvas — stood before me, with a lack of speech. Why weren't they responding? I looked from one to the other, fear sousing my eyes as I anxiously willed them on.

"Take the gem, it's yours," I initiated, mouthing my request directly to Kalen. "All I ask is that in return you get me out of here."

Zach with all his military training was stronger than average, place him against any other human and he would obliterate them, but put him up against these titans and he would die. These were not exactly your regular everyday men, were they!

I was fully aware Zach had held his own against Kalen, but there was only one of him, and surely his luck couldn't last. He had given his utmost and for the majority had kept up, but it was now beginning to show. The strain was hitting hard, he was notably struggling.

Kalen, on the other hand, was full of zeal. He hungered

for that gem and would do anything for it. The gem for my life seemed like a good exchange right now, and if anyone was to remove me from out of this nightmare alive, then it was always going to be him.

Finally, he responded, nodding his head in acceptance to my offer, but it was Zach without thinking or speaking that stepped up, no questions asked.

He had heard every word spoken to Kalen and knew exactly what I had agreed to. He wasn't prepared to stand back and watch as I committed myself to this deal of desperation.

"It's sorted, Zach. You stay where you are, leave this one for Kal," I urged.

Zach didn't care, he didn't register my appeal. He had made his decision and continued to stumble towards me. Zach's movements had also prompted his unrelenting rival to keep to his side of the bargain.

Swivelling his body on the spot, Kalen's back now faced me as he took a few steps forward. He was creating a running jump for himself. Once happy with the distance, he spun his manful body around and launched himself into a sprint. His steps were rapid, and the speed in which he moved was preposterous and most unworldly.

Reaching level with Zach, Kalen attempted to overtake. Like a masterful bird, he projected himself into the air, purposely spiralling into Zach's path and shoulder barging him out of the way.

This malicious disruption caused Zach to tumble, connecting him to the ground with an unsuspecting *smack*. He bawled out in pain as his spine landed on a heap of disused wood.

The barge was intentional, but his efforts to sabotage Zach's rescue attempt, not only knocked Zach out of the running but caused havoc with his own mission. Subsequently throwing himself off balance, he strained to control his composure as he worryingly wobbled and rolled through the air towards me like an out of control bullet.

Although pained, Zach wasted no time on the ground, urgently removing a large wooden clump from under the small of his lacerated back.

With one knee on the floor, he mustered up every last drop of energy into catapulting this substantial piece of wood up into the air. The missile was on point and pigeon-holed for Kalen!

Kalen twisted and twirled as the wood struck against his cranium — smarting his skin as the wood disintegrated into hundreds of tiny shards.

A trickle of blood, the only evidence of a direct hit, flowed from his hairline and rolled down one side of his dirt-ridden face. This was the first time I had seen him bleed red, and weirdly I was kind of turned on! It sounds distasteful to be enticed by such a gruesome bodily fluid, but he was a vision.

Rolling effortlessly down his cheek, the blood glistened brightly, irradiated by thousands of glitzy stars. I wanted to roll my finger in the claret syrup, to feel its sticky crystallised touch between the slender crack of my fingers.

Kalen also felt the unusual presence against his skin, and by his hesitant touch, I guessed this was a first for him too. He raised his hand to investigate the leaky warm gash, dropping his hand to eye level and promptly investigating the tacky puddle of gloop within.

Perplexed, he hurriedly smeared the remaining crimson jelly from off his tarnished skin before anyone else had a chance to notice.

Undeterred, he shakily persevered on with the rescue mission. The aim to save me and in return keep the gem. Well, he made sure half of that agreement was adhered to by snatching the gem from out of my outreached clasp.

Kalen's jump had landed him neatly on a clump of sturdy soil on the opposite side of the portal. He was now stood directly behind me with the gem in tow. With my back towards him, I could no longer see him, but I could feel his eyes burning into the back of my skin.

"You come back here, Snow! We had a deal!" I furiously howled.

∞∞∞

I was dangerously close to death's edge, which I can tell you was not helped by the after jiggle caused by Kalen as he plucked the gem from out of my grip.

As a countermeasure to regain stability, I elongated my arms and levelled myself out.

I was silly to believe that Kalen would stick to his end of the bargain. He had made his priorities clear, tucking the gem safely away on his persons whilst leaving me to perish. With my little island evaporating into nothingness, I was on borrowed time. I turned to my only hope and unlike Kalen, he unselfishly offered a hand.

Gathering all his might, he took one hell of a running jump towards me, athletically bolting overhead and grabbing me firmly by the hand. His legs furiously trod the air as he hoisted me up and over with him — perfectly clearing the gap. We landed on firm ground on the opposite side of the portal, exactly where Kalen had been stood — 'had' being the key word here.

The island I had been stranded upon was literally now a slither of rubble, an uneaten core, flaky and broken. If Zach hadn't of intervened when he had, then unquestionably, I would have met my maker.

"Argh," I warbled — had I spoken too soon?

My left foot slipped on the crumbly ground, dragging me downwards and back into harm's way. I was dangling dangerously within — with the spit of the hissing watery rim licking at my toes.

"I got you, Allie. Hold on!" puffed Zach, as he wearily heaved my body from out of death's reach and back on to stable soil.

In unison, Coral's men simultaneously dropped their heads to their toes, their trancelike state ceasing. The clatter of my loose limbs hitting the gushing aqueous wall of the portal had fortuitously formed a wave of vibrations, breaking the concentration of the men.

Like a domino effect, they one by one reentered reality, expecting my body to have been gobbled up whole, like some sort of greasy burger bap. Unfortunately for them and luckily for me, I was very much alive.

With their focus now distracted, the portal weakened. It's power floundering to function as the ground slowly began to restore to its previous earthy state. One fairy was a tall order to deal with, but to be handed three fairies and angry ones at that — well it was a big ask!

Axel was the first to respond. He openly seethed at their combined mistake as he sharply realised I was far from dead. Hotly, he stomped towards my saviour, and without hesitation, cuffed his fist around the length of his objector's breakable neck.

Effortlessly, he lifted Zach from off the dirt before swinging him like an expendable paper bag over the renewing swirling portal. Although closing, it was still active and capable of withstanding the shape of a human-sized body.

Zach's eyes bulged with the insufferable pressure issued by the deadly squeeze as Axel continued to torturously sway him above the brutal vortex. His feet hopelessly swinging, unable to reach solid ground, unable to fight this animal off.

I had to admire his new-found loyalty, as not once did Zach remove his swollen gaze from off my woebegone image. Anchored, he maintained my attention, reassuring me that all was not lost. We were still here together, no matter how indescribable the situation was. In that one look, he provided me with a plethora of reassurance, and all I could do in return was pathetically watch on as he was to be coldly dropped from a grotesque height.

Noticing my protection was otherwise engaged, and

with Kalen once again on the missing persons list, Mace took his opportunity to attack.

I was in the worst position imaginable, laid flat out on my back with no time to rally myself together.

He stomped heavily towards me, his eyes protruding with excitement as he closed in. Licking his parched lips, he was baying for human sweat as he reached in to claw me.

With quick thinking and the last ounce of spirit I had left, I bent my legs up and in towards my stomach — *oomph* — my feet rammed straight into his bulked-out chest as I dedicated my all into thrusting him up and over my entire body.

He hit the frangible edge of the portal with a bruise-inducing *smack*, but unfortunately for him, he stumbled, tumbling backwards and into a swirling underwater star-infested void.

Unable to regain his balance, he roared in disbelief.

Mace hadn't expected me to fight back nor did he think he would foolishly fall into the very death trap he had created.

Axel's eyes automatically diverted to his comrade's plight. He was dumbfounded as to what had just taken place. This distraction, was however, enough to spur Zach on and raising his once flaccid arm, he hooked his hand onto the middle and index finger of Axel.

Snap!

"Woah, woah, woah!!!" I wailed.

I fumbled with the soaked dirt and gravel as my feet scrambled to reach the skirting of the portal in time.

"No, no, please no!" I hauntingly screeched.

I tried.

I really tried, but it wasn't enough, I couldn't reach him. What had I done, and how could I have let this happen?

Zach must have known it was unlikely he would survive, but he took his chance, boldly breaking the fingers of Axel who in response had heartlessly released his hold.

Was it from the shock of losing Mace? The pain inflicted by Zach? Or because he was pure evil that he relented? Who knows, but his answer really needn't matter, as his conduct was odious and ruthless, nonetheless.

Never would I be able to erase that image. That image of his face, his inconsolable face!! His stretched-out arms, begging to be snatched, just as I had done to him in my hour of need. Only I couldn't reach him when he needed me the most.

That wretch had tossed him away like yesterday's rubbish, leaving only a sharp shrill to echo through the fall and into my fragmented heart.

But wait....

...that shrill didn't pour from the guts of Zach! No, this unrestrained caterwaul had haemorrhaged from Axel as he too was sucked into the pit of no return. In no way was this part of his plan, but the unexpected plummet of Mace was enough to scupper his own vulgar ploy.

On breaking the power-soaked fingers of his adversary, Zach forcibly jerked Axel forwards, ripping him from off his footing. Taken off guard, Axel was in too much pain to recoup control of his mooring, automatically releasing his hold and toppling in after Zach.

Zach noticing Axel's distraction, had seized his opportunity to take down his potential killer, tactfully removing him from causing any further harm to me. It was an act of selfless devotion, and one I was denied of repaying.

Unlike Axel, Zach remained dignified. He didn't scream, he didn't kick, he didn't make a scene — he simply fell.

I had thrown myself to the rim of the portal and extended my arm out to Zach in a feeble attempt to catch him. My hand met with his, our fingertips softly kissing as they stroked skin against skin. Then I felt it, the clasp of hand against ankle and a short tug.

I tussled to fight against the pull, attempting to lock on to Zach, but it was to no avail; without a word, he was gone and so was I.

"No, no, no!" I yelled in denial, unable to swallow the hard realisation of both our fates.

He couldn't have gone. He wouldn't just leave me! Heck, he had survived a red-hot walloping of fire, a blockade of invisible incarceration and a fairy-spanking from Kalen! Please don't tell me a giant grubby hole was his limit?

"Zach! Zachhhh!" I wept loudly, unable to muffle my ineffable grief.

I was emotionally too far gone to care about the pending termination that was now awaiting me.

My fingers weren't even lukewarm from touching Zach's tips, when once again, I was ungraciously dragged by my heels and away from the verge of the disappearing portal.

There was still one of Coral's goons left, and it was apparently my turn to face him. I didn't have the energy to fight no more. I wanted this to be over. I had nothing left to give.

"Get it over and done with, Ike!" I aggressively challenged.

I had seen and lost too much to care about what he could possibly do to me. I was already destroyed.

"What you waiting for, do it already, you spineless wimp!" I egged on.

This was sick, he was prolonging the moment, enjoying the suspense. Emotionally and physically beaten, I mustered up enough strength to flip my body up, over and on to my back. I was intent on confronting my fate face to face. He wasn't going to decide when he would kill me, I wouldn't allow him the satisfaction.

"I'm ready!" I bellowed, arms slack and splayed above my head, eager to accept my slaying.

As brave as I was, I hadn't quite been able to look Ike in

the eyes, but with still no response, I had no choice but to.

Up went my brows, "do it already!" I bawled — this was the last time I would ask...though the person I was asking was not who I was expecting!

"You..." I muttered.

In lieu of Ike, I was met with a rather concerned Kalen. I must admit, I was slightly relieved to see the lesser of the two evils standing above me to summon the final blow. I did, however, feel terribly sickened for Zach, who would have witnessed the person or 'thing' that was stood behind me before I did. I wasn't sure who I would have preferred his last living memory to have been of, but I'm pretty sure it wouldn't have been Kalen.

Zach would have noted his nemesis approaching me from behind as he fell to his sudden and most unwarranted death. What kind of lasting image is that to behold? Then it morbidly dawned on me...if Kalen hadn't of dragged me backwards, I would have stood a good chance of gripping hold of Zach's fingers, rather than only brushing past them!

"Kalen, I could have saved him. Why...? Why would you do such a despicable thing? You got what you came for, you should have left well alone!" I bleated, thudding the ground in protest — devastated and distraught by his careless actions.

He shook his head. He disapproved of how I felt.

"Are you stupid, girl! The suction would have snared you in, and you too would be long gone. Can't you see I saved you!" shouted Kalen.

His words didn't matter. I would have rather died with Zach than live another second with this crippling desolation inside me.

"Help him, please! You're one of them, there must be something you can do!" I desperately ordered.

He adamantly shook his head, rejecting my request without a second thought. Was he concerned in the slightest at how damaged I was? Could he even comprehend what this was doing to me? He was probably incapable of knowing how to feel or how to care. Did his kind even have feelings!

"He's gone, Alanna, let him be!"

Kalen made it clear the events were not up for discussion and forthwith dropped into a crouched position onto the dirt in front of me.

Rather than erase me from my very existence, he told me he was preparing to extract me from out of here.

Gulp, I froze.

A bubble worth of words trapped themselves within my windpipe, unable to release. Jolted into silence, it was visible that tonight was far from over.

As Kalen dropped to the floor, he had revealed an irritable, bug-eyed Ike standing directly behind him. His scrunched fists spasming with unmanageable rage. The trauma of seeing him stood there was apparent on my already resigned face, but luckily enough, had halted any noise from leaving my cracked lips.

Kalen was quick to identify the horror as well as the reflection of Ike in my bulbous eyes. He knew he had to deal with this unrelenting nuisance pronto, and that's exactly what he did.

Up he shot, his clenched fist springing back into the crux of Ike's trachea, causing him to buckle weakly to his knees. Whilst bent over and temporarily out of action, Kalen wasted no time, vigorously booting him in the coccyx. The effects of which saw his opponent clumsily forward roll towards and into the belly of the portal.

With fingernails overfilled with dirt, Ike dug painfully into the edge of the spitting pit as he longingly held on with the hopes of scrabbling to safety. Kalen refusing to let such hopes materialise, moved sinisterly towards his impuissant challenger.

Without so much as a word, he proceeded to raise his condemning foot from off of the ground.

"Wait!" pleaded Ike aggressively.

But it was too late.

Kalen had already decided his future, slamming his boot into Ike's imploring grip.

"Arghhhh!" bellowed Ike, his cry cut short by the zip of the portal's complete closure, which of course resulted in his premature departure.

Was that it? It was over? I had expected a long laborious fight, splattered in blood, gore and entrails!

Kalen was no amateur. He handled the situation efficiently, promptly and with little to no bruising.

Dusting off his raw palms, he diverted his attention back to where he had started by tenderly collecting my dilapidated body. Like a newborn lamb, he cradled me in his arms — my weak, dependent shell collapsing within his embrace on contact.

With a full rotation of three hundred and sixty, Kalen mindfully checked his surroundings, making sure there were no more surprises to be had.

Coral was missing, her men were dead, and so was my precious Zach.

I closed my eyes. I didn't want to accept it. I didn't want to remember the things I had seen or how I would never see his handsome face again.

Yes, Kalen had saved me, but it wasn't enough. He had chosen the gem over my life and hindered my one and only chance to save Zach. If he had delivered what he had promised, then Zach would still be here. There was only one hero for me, and it was not and never would be Kalen, and besides, now that he had me, I wasn't exactly sure what he would do to me.

Thirty-Three

BROKEN

His nimble steps grew quicker and quicker with tempo as he pummelled through the moonlit woods on foot. If it hadn't had been for the sound of his boots slapping against the soggy turf, then I could have sworn we were soaring several feet above soil.

Not a word was exchanged between us as he expeditiously marched on in his promise to relieve me from this hell. If he had spoken, or tried to reassure me that all would be ok, would it have helped? Probably not. Too much had already taken place that not even the most open-minded of people would be able to comprehend the things that I had seen. There was not one word available in my universe or theirs that could possibly excuse Coral, her men or Kalen from their atrocious acts. I would never be able to dismiss from my mind what they had done, nor would I be able to condone it.

A million questions resonated within my over bulging brain, incessantly pecking at my lobes for the answers — the answers I didn't have.

Where was I to go from here, and was I mentally strong enough to pull myself through this ordeal? And how would I find Frank, let alone be the one to tell him his child was dead! My sanity would irrefutably be under scrutiny if I was to ever reveal what really happened in these woods.

Who could I realistically confide in that would understand and most of all believe me? The one person I would have turned to — was the one person I would never see again.

It hurt, it hurt horrifically so to think I would never see his smile again. The way that one side of his lip would curl when he was misbehaving or coming across a little frisky. To never hear his voice call my name over and over was heart-rending. No one could call me Allie — not like he could.

That girl. That bashful, slightly anxious, unsuspecting individual that entered the party was not the same girl that had left. Stricken with grief and poisoned with guilt, I was stripped of life, but most of all I was broken. Crushed into pieces, I couldn't be fixed. Despondent and ashamed, I was losing myself. An alien to the person I used to be.

Unable to stop them, they erupted against my forlorn thoughts and like the cold, glass spherical marbles they were, they began to roll thick and fast.

The wind tenderly brushed against my dehydrated skin, drying my uncontrollable tears as they seamlessly flowed over my tired puffy cheeks and swollen chapped lips.

Not in my darkest of dreams did I imagine tonight would finish in the way that it had! Kalen was back, Zach was dead, and I had entered a world of unicorns, flying pigs and magical pixie dust!

With my eyes wedged shut, I convinced myself I could block the world out. If I couldn't see it, it didn't exist. As long as they were closed, I could remain isolated underneath my umbrella of pretence for as long as I saw fit.

If I could continue to live in this manner for the rest of my life then I would, but it was never going to be feasible, was it! I had to acknowledge the aftermath and accept the realities of what had been and what was yet to come. Besides, my eyelids were struggling to battle against the increasing blow of breath. Flickering to remain sealed, they were unable to withstand the continuous current.

Wearily I conceded, agreeing to open my eyes and welcoming in the new world through waterlogged vision.

∞∞∞

The fullness of the moon was on hand to illuminate our way, reflecting its watchful gaze in the shallow puddles of sorrow that lay beneath Kalen's feet. I darted my attention up towards him, expecting some sort of empty expressional exchange, but his attention wasn't on me, he was instead soundly focused on the route ahead.

He appeared sheepish, his gaze darting from left to right and right to left. He was up to something, and intent that no one else, bar me, should be present to witness what it was he was about to do. Then as expected, there it was....

SWOOSH!

That brief yet recognisable sound rearing itself from behind, though on this occasion, it was three times louder than before.

Imagine a flock of sophisticated swans, harmoniously unfolding and extending their refined pure white feathered wings as one. Now accompany this stately sound with a large looming curvaceous shadow, semi-circled and partially jagged in shape. Its presence flooding out the glow of metallic grey moonlight as it encased my body in a duvet of warmth.

After all that had taken place at Coral's party, I could finally say I felt somewhat safe, draped in the protection of Kalen's cosy embrace. I felt untouchable here, like no one or thing could harm me, and though I knew this evolution taking shape around me was not normal, I didn't feel the need to question it — not yet.

My eyelids heavy in weight — progressively struggled to remain open. My mind and body failing to fight against the arduous exhaustion continued to persevere on — driven by my curiosity, eager not to miss a moment of fairy verification.

Then as luck would have it, I managed to sustain a small slit of sight, enabling me to keep my vision focused for long enough and capture what needed to be seen. No longer able to raise my head through fatigue, I squinted towards the ground, and as blurry as it was, I was able to catch a vital glimpse of Kalen's silhouette in the floodlit pools of watery mud below.

My heart bolted, peeling itself from out the comfort of my chest as I quickly realised we were numerous feet from off the ground! Not only that but his shadow quite frankly snatched my breath away, holding my dropped jaw to ransom.

I wanted to pinch myself — was I dreaming? I willed my droopy lids to open wider. Was I really privy to this magnificent sight?

I drained every last drop of energy into forcing my head up and towards Kalen, but still, he was yet to acknowledge me. His attention firmly focused on his flight path up front.

Seemingly unfazed by my prying eyes, I assumed he no longer deemed it essential to protect his secret against me, after all, I knew all I needed to know. I was viewing him for exactly what he was, what Zach had arguably believed he always was.

I had since bought into the fact that he was this rather fickle enchanted creature, but to actually see his truth for myself was utterly sensational.

Now, these things were huge, and I mean huge! Elegant and imaginative, they were an unthinkable sight to behold. Formed like the wings of a butterfly, they were the colour of ice, transparent and leaflike. Lined with a network of crystal glass veins, they surged with light, palpitating with glitter.

Reminiscent of twigs and branches, they shimmered with a scarce opal dusting, similar to that of iridescent cellophane. Majestic and unforgettable, they separated the fairy from the human.

I was keen to take a closer look, but with my failing eyesight and limited view, I was only able to catch snippets of his angelic wings as they glided back and forth overhead.

However, with the increase in altitude came my lucky break as his fluttering shadow came into full view on the woodland landscape below. I had an inkling this rare sighting was likely to be the closest I would come to see them in their full entirety.

They sliced through the barrage of tree growth, careful not to scathe their papery form on the many rogue offshoots waiting to slash. Well-practiced, he was untouchable, slipping through every twist and turn with ease.

With my mind elsewhere, I had completely failed to notice a swarm of tiny opal citrine lights coming into view from the rear. Suspended mid-air like stringless baubles, they burned brightly as they merged with our flight.

"Fireflies!" I blurted.

Never had I sighted one in Eldercrest, let alone an army of these twinkly little bugs!

Encompassing our bodies with their illumination, they chaperoned the remainder of our journey, guiding us through the web of wood and petals with their beaming abdomens on show. They radiated sparks of goodwill, allegiance and solidarity via their bulbs of golden sunset, lighting the way to liberty before dispersing without warning into nothingness.

Noting their departure, Kalen bowed his brow in gratitude, spread his heavenly wings and burst through the wood verge into open land.

We were free!

Unshackled from my chains, the weight of entrapment lifted from off my stacked shoulders. I was relieved — not only were we unconfined from the clenches of greenery but we were also alone, if only for a brief moment or two....

"Coral!" I gasped.

There she was, stood frothing with irritability at the entrance of 'Hags Alley'. Fully aware of our presence above, her evilness took an unconquerable swing, threatening to stab me as my feet skimmed the top of her inflamed head.

I pressed my eyes shut in a desperate bid to erase her, propping back open my brolly and sheltering myself from her scorn.

Squeezing Kalen tightly, I hoped she wouldn't touch me. I figured if I was glued to him, she might spare me for fear of the repercussions he would impose.

"Stay strong, you're almost home," I told myself, whilst drowning out her nocuous image and replacing hers with the decency of Zach.

He once said, 'if you get really scared, close your eyes and think of me' — so I did.

Granted, the first attempt with those beastly Mapleby brothers had failed, but with nothing else to lose, I could but try.

"Zach!" my heart cried.

With my temples lifted, my eyes ballooned as they absorbed him in.

An apparition, yes — though remarkably realistic. It was like I could actually see him with his fervidly distraught expression frowning upon me as I needily clung to Kalen.

I pressed my eyes shut to block out his disdain, and this time I refused to reopen them.

Crackle!

Kalen landed softly on the leafy smothered porch outside my bedroom window.

I was home!

He had kept true to his word, removing me from Coral's domain — eventually!

Smoothly he dropped his hand from underneath my feeble legs and stabilised my footing to the cladding. I had pretty much lost all track of my bearings as he had carved through the night air, teasing me with scraps of his enchanting wings.

'Hags Alley' was pretty much on my doorstep but far enough away for me to feel relieved that both her and 'it' were out of view, and once steady on my feet, my eyes zoomed in on Kalen...or should I say those wings of his! Coral's locality was the now the least of my worries as I finally had the opportunity to capture Kalen in all his fairy tale glory.

He, on the other hand, had other plans, and like a handheld Japanese fan, his wings immediately collapsed. They retracted back through his punctured clothing and into his versatile skin.

Out of view, it was as if they had never been there in the first place, and in no way was he waiting around for me to view them! They were his wings; they were private and most of all they were unheard of. I guess I could kind of understand why he didn't want them on show!

"I best leave, Alanna," he soothed, pushing up the frame of my window and urging me through.

"Come in...?" I innocently asked.

I didn't want to be alone, I wasn't ready, especially with Coral lurking by.

"Are you sure? I wouldn't have thought I would be welcome after everything that's gone on tonight?"

"Please. I don't feel strong enough to make it into my bed alone," I prompted.

For goodness sake, I wasn't inviting him in for an early morning fumble. It was the company I needed more than anything right now, and after giving it some thought, he finally accepted.

Quietly he led me in, gently easing me upon my quilt and affectionately brushing the loose strands of hair from off my grime splattered face.

"Am I dreaming, Kal?" I questioned.

I hoped he would say yes, informing me that all this was some sort of silly made up fiction.

"No, Alanna, I'm afraid you're not. I'm only sorry you were caught up in all of this," he apologised.

"Was it worth it?"

I needed to know.

"The gem...yes, yes it was, and one day you will understand," he promised.

"Coral...?" I stammered.

"Coral won't be back, I'll make sure of that," he assured.

"And Zach, he...he's dead, isn't he?" I whimpered.

"I would presume so, but if he had anything to do with Coral, then believe me, he was bad news. You'll do well without him!" he spat.

"No, you've got him all wrong. He told me all about Coral, their relationship was purely platonic...well on his side anyway. He had his own personal reasons for being associated with her. He's not...he wasn't...one of you!" I defended.

"One of me? I'm not a dirty word, Alanna! That person in the woods, it wasn't me, not the real me. I did what I had to do to survive, you do know that, don't you?" he sorrowfully replied.

"I don't know what to think anymore," I argued.

Part of me wanted to believe him, but I couldn't forget the way he had acted or the dreadful things he had done to Zach.

"Understand that the earthy hole you witnessed was not a hole at all. It was a portal, leading you to my world, my kind, my way of life. It's not for your eyes or for your people," he harshly revealed.

I knew it! I knew there was more to its existence than just the muddy grave it portrayed itself to be.

"Yes, in years gone by the odd human has wandered in, but they have never wandered out. Can you comprehend what I'm trying to say?" he sinisterly informed.

"You mean you won't let them leave?" I questioned.

He didn't answer, he didn't have to. Zach didn't just 'wander' in, and I didn't happen to have haplessly found myself stranded on a plot of disintegrating terra firma. If Zach hadn't of intervened, would Kalen have reacted and followed through on our deal? People didn't just fall into these portals, they were trapped, stranded or pushed!

"Alanna, don't believe all you've been told. It would seem I wasn't the only one keen to keep hold of the gem!" he suggested.

"No, again you're wrong! Zach was helping me. He knew how much that gem meant to me, and what it would do to me if I was to lose it," I advocated.

"You really believe that?" he laughed.

"Yes, yes, I do!" I bit.

"Ok, well what exactly did Zach gift to the birthday girl then? If you didn't see it with your own eyes, then chances are you or the gem were it!" he blared.

"I don't need to explain myself or Zach to you!" I thundered, embarrassed by his accuracy.

"You've had a lot to take in, not all will make sense, but all I will say is be careful. This Zach isn't all he seems to be, and if it appears peculiar, then it most likely is. Trust within here," he finished, pointing to my heart.

If Kalen was saying what I think he was saying, then he was way off the mark.

"I know this is seriously bad timing, but there are things I must do," he declared, holding the gem tightly against his chest.

I didn't argue. I knew the gem was key to whatever it was he needed to do, and now he had what he wanted, he might as well go.

"Please keep all of this...between us?" he requested, worriedly.

"If your people were to find out about my kind, that we even existed, then without a doubt, we would be smoked out. In defence, the portal to my realm would shut, our worlds terminating to coexist, never to open, and I would hate to never see you again," he whispered.

My heart sank as I nodded in compliance. My eyes drowning within their own tears at the thought of him leaving and never returning, regardless of what he had done.

Leaning into say his goodbyes, he parted his lips, hovering them nervously in line with mine. Then it happened.

The moment I had yearned for, for so very long.

He kissed me.

I didn't respond. I couldn't, and so he kissed me again.

Still nothing.

On the third attempted kiss, I tearfully caved in, reciprocating his soft clinch, our lips barely touching as we floated in between sweet delicate pecks.

A pear-shaped tear of guilt escaped me, trickling onto my rough lips as the heat between our bodies began to blaze. Kalen incited with sensual want, took control of my reclined body, weaving his hand underneath my neck and gently thrusting me deeper into his mouth.

With my head raised off the pillow, and my neck rested firmly in the scoop of his palm — I was completely at his disposal. Gentle, yet firm, he moulded my mouth to his. I fizzed inside with spurts of adrenaline.

Kalen's kisses were hardly fairylike, in fact, there was vaguely any difference between the taste of him and that of Zach. Although, you could say there were more sweetness and less spice to Kalen's lick!

I'm not really sure what I envisaged his kiss to entail, but I guess I was kind of expecting to savour the flavour of earthy mushrooms, mouthwatering strawberries and sticky golden honey. Instead, my tongue was basted with the dry, strong flavour of man as he commandeered me, tingling my bottom lip with his.

Kalen was very experienced for just a little fairy. He knew how to hold me, how to kiss me and how to make me quiver for more. Surprisingly, he wasn't that much different from the likes of me and you, as he too possessed those animalistic urges.

With his nose now nuzzling against mine, I could censor my remorse no more, and via the use of his thumbs, he lovingly rubbed away my drops of shame as they failed to stop, streaming down my skin, one after the other. He rubbed and he rubbed, but it was to no use, they were unmanageable. Realising he was facing a losing battle, he pulled away, closed his eyes and blew upon my abashed face.

His slight touch warmly dried my dampened skin, instantly reversing my tumbling tears, rolling them neatly up and over the curvature of my stinging cheeks. They nestled back into the overfilled ducts of my swollen, vein blotched eyes; with the chances of a repeat spillage highly unlikely.

This was the very first time I was conscious of Kalen using any form of fairy wizardry on me. I would hate to have guessed how many other times his magic had gone unnoticed.

Another time, another place and this kiss would have been perfect. Don't get me wrong, it was everything I had hoped it would be and some — unexpected, romantic and tingly. But as incredible as it felt, our time had surely come and gone? Problem is, I couldn't stop myself, maybe it was my emotions riding high or the fact I simply couldn't resist his hot and cold mixed-up signals!

The sad thing was, Zach had not even been gone an hour, and I was already cosying up elsewhere. I was a disgrace. I never really deserved him. Kalen wasn't even human and what's more he had tried to kill Zach on several occasions, but yet here I was clinging on to his lip like a wet lettuce. I was so confused; I didn't know what I was doing or who I should trust? It all just kind of happened, and with the little self-control I had, I went along with it.

∞∞∞∞

With no time to assess the situation, to stop or discipline myself, history had only gone and repeated itself. Kalen like he had done that one time in 'Blossomvale' — did it again.

He had left, jumping out of the window and vanishing into the thin of night.

"Kalen!" I beckoned.

It was a long drop to the ground but nothing a little fairy couldn't handle.

"I'll come for you," he replied.

"Promise?" I shot back.

"Forever," his voice hummed as he disappeared into the far-off distance.

SWOOSH!

I raced to the window, hoping to catch sight of him, but he was nowhere to be seen. Fast and cautious, he vanished within the early hours of the morning, ensuring his secret would remain exactly that.

"Urgh," I sighed, lowering my head as I rested my arms limply onto the windowsill. The charm from Kalen's bracelet clanked the surface on contact, serving as a reminder of the irreversible bother he had caused me.

What a way to go and mess your life up, eh! If only I could speak to Nan — bleed my heart out to her. She would know exactly what to say. She wouldn't judge either, but I had, however, promised Kalen I wouldn't blab. After all, he had saved me. I at least owed him my word in return.

Vowing to honour my oath of secrecy, I elevated my head and sucked in the fresh crunchy birth of a new day. The sky was still, Jed was oblivious, and my home was silenced. My little world was once again calm. For the rest of Eldercrest, they were none the wiser, life would go on for them, but I, of course, knew different.

I couldn't help but return my thoughts to Zach and what Kalen had insinuated. There was no way he was one of them. No way! Yes, he had a habit of appearing from out of nowhere but that was hardly a crime. Ok, he had skipped death on a couple of occasions but that was down to fate and a little luck...besides Kalen had gone easy on him. Anyway, why would he create such an elaborate story about the whereabouts of his brother? It seemed like too much trouble for the sake of a keepsake.

Zach was merely thinking of my best interests. He liked me! There was no underhand activity going on. He cared! That's all. He had exposed the identity of Coral, her men and Kalen to me, undertaking what was required in order to protect me. No, it was silly to even contemplate that Zach was anywhere near the likes of one of them. It was a ridiculous claim, and one I would not accept.

SWOOSH!

That familiar sound again...had Kalen forgotten something?

"Hello..." I cautiously whispered.

I could have sworn I'd heard the distinctive sweeping tone of his wings.

"Kalen...is that you?" I lightly called, but still, there was no response.

I was exhausted and evidently so was my mind, especially now it had resorted to playing tricks on me. I wasn't in the mood for any more games, and agreeing with my inner voice, I headed back to bed. I desperately needed sleep!

SWOOOOSH!

I had definitely heard it this time. It stopped me in my tracks, forcing me to tiptoe back to the window with heed.

SWOOSH!

SWOOSH!

Back and forth past my window he flew. His pronounced wings piercing through the sky as he aimed directly for me. I bolted my head back in shock as he swooped for my face, abruptly stopping inches from the tip of my rosy flushed nose.

Mighty and persistent, they flapped hysterically at me, leaving me gasping for air as he extracted each and every breath away.

"Baxley! It's you!" I spluttered, the remnants of oxygen within my lungs quickly evaporating with each word spoken.

"You made it!" I choked; I was completely overwhelmed to see him.

The last I saw of him was when he had heroically teamed up with Kalen to fight against the sinister fairy ring.

Poor Baxley had taken the brunt of Coral's anger! That dragon had viscously assaulted him, and in all honesty, I hadn't thought he had made it.

"Why are you here — little fella? What's — wrong?" I wheezed, still vying to catch my breath.

How on earth did he know where to find me? Had he followed me home? This wasn't right. Something was wrong. I could feel it!

Never had I seen Baxley act out of sorts like this, it was almost like he was trying to tell me something. If only I knew what it was! I wanted to be able to help him — like he had done for me on so many prior occasions.

It took a few more frantic flaps to pacify him, but gradually Baxley began to relax, slowing down the pace and easing his wings into a steady, composed rhythm.

"That's it. Easy does it," I prompted, grateful to recover my breath and finally be able to take a closer inspection of him.

Well, his wings seemed to be functionally intact, and he didn't appear to be grazed or carrying a broken leg or crooked antennae. So, if he wasn't injured or in pain, then was he trying to forewarn me of something?

∞∞∞

His midnight black eyes drilled deeply into mine. He was transfixed as I was with him, but the reasons for his unforeseen show were still unknown — and no sooner had I questioned his unexpected arrival, then did the most peculiar of things happen....

It began with the watery darkness of his irises rapidly drying out. Cracked, drought-stricken and broken into shards, they resembled a barren land. Desiccated, they were painfully sore to view, as were the whites of his eyes which were riddled with speckles of roaming grit.

From the pitch-black of coal, his eyes began to alter, lightening in colour. Without haste, they blended into a wooden roasted chestnut brown, churning into a fresh pea seaweed green before settling on a shivering icy-eggshell blue.

"What's happening?" I warbled, knowing full well he wouldn't be able to answer.

Instead, his newly acquired sapless chilly blues slowly began to replenish, soaking in a deluge of moisture and recapturing the vitality they once had.

Baxley was starting to scare me! Was he sick, dying or transitioning into some sort of undiscovered imperial bug?

I remained silent as my fretful friend wafted inches in front of the bridge of my nose.

Floating effortlessly, his wings barely fluttered as he secreted a glittery dusting of sparkly black flakes. With flashes of silver, they emanated with fascination from the wave of each one of their glorious sedated flits.

These shiny confetti particles of light drifted to earth like a gleaming shower of stray fallen stars. Dissolving like powdery soft white snow, their spectacular performance left no trace, much like the whereabouts of Zach's empty shell.

Then, *puff!*

Baxley's body denoted like a baked colour-infused bath bomb, smouldering in a haze of lavender and liquorice smoke.

With no words or reasoning to his untoward behaviour... he was gone. Leaving me only with the image of his doleful glacial blues as they gradually faded away into the loneliness of the early morning sky.

Muddled, my mind throbbed with astonishment, unable to explain what the hell I had just witnessed. It wasn't 'normal' — it was unheard of!

Who or what exactly was Baxley? The strength that little fella had was unrealistic, he also had more lives than a cat! He would appear at the most pivotal of times, and let's face it, he wasn't exactly 'bug' like, was he!

Baxley wasn't just any old butterfly now was he, and come to think of it, I had only ever seen him when Zach wasn't around. What's more, I knew those eyes, I knew them more than anyone....

THE END.

Acknowledgements

Robbie,
Mum and Dad,
Chris,
Scotty and Nat-Nat,
Lou, Sami, Helen, Vicky and Joe.

Thank you for your never-ending support, and
most of all, thank you for believing in me.

Printed in Poland
by Amazon Fulfillment
Poland Sp. z o.o., Wrocław

54601011R00247